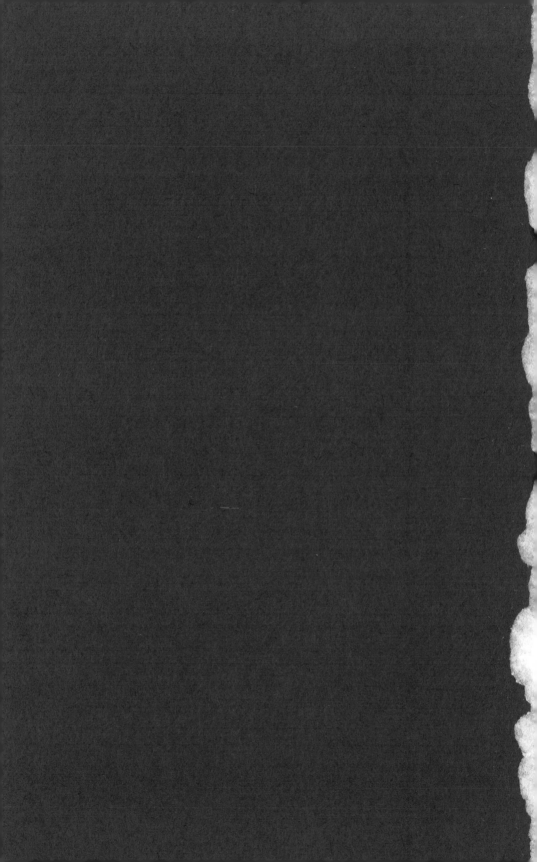

Microcomputer Structures

by
Henry D'Angelo

Associate Dean of the College of Engineering
and Professor of Manufacturing Engineering
at Boston University

BYTE BOOKS
Subsidiary of McGraw-Hill

Microcomputer Structures

Library of Congress Cataloging in Publication Data

D'Angelo, Henry, 1932-
    Microcomputer structures.

    Includes index.
        1. Microcomputers.   2. Logic design.   3. Computer
architecture.   I. Title.
TK7888.3.D295   621.3819'53   80-28985
ISBN 0-07-015294-2

Test set in Paladium Medium
by BYTE Publications

Edited by Blaise Liffick and Bruce Roberts

Design and Production Supervision
by Ellen Klempner

Cover Illustration
by Gail D'Angelo

Copy Edited by Peggy McCauley

Printed and bound
by Halliday Lithograph Corporation,
Arcata Company, North Quincy, Massachusetts

CONTENTS

0. Introduction to Electricity   1

   0.1   Physical Quantities and Units

   0.2   Electric Charge

        0.2.1 Coulomb's Law

        0.2.2 Electric Field

   0.3   Electric Potential

        0.3.1 Work and Energy

        0.3.2 Voltage (Electric Potential)

        0.3.3 Electromotive Forces (emf)

   0.4   Electric Current

        0.4.1 Electric Current: Definition

        0.4.2 Ohm's Law

        0.4.3 Resistance and Resistors

        0.4.4 Power to a Resistor

   0.5   Practicalities I

        0.5.1 Temperature Effects on Resistors

        0.5.2 Nonlinear Resistors

        0.5.3 Resistor Identification

        0.5.4 Variable Resistors

        0.5.5 DC and AC

   0.6   Electric Networks

        0.6.1 Network Diagrams

        0.6.2 Kirchhoff's Laws

        0.6.3 Network Analysis: Examples

        0.6.4 Real Voltage Sources

        0.6.5 Potentiometers

        0.6.6 The Solderless Breadboard

   0.7   Simple Electical Measurements: The VOM

        0.7.1 The Meter Element

        0.7.2 The Ammeter

        0.7.3 The Voltmeter

        0.7.4 The Ohmmeter

   0.8   The Capacitor

        0.8.1 Dynamic (Energy-Storing) Network Elements

        0.8.2 The Capacitor

        0.8.3 Capacitor Construction: Basic Principles

        0.8.4 Series and Parallel Capacitors

        0.8.5 Stored Energy

0.9   The Inductor
      0.9.1 Inductor Construction: Basic Principles
            0.9.1.1 The Magnetic Field: Ampere's Law
            0.9.1.2 Induced Voltage: Faraday's Law
      0.9.2 Series and Parallel Inductors
      0.9.3 Stored Energy
      0.9.4 Transformers
0.10 Dynamic Networks
      0.10.1 Charging and Discharging a Capacitor (The *RC* Circuit)
      0.10.2 Current Through an Inductor (The *RL* Circuit)
      0.10.3 *RLC* Networks
0.11 Dynamic Electrical Measurements
      0.11.1 The Function Generator
      0.11.2 The Pulse Generator
      0.11.3 The Oscilloscope
0.12 Practicalities II
      0.12.1 Parasitic Elements
      0.12.2 Grounding
      0.12.3 Oscilloscope Probes
      0.12.4 Identifying Capacitors

1. Introduction to Digital Electronics   87
   1.1   Implementation of Switches
   1.2   Semiconductors
   1.3   The Semiconductor Diode (The pn Junction)
   1.4   A Simple Diode Circuit
   1.5   Simplified Diode Models
   1.6   Regulated DC Power Supplies
         1.6.1 DC Power Supplies (AC to DC)
         1.6.2 Voltage Regulators
   1.7   The Transistor
   1.8   The Transistor Switch
   1.9   Transistor-Circuit Sensitivity
   1.10 Simplified Transistor-Switch Analysis and Design
   1.11 Inverter Design
   1.12 The Resistor-Transistor NOR Circuit
   1.13 The Building-Block Approach to the Design of Complex Digital Logic Networks
         1.13.1 Cascading
         1.13.2 Fan-out
   1.14 Transistor Switching Speed
         1.14.1 Switching Delays Caused by Transistor Parameters
         1.14.2 Switching Delays Caused by Loading

2. Digital-Logic Networks   155
   2.1   Switching Algebra
   2.2   Fundamental Digital-Logic Circuits and IC Logic Families
         2.2.1 Resistor-Transistor Logic (RTL)

2.2.2 Diode-Transistor Logic (DTL)

2.2.3 Transistor-Transistor Logic (TTL)

2.2.4 Loading TTL Devices

2.2.5 Complementary Metal-Oxide Semiconductor (CMOS)
   Logic
   2.2.5.1 The MOS Transistor
   2.2.5.2 CMOS Logic

3. Logic Design With Integrated Circuits: Combinational Logic   **203**
   3.1   Combinational Logic
   3.2   Combinational-Logic Design Using ICs
      3.2.1 The Half-Adder
      3.2.2 The Full-Adder
      3.2.3 The Comparator (the Exclusive-NOR: XNOR)
      3.2.4 The Seven-Segment Display
      3.2.5 Digital Multiplexers and Demultiplexers

4. Logic Design With Integrated Circuits: Sequential Logic   **235**
   4.1   Sequential Logic
      4.1.1 Memory
      4.1.2 State
      4.1.3 Sequential Logic versus Combinational Logic
      4.1.4 General-Purpose Sequential-Logic Systems: Introduction
         to Programming
         4.1.4.1 Design of Sequential-Logic Systems from Sequences
         4.1.4.2 A Programmable General-Purpose Sequential-Logic
            System
   4.2   Clock Structures
   4.3   Memory
      4.3.1 Debounced Switch
      4.3.2 Two-State Logic
      4.3.3 Flip-Flops
         4.3.3.1 RS Flip-Flop
         4.3.3.2 D Flip-Flop (T-Delay)
         4.3.3.3 Master-Slave Flip-Flop and Edge-Triggered Flip-Flops
         4.3.3.4 T Flip-Flop (Toggle)
         4.3.3.5 JK Flip-Flop
         4.3.3.6 Preset and Clear
   4.4   Applications of Flip-Flops
      4.4.1 Registers
      4.4.2 Latching
      4.4.3 Counters
      4.4.4 Read/Write Memory
      4.4.5 Dynamic Read/Write Memory

5. Bus Structures   **305**
   5.1   RTL-Based Bus Structures
   5.2   TTL Open-Collector Logic

5.2.1 Use of Open-Collector Logic Devices to Drive Other TTL Devices
5.2.2 Open-Collector Bus Drivers
5.3   TTL Tristate
5.4   CMOS Tristate Logic
5.5   Tristate Logic Applications
5.5.1 Memory Design
5.5.2 Bi-Bus Drivers

6. Computer Architecture   **339**
6.1   Architectures
6.2   von Neumann Architecture
6.2.1 A Simple Processor Architecture
6.2.2 Program Execution
6.2.3 Register Notation
6.2.4 A Simple Instruction Set
6.2.5 Program Execution
6.2.6 Indirect Addressing
6.2.7 Index Registers
6.2.8 Subroutines and Stacks
6.2.9 Interrupts
6.2.10 Reset and Bootstrap Programs
6.2.11 Status Register (Flags)
6.2.12 Processor Bus Structures
6.3   Microprocessors
6.4   A Simple Microcomputer

Appendix   **379**
A1   Solution of Linear Differential Equations
A1.1 First-Order Linear Differential Equations
A1.2 Second-Order Linear Differential Equations
A2   Numerical Solution of a Simple Integral Equation
B   Laboratory Components, Instruments, and Supplies

Index   **389**

PREFACE

The remarkable advances in the manufacture of microelectronics have made the small, low-cost digital computer system a reality. Digital computers are now affordable to many small enterprises that cannot afford the technical consulting and maintenance services typically purchased along with the expensive large machines. As a result, there is an increasing demand for computer users who are not only well versed in software, but who can also maintain, modify, and design their own computer systems. This book is intended for those computer users (programmers, system analysts, managers, engineers, scientists, etc) who plan to maintain, modify, or design a microcomputer system. It is particularly directed to those who have little or no background in digital computer hardware and, as a result, would find it difficult to obtain a working knowledge of microcomputers. The object of this book is to introduce computer users to the basic computer structures used in microcomputer design and in microcomputer interfacing.

The book is based on a one-semester computer science course which I designed for students with some programming experience. In several instances, however, students have taken this course along with their first programming course. Importantly, the course has had a strong laboratory component associated with it, and the book reflects this both in its point of view and in the laboratory problems included at the end of each chapter. The book, like the course, assumes no electronics background and is designed to guide the reader through a series of laboratory exercises beginning with exercises on elementary electric circuits and electric measurements, proceeding to exercises on digital electronics and logic design, and ending with exercises on microcomputer design and interfacing.

Although a one-semester course spanning such broad areas of computer science and electronics is not a substitute for major concentrations in computer science and electrical engineering, the material presented here does provide a foundation for microcomputer design and microcomputer interfacing. Importantly, the combination of subjects presented and the relationships between them provide a framework within which several important technologies come together. Without such a framework, a quantitative study of microcomputers could be formidable, especially if the study is undertaken in a traditional manner. Specifically, consider the problem of having to take courses in electric circuits, electronics, logic design, computer architecture, and computer programming in preparation for a study of microcomputer design and microcomputer interfacing. At most universities such a program of study would take two to three years, with the objectives being broader than just to provide background for a study of microcomputers. This book is based on the premise that only a small subset of the material normally covered in a traditional electrical engineering program is fundamental to the limited objective of obtaining a background for microcomputer design and microcomputer interfacing.

Although the laboratory exercises are considered to be an essential part of this study of microcomputer structures, those without access to an electronics laboratory should not be discouraged. The cost of the electronic components and instruments necessary to set up a laboratory suitable for carrying out most of the suggested exercises is minimal. In fact, the course on which this book is based was initially taught to nine students in a department of mathematical sciences which at that time had no electronic laboratory facilities. Those students conducted most of the laboratory exercises using my eleven-year-old son's collection of electronic laboratory equipment. The main items in this collection included a $19 Radio Shack multimeter, a $15 solderless breadboard, an $11 Edmond's variable DC power supply, and a random assortment of resistors, capacitors, integrated circuits (ICs), and wire. Before the semester was over an additional $600 was spent. These funds were used primarily for additional solderless breadboards, components to build 5-volt power supplies, ICs, and some general-purpose tools. In addition, four microcomputers were available for the later interfacing exercises. The point is that a laboratory necessary to carry out the major laboratory exercises described in this book is neither complex nor expensive. In fact, the cost of many short courses on microprocessors and microcomputers is greater than the cost of setting up a modest digital-electronics laboratory.

I confess that, given a choice, I would have selected better laboratory equipment than that used initially; the laboratory I eventually developed was rather well equipped. It is especially helpful to have access to a good high-frequency oscilloscope at the time that the microcomputer exercises are being conducted; almost any inexpensive oscilloscope is adequate for the study of electric circuits, electronics and digital logic. However, it is interesting that the students who took that first course developed rather ingenious latching schemes which did not require the use of an oscilloscope to test their sequential-logic and interface designs. It is perhaps significant that most of these students had never used an oscilloscope and, at this introductory level, did not feel handicapped without one. Nevertheless, the oscilloscope is the most versatile of all electronic instruments, and if it is at all possible to arrange to have access to one during this study, do so. Appendix B provides a list of electronic components, instruments, and supplies suitable for conducting the suggested laboratory exercises.

The material on which this book is based has been taught for three years as a one-semester (42-session) course. The following schedule has proved effective:

Chapter	0	1	2	3	4	5	6
Number of Sessions	7	7	6	4	6	4	5

The students were assigned to do all the exercises at the end of each chapter. In addition, one session was used to introduce the course, and two sessions were used for exams. The Instructor's Manual for this book details the material covered in each session and the homework problems assigned.

This book contains seven chapters, numbered 0 through 6. In starting the numbering of the chapters with 0 rather than 1, as is customary, the thought was that readers with backgrounds in electric circuits (eg: engineers who have taken an electrical engineering course in circuits, scientists who have taken a physics course in circuits, technicians, etc) would wish to skip the introduction to electric circuits and begin with Chapter 1 on digital electronics. Since most students I have taught have been computer science majors and have not had a strong background in electric circuits, I have always started teaching the course with Chapter 0. However, a number of graduate electrical engineers (none with significant experience in digital computer hardware) have taken the course; all felt that Chapter 0 was a worthwhile review and would not have chosen to skip it. Nevertheless, I would not recommend Chapter 0 to those who have just recently completed a study of electric circuits.

In teaching this course I have been using the KIM-1 microcomputer for the laboratory exercises requiring a microcomputer. The KIM-1 has proved to be excellent for this purpose. Any other microcomputer which provides easy access to the data bus, the address bus, and all the important control signals would be equally effective.

In carrying out this project I have had many rewarding interactions with students, colleagues and friends. I am indebted to many and with pleasure acknowledge my gratitude to them. I am indebted to Stanley P. Franklin, Chairman of the Department of Mathematical Sciences at Memphis State University, for the opportunity to introduce the course on which this book is based. At the time that the course was introduced, the department had no hardware laboratories. Dr. Franklin made space, equipment, and time available to me for carrying out the project. Can an administrator do more? I am indebted to Thomas G. Windeknecht who, as a close colleague and friend, played a major role in determining the type of hardware course needed by computer science majors. It is difficult to imagine that the project would have begun without Dr. Windeknecht's enthusiastic encouragement and support. I am indebted to Leonard R. Marino, whose two magnificent lectures introduced me to the marvelous world of microprocessors. Then, over the next several years, Dr. Marino allowed me access to his formidable collection of early microprocessor literature, including his own excellent notes. I am indebted to Gregg Williams, a student in the first course and now an editor of BYTE magazine. Mr. Williams' enthusiasm for the course was a major factor in my decision to write the book, and his bringing the manuscript to the attention of the editors of BYTE Books aided in publication. I am indebted to Michael J. Connolly, an excellent student who endured the first complete draft. Mr. Connolly generously gave me his well-written problem solutions to use in preparing the Instructor's Manual. I am indebted to Mary Thorpe, Secretary of the Department of Mathematical Sciences at Memphis State University, for her infinite patience in handling the many logistical problems involved in copying and distributing notes to the students and in purchasing and maintaining laboratory equipment and supplies. I am indebted to David Saxton, a close friend and philosopher, who contributed several days of a precious short vacation to the cause: he constructed power supplies. I am indebted to my students whose enthusiasm for the course in general and whose skepticism toward particulars stimulated and directed the project. I am especially indebted to Gail Cepnik, Charles Crowe, Linda Edminster, Andrew Halford, Gordon Helyer, Pik Chi Hui, Dan Lasley, Yaw Lin, Marjorie Martin, Timothy McCain, Sid Moody, Austin Smith, Donald Swearingen, Sammy Turner, and David Tzai.

I am indebted to my four children, Gus, Jim, Peter, and Paul, for the many hours they spent helping to get the laboratory started and then helping to keep it going. They wired, sorted parts, swept floors, assembled kits, put up shelves, and made repairs. I am especially indebted to Jim, whose sustained contribution to the laboratory over a three-year period, often requiring an afterschool bus ride to the University, was an important factor in the success of the laboratory operation.

It is a gross understatement to say that the project could not have been completed without the collaboration and cooperation of my wife, Gail. The fact is that the project would not have ever been started. Gail argued strongly that we undertake the project. This was at a time when, in view of other conflicting demands, it seemed prudent not to do so. Her offer to support the effort by taking total responsibility for all the editing, typing, and layouts, was monumental. Considering the magnitude of her contribution (note that even the cover illustration is hers), Gail should rightfully be a coauthor. Since her modesty doesn't allow that, I lovingly dedicate the book to her.

To Gail

Microcomputer Structures

Chapter 0

Introduction to Electricity

Digital electronics is a special area of electronics which deals with the design of logic devices used in digital computers and other digital equipment. Even though the general field of electronics is a complex subject embedded in an intricate mosaic of mathematics, physics, and engineering, it is possible to obtain a fundamental working knowledge of *digital* electronics in a relatively short time. For example, compared with the mathematical models used in the design of electronic amplifiers for high-fidelity sound equipment, rather simple models can be used to analyze and design digital electronic networks. In fact, the models used for digital networks seldom need to be precise and rarely take into account second-order effects.

Because the functional accuracy of a digital device rarely depends, within large ranges of variation, upon the accuracy of the components used in its construction, it is possible to use coarse models to analyze and design digital networks. For example, a typical electronic logic component is considered to be functional if its only two possible output states, *HIGH* and *LOW*, can be distinguished from each other. Thus, in a 5 V logic system, one might define any voltage between 2.5 and 6.0 volts as the HIGH state and any voltage between 0 and 1.0 volts as the LOW state; a voltage in the *forbidden region* lying between 1.0 V and 2.5 V would be indicative of a malfunction. With such wide ranges of voltage possible in defining a HIGH and a LOW, low-precision components can be used to construct logic devices. From the standpoint of analysis and design, the need for high-precision models is diminished. Nevertheless, many rather sophisticated digital electronic problems frequently arise that cannot easily be solved without a fundamental understanding of electricity. As background for the study of digital electronics, this chapter presents the fundamentals of electricity, electric networks, and electrical measurements.

0.1   Physical Quantities and Units

In the study of electricity, only four fundamental physical quantities need to be defined: *length, mass, time,* and *electric charge.* A unit of a physical quantity is a standard of measurement defined for that physical quantity. In this text the MKS (meter-kilogram-second) system of units is used. The following table gives the MKS units for the four fundamental physical quantities.*

Physical Quantity	MKS Unit
Length	Meter (m)
Mass	Kilogram (kg)
Time	Second (s)
Electric Charge	Coulomb (q)

Table 0.1: *The MKS system of units.*

All other physical quantities can be expressed through definitions or physical laws in terms of these four fundamental physical quantities.

For example, *velocity* is defined as the rate at which distance is traversed. Thus, if the variable x represents the distance in meters from a point on a line (ie: a point representing the position of an object on that line) to a fixed point of reference on that line, and the variable t represents time in seconds, then the velocity v of that object as it moves along the line is given by

$$v = \frac{dx}{dt}$$

Therefore, a unit of velocity is expressed in meters per second (m/s). Similarly, *acceleration a* is defined as the rate of change of velocity:

$$a = \frac{dv}{dt} = \frac{d^2x}{dt^2}$$

Therefore, a unit of acceleration is expressed in meters per second per second (m/s²). Thus, velocity and acceleration are *defined* in terms of the fundamental quantities *length* and *time.*

The physical quantities of velocity and acceleration are *mathematically*

---

*Temperature, a fifth fundamental quantity, which, in the MKS system, is measured in degrees Kelvin (°K), is not essential to most electric network modeling. It is generally assumed that all networks are at room temperature (ie: at approximately 300°K).

defined physical quantities, but the physical quantity *force* is more subtly defined. It seems somewhat natural for masses to be at rest and to be inclined to remain at rest. More interesting and mysterious, however, is a moving mass. The concept of a force was invented to describe the phenomenon that causes a mass to be set in motion from its apparently natural state of rest. Through the ages many ingenious mechanisms for developing useful forces have been devised (eg: levers, pulleys, screws, magnets, air foils). It was not until the seventeenth century that Sir Isaac Newton proposed that a simple relationship exists between force, mass, and acceleration. Newton hypothesized that force is proportional to the product of mass and acceleration. This is now called *Newton's second law of motion*. In the MKS system, Newton's second law of motion provides a convenient definition for force:

$$f = ma$$

Therefore, a unit of force is expressed in kilogram-meters per second per second (mk/s^2). This unit of force is appropriately called a *newton*.

For many applications, the MKS units of measure are awkward in that the quantities used are either several orders of magnitude larger or smaller than the standard unit. For example, the time required for a typical electronic logic device in a digital computer to respond to a command signal is on the order of 20×10^{-9} seconds. Thus, 20 *nanoseconds* (or simply 20 ns), where *nano* (or n) is defined to be a factor of 10^{-9}, is 20×10^{-9} seconds. Table 0.2 summarizes some of the more common symbols for such factors.

Terminology	Symbol	Factor
pico	p	10^{-12}
nano	n	10^{-9}
micro	μ	10^{-6}
milli	m	10^{-3}
centi	c	10^{-2}
kilo	k	10^{3}
mega	M	10^{6}
giga	G	10^{9}

Table 0.2: *Scale factor symbols.*

0.2 Electric Charge

The observation of certain forces other than those well known in mechanics (eg: inertial forces, gravitational forces, spring forces, frictional forces, etc) led to the hypothesis of the existence of the physical quantity called *electric charge*. Specifically, very lightweight object such as pith balls repel each other after being touched by a glass rod that has been rubbed with silk. Similarly, very lightweight objects repel each other after being touched by a hard rubber rod that has been rubbed with fur. Such objects are said to be *electrically charged*. Furthermore, an object charged by the glass rod *attracts* an object charged by the rubber rod. The existence of both forces of attraction and repulsion led to the conclusion that there are two distinct types of electric charge. Arbitrarily, the glass rod is said to be *positively* charged and the rubber rod is said to be *negatively* charged. A qualitative model is now clear: a force of repulsion exists between two similarly charged bodies (ie: either two positively charged bodies or two negatively charged bodies), and a force of attraction exists between two dissimilarly charged bodies.

In 1913, Niels Bohr modeled the atom as a planetary structure in which negatively charged particles, called *electrons*, whirl around a nucleus which consists of positively charged particles, called *protons*, and uncharged particles, called *neutrons*. Although the proton is considerably heavier than the electron (1.674×10^{-27} kilograms versus 9.11×10^{-31} kilograms), both have the same magnitude of charge. The charge on an electron is a small fraction of a coulomb; it takes the charge of 6.25×10^{18} electrons (or protons) to make a coulomb.

0.2.1 Coulomb's Law

In the eighteenth century, Charles A. Coulomb hypothesized a mathematical model from which a quantitative measure of charge could be obtained. Now known as *Coulomb's law*, this model is based upon the observation that the force f between two point charges, q_1 and q_2, is proportional to the product of the charges and inversely proportional to the square of the distance r between them, as follows:

$$f = \frac{q_1 q_2}{4 \pi \epsilon r^2}$$

The constant of proportionality, $4\pi\epsilon$, depends upon the medium in which the charges are placed. The constant ϵ is called the *permittivity* of the medium. The permittivity of free space (ie: a vacuum) has been experimentally determined to be $\epsilon_v = 8.854 \times 10^{-12}$ (approximately $10^{-9}/36\pi$). For all practical purposes the permittivity of air can be assumed to be equal to that of free space.

Clearly, the forces that charges exert on each other are inversely proportional to the permittivity of the medium. It is convenient to compare the permittivity of a material to that of free space. The ratio of the permittivity of a material to that of free space is called the *dielectric* constant. Table 0.3 gives the dielectric constants for some common materials.

Material	Dielectric Constant
Glass	5 - 10
Hard Rubber	2.9 - 3.1
Mica	5.7 - 8.7
Paper	2 - 2.5
Paraffin	2 - 2.3
Water (pure)	81

Table 0.3: *The dielectric constants for some common materials.*

Example 0.1

Two point masses, each with a positive charge of 1 coulomb, are separated by a distance of 1 meter, as shown in figure 0.1. The force of repulsion on each charged body is determined by the application of Coulomb's law:

$$f = \frac{q_1 q_2}{4\pi \epsilon r^2} = \frac{(1)\,(1)}{4(3.142)(8.854 \times 10^{-12})(1)^2} = 9 \times 10^9$$

Figure 0.1: *Force between two charged bodies.*

Thus, the force on q_1 is 9×10^9 newtons at an angle of $180°$ (a vector directed horizontally and to the right is said to be at $0°$; all other angles are measured in a counterclockwise direction from this $0°$ reference) and the force on q_2 is also 9×10^9 newtons, but at an angle of $0°$. The angle of force is always in the direction of a straight line drawn between two charges, away from the charges if both charges are positive or both are negative, and toward the charges if one is negative and the other is positive.

A force of 1 newton is equivalent to the force produced by the earth's gravitational field on a weight of 0.2248 pounds at sea level. Thus, a force of 9×10^9 newtons is an extraordinarily huge force (over 1 million tons) and, consequently, a charge of 1 coulomb is an extraordinarily huge charge.

Example 0.2

Three point masses, two with positive charges of 1 coulomb each and one with a negative charge of 1 coulomb, are separated from each other by distances of 1 meter, as shown in figure 0.2. The force f_2 on charge q_2 is determined as the vector sum of the force f_{12} (exerted on q_2 by q_1) and the force f_{32} (exerted on q_2 by q_3). Therefore, $f_{12} = 9 \times 10^9$ newtons at $300°$ (q_1 and q_2 repel each other), $f_{32} = 9 \times 10^9$ newtons at $180°$ (q_3 and q_2 attract each other), and the resultant force $f_2 = 9 \times 10^9$ newtons at $240°$.

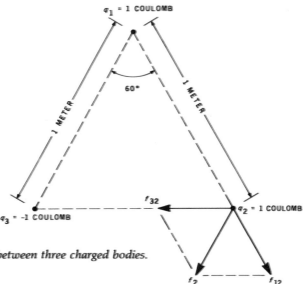

Figure 0.2: *Forces between three charged bodies.*

0.2.2 Electric Field

Although the application of Coulomb's law is sufficient to determine the forces on stationary point charges,* the concept of an *electric field* is convenient in situations where a large number of charges are distributed in complex geometric patterns. An electric field is defined as an infinite set of vectors such that, corresponding to each point in space, there is a vector equal to the force that would be experienced by a positive unit charge placed at that point in space. Such forces produced by interactions with other charges can be determined by using Coulomb's law. Knowledge of the electric field produced by a stationary distribution of charges in space is thus equivalent to a description of the charge distribution. However, knowing what the

---

*Moving charges can experience additional forces due to the presence of *magnetic fields* (see section 0.9.1.1).

electric field vectors are in a specific location in space, such as in the region where electrical measurements are to be made, is often more useful than having all the details pertaining to a complex charge distribution.

If the magnitude of the electric field vector at a certain point in space is denoted by $\mathcal{E}$, then the force f experienced by a charge q placed at that point is simply

$$f = \mathcal{E}q$$

In example 0.1, the electric field vector produced by charge q_1 at the point where q_2 is placed is $\mathcal{E}_1 = 9 \times 10^9$ newtons/coulomb at an angle of $0°$.

In example 0.2, the electric field vector produced by charges q_1 and q_3 at the point where charge q_2 is placed is $\mathcal{E}_2 = 9 \times 10^9$ newtons/coulomb at an angle of $240°$. If, in example 0.2, q_2 is a charge of -2 coulombs, the force on q_2 as computed from $f = \mathcal{E}q$ is -18×10^9 newtons at an angle of $240°$ or, equivalently, $+18 \times 10^9$ newtons at an angle of $60°$. (The negative sign can be used to reverse the direction of the vector, shifting it $180°$.)

0.3   Electric Potential

An energy transfer occurs when a charged body is transported in an electric field. *Electric potential*, or *voltage*, provides a measure of that energy.

0.3.1   Work and Energy

Energy is expended (or, equivalently, *work* is done) when a force is applied to move an object. Thus work is done, for example, in pushing or pulling a wagon, lifting a weight, or compressing a spring. If the force is constant and is applied in the direction of motion, then the work done is defined as the product of the force applied and the distance moved. Thus, if (as in figure 0.3) force f is applied to move a body from point b to point a, the work done is given by

$$w_{ab} = fl$$

where l is the length of the path from point b to point a. Note the convention: if work is done in moving from b to a, then w_{ab} is positive. Conversely, a negative w_{ab} implies that energy has been obtained from this system.

Figure 0.3: *Work done by a constant force applied along the trajectory of motion.*

For example, if the body somehow moves from point a to point b with force f applied in the direction shown in figure 0.3, then w_{ab} is negative. When force is in newtons and distance is in meters, the unit of work is a newton-meter. A newton-meter is called a *joule*.

Forces applied perpendicularly to the trajectory of motion do not contribute to the work done. Thus, if a force is not directed exactly along the trajectory of motion, only the vector component of the force along the trajectory of motion contributes to the work done. Also, the force applied may not be constant over the entire trajectory of motion. Under such conditions, where the force is neither constant nor applied along the trajectory of motion (see figure 0.4), the computation of work can be quite complex. In this general case, integration of the component of the force vector along the trajectory of motion is required,

$$w_{ab} = \int_b^a f \, dl \cos \theta$$

where θ is the angle between the force vector f and the incremental distance vector dl.

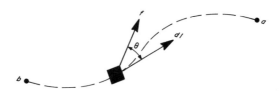

Figure 0.4: *Work done by a variable force.*

Example   0.3

A constant 1-newton force is applied to a body (see figure 0.5) to move it around square *abcda* having 1-meter edges. The application of the work equation is illustrated below by finding the work expended to move the body along each edge of the square:

$$w_{ba} = fl \cos \theta = 1 \times 1 \cos 45° = .707 \text{ joules}$$
$$w_{cb} = 1 \times 1 \times \cos 315 = .707 \text{ joules}$$
$$w_{dc} = 1 \times 1 \cos 225 = -.707 \text{ joules}$$
$$w_{ad} = 1 \times 1 \cos 135 = -.707 \text{ joules}$$

The total work expended to move the body once around the square, starting in corner a, is given by

$$w_{\text{total}} = w_{ba} + w_{cb} + w_{dc} + w_{ad} = 0$$

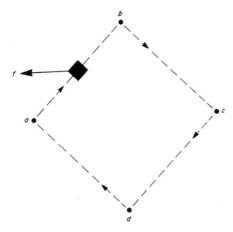

Figure 0.5: *Work done by a constant force applied to move a body once around a square.*

0.3.2 Voltage (Electric Potential)

The *voltage*, or *potential difference*, between two points is defined as the amount of work necessary to move a unit charge from one point to the other; a unit of voltage is a joule per coulomb, or *volt*, and is represented by *v*. Thus, if a nonzero voltage exists between two points, energy can be obtained by moving charges between these two points in the appropriate direction.

Voltage is a relative quantity in that it describes the property of one point in space with respect to another. Nevertheless, it is quite common to speak of the voltage of a single point (eg: a terminal, a wire, etc). In such cases there ought to be no ambiguity as to the *zero-voltage point* (ie: the agreed upon reference point with respect to which the voltages of all other points are measured). Frequently, the earth's surface provides such a reference point.

If a charge q is moved from point b to point a, then the work done in moving charge q is

$$w_{ab} = \int_b^a f \, dl \cos \theta$$

and the potential difference or voltage between point a and point b is

$$v_{ab} = \frac{w_{ab}}{q} = \frac{1}{q} \int_b^a f \, dl \cos \theta$$

The convention is that if work is done in moving a positive charge from point b to point a, then v_{ab} is positive.

Consider moving a charge through an electric field. Recall that the force on charge q caused by the electric field vector $\mathcal{E}$ is $\mathcal{E}q$. Thus, to move charge q, the force exerted on the charge by the electric field must be overcome. The force applied must be equal in magnitude and opposite in direction to the force exerted by the electric field, ie: $f = -\mathcal{E}q$ and

$$v_{ab} = \frac{1}{q} \int_b^a -\mathcal{E}q \, dl \cos \theta = -\int_b^a \mathcal{E}dl \cos \theta$$

The minus sign reflects that work is done in moving a positive charge from point b to point a. This will yield a positive value for v_{ab}.

Example 0.4

A uniform electric field of 10 newtons per coulomb exists in the space between points b and a; these two points are separated by a distance of 3 meters (see figure 0.6). Determine the voltage v_{ab}.

$$v_{ab} = -\int_b^a \mathcal{E} \, dl \cos \theta$$

Since $\mathcal{E}$ is constant (-10 newtons/coulomb) along the straight line path from point b to point a, the integral can be replaced by a product:

$$v_{ab} = -\mathcal{E}l \cos(\theta) = -(10) \times 3 \times \cos(180) = 30 \text{ V}$$

Therefore, the energy required to move a positive charge of 2 coulombs from point b to point a is

$$w_{ab} = qv_{ab} = 60 \text{ joules}$$

On the other hand, 60 joules could be obtained from this system by moving a positive 2 coulombs from point a to point b.

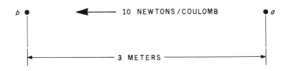

Figure 0.6: *A uniform electric field.*

Example   0.5

Use the law of conservation of energy to show that the path traveled in determining the potential difference between two points is arbitrary.

Figure 0.7 shows two arbitrary paths between point b and point a. Suppose $v_{ab}^{(1)} > v_{ab}^{(2)}$, where $v_{ab}^{(1)}$ is the voltage v_{ab} computed along path (1), and $v_{ab}^{(2)}$ is the voltage v_{ab} computed along path (2). In carrying a unit charge from point b to point a along path (2), an amount of energy equal to $v_{ab}^{(2)}$ is expended. The unit charge can then be returned from point a to point b along path (1), and an amount of energy equal to $v_{ab}^{(1)}$ can be taken from the system. Thus, in traversing the circuit from point b to point a and back to point b, a net energy equal to $v_{ab}^{(1)} - v_{ab}^{(2)}$ can be taken from the system. If this were the case, an infinite energy source would be implied in which any amount of energy could be obtained simply by traversing this circuit the appropriate number of times with a unit charge. Clearly, the assumed inequality $v_{ab}^{(1)} > v_{ab}^{(2)}$ violates the law of conservation of energy. The inequality $v_{ab}^{(2)} > v_{ab}^{(1)}$ similarly violates the law of conservation of energy. Thus, the only possibility is that $v_{ab}^{(1)} = v_{ab}^{(2)}$.

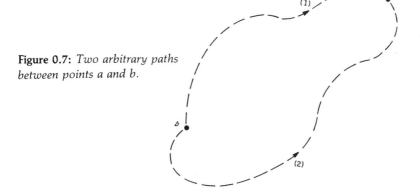

Figure 0.7: *Two arbitrary paths between points a and b.*

Figure 0.8 shows the symbolic network notations commonly used to depict voltage differences in electric network diagrams.

Figure 0.8: *Symbolic network notations for voltage.*

0.3.3   Electromotive Forces (emf)

Sources of electric potential are called electromotive forces (emf) or *voltage sources*. Since they establish electric fields which exert forces on charges and cause them to move, voltage sources are sources of energy. A voltage source is typically a two-terminal device which generally transforms a nonelectrical source of energy into electrical energy. Some common voltage sources are:

- Batteries: chemical energy is transformed into a constant (DC) voltage source.
- Generators: mechanical energy is transformed into varying (AC) and constant (DC) voltage sources.
- Thermocouples: thermal energy is transformed into a DC voltage source.
- Photo cells: light energy is transformed into a DC voltage source.
- Power supplies: an AC voltage source is transformed into a DC voltage source.

Figure 0.9 shows two network symbols commonly used for representing voltage sources.

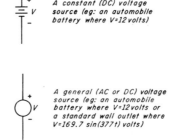

Figure 0.9: *Network symbols for voltage sources.*

A constant (DC) voltage source (eg: an automobile battery where V=12 volts)

A general (AC or DC) voltage source (eg: an automobile battery where V=12 volts or a standard wall outlet where V=169.7 sin(377t) volts)

0.4   Electric Current

Because energy is transferred when charges are moved in an electric field, *electric current*, a defined quantity which describes the rate of charge motion, assumes great importance in the study of electricity.

0.4.1   Electric Current: Definition

Electric current is defined as the rate at which charge traverses a given cross-sectional area:

$$i = \frac{dq}{dt}.$$

A unit of current is a coulomb per second, or *ampere*, and is symbolized by A. The direction of positive current is historically defined as the direction in which positive charges flow. However, electric currents are the results of *electron* motion, and electrons are negatively charged, so positive current is really opposite to electron motion (actual flow). Logically, the direction of "positive" current should be in the same direction as the actual flow that occurs, and in some literature it is defined as such. But this convention is rare in the general engineering and scientific literature, and the historical definition is commonly preferred.

0.4.2 Ohm's Law

Consider a two-terminal object, such as the one shown in figure 0.10, which has a voltage applied across its terminals. The existence of a voltage across the object implies the existence of an electric field everywhere within the object. Thus, any charges present experience forces caused by the electric field. Under the influence of these forces, the charges that are free to move will do so. This results in the flow of current through the object and the expenditure of energy by the source of the applied voltage. In other words, applying a voltage across an object containing charges which are free to move causes current to flow through the object and energy to be dissipated in the object. For most materials, under "normal" environmental conditions, the current flowing through the material is proportional to the voltage applied across it. This proportionality, known as *Ohm's law*, is expressed by

$$i = \frac{1}{R}\, v$$

where the constant of proportionality R is called the *resistance* between the two points. The unit of resistance is a volt per ampere, or *ohm*, and is symbolized by the Greek letter Ω.

0.4.3 Resistance and Resistors

The resistance between two points (ie: two equipotential surfaces) depends upon the material between those two points and the geometry of that material. In fact, for a given material, the resistance of an object can be completely determined from its geometry. If an object has a constant cross-sectional area, as shown in figure 0.10, the resistance is given by

$$R = \rho \frac{l}{A}$$

where l is the length of the object, A is its cross-sectional area, and ρ is the *resistivity* of the material.

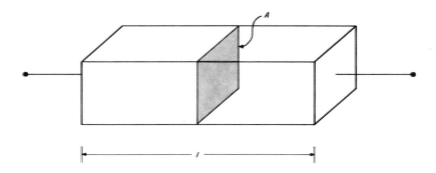

Figure 0.10: *Resistance and physical dimensions.*

The resistivity of copper is approximately 1.7×10^{-8} ohm-meter; the resistivity of silicon is approximately 2.3×10^3 ohm-meter; the resistivity of glass is practically infinite. Because of a wide variation in resistivity, materials are frequently categorized according to their resistivity. For materials of the same shape with the same voltages applied to them, large currents flow through the *conductors* (copper, aluminum, steel, etc), relatively small currents flow through the *semiconductors* (silicon, germanium, etc), and essentially no current flows through the *insulators* (rubber, glass, teflon, etc).

A *resistor* is a two-terminal device placed between two points to provide a known resistance path between those two points. The network symbol used for representing a resistor in a network diagram is shown in figure 0.11. The convention for denoting the current through the resistor and the voltage across the resistor is also shown. Note that a voltage *drop* is observed in traversing a resistor in the direction of positive current flow.

Figure 0.11: *Network symbol for a resistor.*

Example 0.6

Wires used in making electrical connections are categorized by their AWG (American Wire Gauge) Number, with larger numbers representing thinner wires. For example, an AWG No. 22 wire has a diameter of 25.3 mils (1 mil = 0.001 inch). Thus, in accordance with the equation $R = \rho l/A$, the resistance of a foot of No. 22 copper wire is 0.016 Ω. Therefore, if 10 feet of this wire is used to carry 1 ampere of current, then in accordance with Ohm's law, the voltage drop across the wire is 0.16 V.

0.4.4 Power to a Resistor

When voltage is applied across the terminals of a resistor, current flows (ie: charge moves from one terminal to the other), and energy is transferred from the voltage source to the resistor. This energy is released by the resistor in the form of heat. The amount of energy dissipated by a resistor can be easily computed.

Recall, in accordance with the definition of potential difference,

$$w = vq$$

Consider the case of a two-terminal device having voltage v applied across it. Here w is defined as the energy that must be expended to move charge q through the two-terminal device. *Power* is defined as the rate at which energy is expended. Thus,

$$p = \frac{dw}{dt}$$

A unit of power is a joule per second, or *watt*. Thus, the rate at which energy is transferred to the two-terminal device is*

$$p = v\frac{dq}{dt}$$

Since current is defined as the rate of transferring charge, ie:

$$i = \frac{dq}{dt}$$

the power transferred to the two-terminal device is

$$p = vi$$

The energy supplied to the two-terminal device during the time interval $[0, t]$ is

---

*Note that $\frac{d(vq)}{dt} = v\frac{dq}{dt} + q\frac{dv}{dt}$. However, the second term, $q\frac{dv}{dt}$, is zero because we assume the *net* charge in the two-terminal device to be zero. Although charge is moving through the two-terminal device, the rate at which charge enters one terminal is the same as the rate at which it leaves the second terminal (see section 0.6.2 for Kirchhoff's current law).

$$w = \int_0^t p \, d\tau = \int_0^t vi \, d\tau$$

For the case that the two-terminal device is a resistor R, voltage and current are related by Ohm's law, and the energy to the resistor is

$$w = \frac{1}{R} \int_0^t v^2 \, d\tau$$

or equivalently,

$$w = R \int_0^t i^2 d\tau$$

Since R and t are always positive, $w \geq 0$. Therefore, a resistor is always the recipient of electrical energy. When the voltage v across the resistor is constant, the integral can be replaced by a product. Thus,

$$w = \frac{v^2 t}{R} = i^2 R t$$

and therefore,

$$p = \frac{v^2}{R} = i^2 R$$

Example   0.7

Determine the energy dissipated during a 2-minute period by a 300-ohm resistor carrying a current of 10 mA.

$$p = i^2 R = 0.03 \text{ watts}$$
$$w = pt = 3.6 \text{ joules}$$

0.5   Practicalities I

In the laboratory use of resistors, problems arise that are not always accounted for by the application of Ohm's law. For example, temperature changes produce resistance changes that can cause electric networks to malfunction. Also, for resistors made of certain materials, the relationship between voltage and current is not linear, and Ohm's law is not satisfied. Thus, for some electric networks the possibility exists that the values of the resistors will change as the voltage and current levels in the network change. For the uninitiated, even the relatively simple task of identifying a coded resistor can be puzzling. Finally, coping with jargon that tends to develop in as esoteric a field as electronics can sometimes be more difficult than dealing with the fundamental principles and concepts; abbreviations such as DC and AC, which tend to take on specialized meanings, can become a source of confusion.

0.5.1 Temperature Effects on Resistors

Temperature changes result in resistivity changes in practically all materials; thus, the value of a resistor is a function of temperature. The resistance of a conductor generally increases as temperature increases. Figure 0.12 shows the temperature-resistance characteristics for standard annealed copper wire.

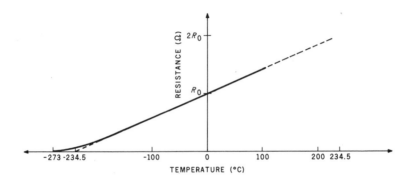

Figure 0.12: *Temperature-resistance characteristics of standard annealed copper.*

Resistance changes caused by temperature changes can produce some seemingly strange dynamic effects in an electric network. For example, suppose a constant voltage V is applied to a resistor whose nominal value R_0 at room temperature (ie: at 25 °C) is known. This voltage causes current V/R_0 to flow. Consequently, energy is dissipated in the resistor as heat, and the temperature of the resistor rises. The rise in temperature causes the resistance of the resistor to increase; accordingly, the current decreases. Reducing the current causes less energy to be dissipated; hence, the temperature and the resistance of the resistor drop. The current now increases, and so forth.

Therefore, under certain environmental conditions, temperature variations can cause oscillatory variations in the current flowing through the resistor. The period of these oscillations depends primarily on the heat-dissipating capabilities of the resistor. With proper cooling of the resistor, the temperature variations in the resistor and the associated current variations can be avoided.

0.5.2   Nonlinear Resistors

For some materials the assumption of linearity (ie: the assumption that current through a two-terminal device is proportional to the voltage applied across it, in accordance with Ohm's law) is not valid. Figure 0.13 shows the voltage-current characteristics of a linear resistor and the voltage-current characteristics of two nonlinear resistors. The resistance of a 75-watt incandescent lamp is not nonlinear by design. However, when used in its intended application, 120 volts AC is always applied to the lamp. Thus, the fact that resistance varies with variations in applied voltage is of little concern. Conversely, the silicon diode, a device examined in detail in Chapter 1, is nonlinear by design, and the nonlinearity is utilized to great advantage in many applications (see section 1.3).

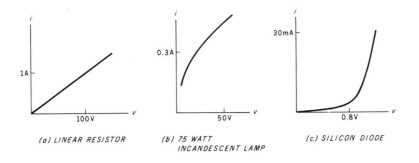

Figure 0.13: *Nonlinear resistors.*

0.5.3   Resistor Identification

Resistors can be purchased in many sizes and shapes. The three important identifying parameters of a resistor are *nominal value, tolerance,* and *maximum power rating.* The uninitiated, however, will have difficulty in identifying a resistor unless they are familiar with the codes used. The most common resistor used is the cylindrical carbon-composition resistor, which is identified by the three or four color bands encircling its cylindrical body and by its size. The first three color bands identify the *nominal value* of the resistor; the fourth color band, when present, identifies the *tolerance* of the resistor. The size of the cylinder determines the maximum power that can be dissipated in the resistor. The formula for identifying the nominal value and the tolerance of a resistor is

$$R = (10a + b)10^c \pm t\%$$

where the values a, b, and c are determined from the colors of the first, second, and third color bands, respectively, and t is determined from the fourth color band (not present for 20% resistors). Figure 0.14a gives the color codes. For example: a red, violet, black, and gold banded resistor is a 5%, 27-ohm $((20 + 7) \times 1)$ resistor; a green, black, and yellow banded resistor is a 20%, 500 kΩ resistor.

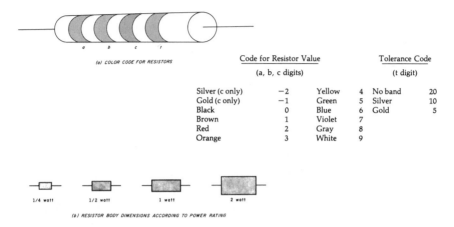

(a) COLOR CODE FOR RESISTORS

Code for Resistor Value (a, b, c digits)				Tolerance Code (t digit)	
Silver (c only)	−2	Yellow	4	No band	20
Gold (c only)	−1	Green	5	Silver	10
Black	0	Blue	6	Gold	5
Brown	1	Violet	7		
Red	2	Gray	8		
Orange	3	White	9		

1/4 watt   1/2 watt   1 watt   2 watt

(b) RESISTOR BODY DIMENSIONS ACCORDING TO POWER RATING

Figure 0.14: *Resistor parameters.*

The other important resistor parameter is the *maximum power rating,* which is the maximum power that a resistor can dissipate without burning out or changing its value beyond the specified tolerance. Common carbon-composition resistors are typically supplied in four wattage sizes: ¼, ½, 1, and 2. The power rating is determined from the physical size of the resistor. Figure 0.14b shows the resistor body dimensions for each of these four power ratings.

0.5.4   Variable Resistors

The need frequently arises for a resistor whose value can be easily varied. Such a resistor is commercially available and is called a *potentiometer* (or a "pot"). A potentiometer is, in fact, more than simply a variable resistor. A potentiometer is a three-terminal device which can be used to *divide* a voltage (see section 0.6.5). Two terminals of the potentiometer are connected to opposite ends of a resistor, and the third terminal is connected to a contact which can slide along the body of the resistor. Thus, a two-terminal variable resistor can be obtained from a potentiometer by using the terminal connected to the sliding contact and either one of the end terminals. The network symbol for a potentiometer is shown in figure 0.15a; the network symbol for a two-terminal variable resistor appears in figure 0.15b, and a common potentiometer is illustrated in figure 0.15c. The moving contact is positioned by rotating the shaft.

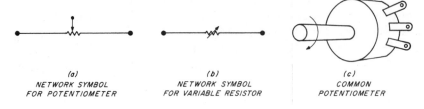

(a)
NETWORK SYMBOL
FOR POTENTIOMETER

(b)
NETWORK SYMBOL
FOR VARIABLE RESISTOR

(c)
COMMON
POTENTIOMETER

Figure 0.15: *The potentiometer.*

0.5.5 DC and AC

The abbreviations DC and AC literally stand for *direct current* and *alternating current*. However, over the yéars DC has come to be used as a synonym for *constant*. Thus, *DC current* means *constant current* rather than the redundant *direct-current current* and *DC voltage* means *constant voltage* rather than the nonsensical *direct-current voltage*. Similarly, AC is not interpreted literally, but has come to be used most commonly as a synonym for *time varying* and, perhaps most frequently, for *sinusoidally time varying*. Thus, if a voltage v is said to be an *AC voltage*, generally that voltage is varying sinusoidally with respect to time, ie:

$$v = V_m \sin(2\pi ft)$$

where V_m is the peak voltage and f is the frequency of the sinusoid in hertz, abbreviated Hz (ie: in cycles per second).

Interestingly, the common electrical wall outlet in most United States homes, referred to as 120 volts AC, supplies a sinusoidal voltage having a peak of approximately 169.7 V and a frequency of 60 Hz. This sinusoidal voltage is called 120 V because it dissipates as much heat in the resistor as does a 120 volt DC source. Consider the average power supplied to resistor R by the sinusoidal voltage source (figure 0.16)

$$p_{avg} = \frac{1}{T} \int_0^T p \, d\tau$$

where $T = 1/f$ is one period of the sinusoid. Since $p = v^2/R$,

$$p_{avg} = \frac{1}{T} \int_0^T \frac{V_m^2}{R} \sin^2(2\pi f\tau) d\tau = \frac{V_m^2}{2R} = \frac{(V_m/\sqrt{2})^2}{R}$$

In contrast, the power supplied to resistor R by the DC voltage source $V_m/\sqrt{2}$ (figure 0.16b) is $p = (V_m/\sqrt{2})^2/R$. Thus, the average power supplied to the resistor R by the AC sinusoidal voltage source having a peak voltage of 169.7 V is equivalent to the power supplied to the same resistor by a DC voltage source of 120 V: hence, 120 volts AC.

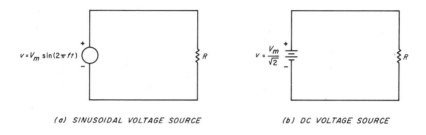

(a) SINUSOIDAL VOLTAGE SOURCE   (b) DC VOLTAGE SOURCE

Figure 0.16: *Power to a resistor from a sinusoidally varying voltage source.*

0.6 Electric Networks

Electric networks are interconnections of electrical components. For our purposes it is convenient to constrain the definition of a network to include only those interconnections in which every component of the network is included in a *circuit*. A circuit is any closed path of a network. A fairly common practice is to use the word *circuit* as a synonym for *network* when a single circuit spans the entire network (note that a circuit can go through a component more than once). Thus far, only two electrical components have been introduced: the resistor and the voltage source. Many important electric networks are composed of only resistors and voltage sources. Figure 0.17 shows some typical *resistor networks*.

0.6.1 Network Diagrams

In a network diagram the lines connecting the various electrical elements to form the electric network are assumed to be conducting wires with zero resistance. Assuming that real wires have zero resistance is a reasonable assumption in most cases. As seen in example 0.6, 1 foot of No. 22 copper wire has a resistance of less than two-hundreths of an ohm; such a resistance is generally negligible. The voltage drop across this wire when carrying a current of 1 ampere, a very large current in digital networks, is less than 20 millivolts, also generally negligible. Thus a 1-foot length of No. 22 copper wire can be generally assumed to be an ideal wire having zero resistance and no voltage drop across it. We will assume from here on that all wires are ideal. An ideal wire represents a single electrical point, in that all points on the wire are at the same voltage with respect to any reference point. Clearly, no energy is required to pass current through an ideal wire.

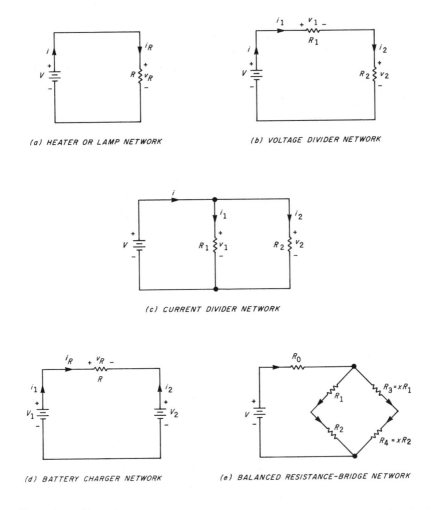

(a) HEATER OR LAMP NETWORK

(b) VOLTAGE DIVIDER NETWORK

(c) CURRENT DIVIDER NETWORK

(d) BATTERY CHARGER NETWORK

(e) BALANCED RESISTANCE-BRIDGE NETWORK

Figure 0.17: *Some resistor networks.*

0.6.2   Kirchhoff's Laws

Kirchhoff's laws provide the mathematical models, based on the principles of conservation of energy and conservation of charge, that are fundamental in the analysis of *all* electric networks.

Kirchhoff's voltage law (KVL): the sum of all voltage around any closed path is equal to zero (ie: conservation of energy).
Kirchhoff's current law (KCL): the sum of all currents entering any enclosed volume is zero; currents leaving are considered to be negative currents entering (ie: conservation of charge).

A notable exception to Kirchhoff's current law is the case in which the surface of an enclosed volume cuts between the plates of a capacitor (see section 0.8.2). In studies of electromagnetic fields, Kirchhoff's current law is generalized to account for this exception. However, our objectives are well met by not allowing the surface of the enclosed volume to cut through any circuit elements. In this text the enclosed volume is always a single *node*, a single point where several wires are connected together.

0.6.3   Network Analysis: Examples

Several illustrative examples follow in which Kirchhoff's laws are applied to resistor networks to determine all network currents and voltages.

Example   0.8

Find the current through and the voltage across each resistor in each network of figure 0.17.

Network   (a)

By Kirchhoff's voltage law,

$$V - v_R = 0$$

Thus,

$$v_R = V$$

By Ohm's law,

$$i_R = \frac{v_R}{R} = \frac{V}{R}$$

By Kirchhoff's current law,

$$i - i_R = 0$$

Thus,

$$i = i_R$$

For the case that $V = 5$ volts and $R = 270\ \Omega$,

$$v_R = 5\ \text{V} \qquad \text{and} \qquad i_R = 18.5\ \text{mA}$$

Network (b)

By Kirchhoff's voltage law,

$$V - v_1 - v_2 = 0$$

By Kirchhoff's current law,

$$i = i_1 = i_2$$

By Ohm's law,

$$v_1 = iR_1 \quad \text{and} \quad v_2 = iR_2$$

Therefore,

$$V = iR_1 + iR_2 = i(R_1 + R_2)$$

or

$$i = \frac{V}{R_1 + R_2}$$

For the case that $V = 5$ V, $R_1 = 270$ Ω, and $R_2 = 680$ Ω,

$$i = 5.26 \text{ mA} \quad v_1 = 1.42 \text{ V} \quad \text{and } v_2 = 3.58 \text{ V}$$

In this network, the voltage supply (V volts) is supplying a current i of $V/(R_1 + R_2)$ amperes. Thus, the voltage supply is connected to an *equivalent resistance* of

$$R = \frac{V}{i} = \frac{V}{V/(R_1 + R_2)} = R_1 + R_2$$

Therefore, the two-terminal electrical device made up of two *series* resistors is electrically equivalent to a single resistor whose resistance is the sum of the two. In general, the equivalent resistance of n series resistors, $R_1, R_2....,$ R_n (see figure 0.18a) is given by

$$R = \sum_{i=1}^{n} R_i$$

Obviously, the equivalent resistance of a set of series resistors is greater than the largest resistance of the set.

Network (c)

By Kirchhoff's current law,

$$i - i_1 - i_2 = 0$$

By Kirchhoff's voltage law,

$$V = v_1 = v_2$$

By Ohm's law,

$$i_1 = \frac{V}{R_1} \quad \text{and} \quad i_2 = \frac{V}{R_2}$$

Therefore,

$$i = \frac{V}{R_1} + \frac{V}{R_2} = V\left(\frac{1}{R_1} + \frac{1}{R_2}\right)$$

For the case that $V = 5$ V, $R_1 = 270$ Ω, and $R_2 = 680$ Ω,

$$i = 25.9 \text{ mA} \quad i_1 = 18.5 \text{ mA} \quad \text{and } i_2 = 7.4 \text{ mA}$$

In this network, the voltage supply (V volts) is supplying a current i of $V(1/R_1 + 1/R_2)$ amperes. Thus, the voltage supply sees an equivalent resistance of

$$R = \frac{V}{i} = \frac{V}{V(1/R_1 + 1/R_2)} = \frac{1}{1/R_1 + 1/R_2} = \frac{R_1 R_2}{R_1 + R_2}$$

Therefore, the two-terminal electrical device made up of two *parallel* resistors is electrically equivalent to a resistor whose resistance is the reciprocal of the sum of the reciprocals of the two. In general, the equivalent resistance of n parallel resistors (see figure 0.18b) is given by

$$R = \frac{1}{\displaystyle\sum_{i=1}^{n} \frac{1}{R_i}}$$

Note that the equivalent resistance of a set of parallel resistors is less than the smallest resistance of the set.

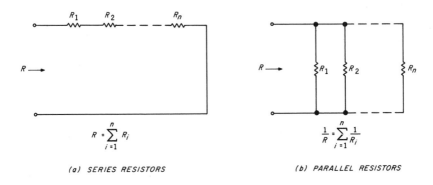

$$R = \sum_{i=1}^{n} R_i$$

(a) SERIES RESISTORS

$$\frac{1}{R} = \sum_{i=1}^{n} \frac{1}{R_i}$$

(b) PARALLEL RESISTORS

Figure 0.18: *Series and parallel resistors and equivalents.*

Network (d)

By Kirchhoff's current law,

$$i_1 = i_R = -i_2$$

By Kirchhoff's voltage law,

$$v_R = v_1 - v_2$$

By Ohm's law,

$$i_R = \frac{v_R}{R}$$

Therefore,

$$i_R = \frac{v_1 - v_2}{R}$$

For the case that $v_1 = 5$ volts, $R = 2\ \Omega$, and $v_2 = 4.5$ V,

$$v_R = 0.5 \text{ V} \qquad \text{and} \qquad i_R = 0.25 \text{ A}$$

Network (e)

The analysis of this balanced *bridge* network is simplified by identifying the series and parallel combinations of resistors. For example, noting that R_1 and R_2 are in series, and R_3 and R_4 are in series, the network could be redrawn as in figure 0.19b, where

$$R_{S1} = R_1 + R_2 \quad \text{and} \quad R_{S2} = R_3 + R_4$$

Similarly, the network of figure 0.19b can be further simplified (as in figure 0.19c) by noting that R_{S1} and R_{S2} are parallel,

$$R_P = \frac{1}{1/R_{S1} + 1/R_{S2}}$$

Finally, the equivalent resistance R is the series combination of R_0 and R_P, as in figure 0.19d,

$$R = R_0 + R_P$$

For the case that $V = 5$ V, $R_0 = 100\ \Omega$, $R_1 = 680\ \Omega$, and $x = 2$ (and thus, $R_3 = 540\ \Omega$, and $R_4 = 1360\ \Omega$), the computation follows:

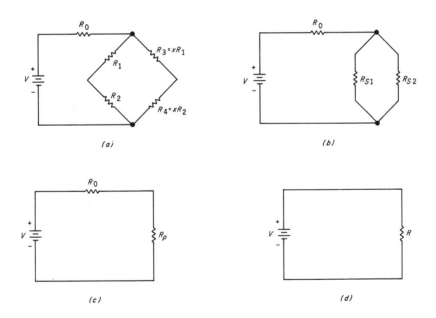

Figure 0.19: *Network simplification.*

$$R_{S1} = 950 \ \Omega \qquad \text{and} \qquad R_{S2} = 1900 \ \Omega$$
$$R_P = 633.3 \ \Omega$$
$$R = 733.3 \ \Omega$$

$$i = \frac{V}{R} = 6.8 \ \text{mA}$$

$$v_0 = iR = 0.68 \ \text{V}$$
$$v_P = iR_P = 4.32 \ \text{V}$$

$$i_{S1} = i_1 = i_2 = \frac{v_P}{R_{S1}} = 4.5 \ \text{mA}$$

$$i_{S2} = i_3 = i_4 = \frac{v_P}{R_{S2}} = 2.3 \ \text{mA}$$
$$v_1 = i_1 R_1 = 1.23 \ \text{V}, \ v_2 = i_2 R_2 = 3.09 \ \text{V}$$
$$v_3 = i_3 R_3 = 1.23 \ \text{V}, \ v_4 = i_4 R_4 = 3.09 \ \text{V}$$

By Kirchhoff's voltage law,

$$v = v_1 - v_3 = 0$$

Not all resistor networks can be analyzed by a sequence of series and parallel reductions: there are interconnections that are not combinations of parallel connections, and for such interconnections a proper analysis demands that Kirchhoff's laws be applied directly. In other words, the equations for series and parallel connections of resistors are special cases of Kirchhoff's laws, but even when taken together are not equivalent to them. An example of an important network in which a series-parallel reduction is not possible is the unbalanced *bridge* network shown in figure 0.20, where resistor R_b is connected across the bridge and where R_3 and R_4 are not given by the products xR_1 and xR_2. This network provides the basis for the resistance bridge, an instrument used for making accurate resistance measurements. An analysis of this network requires three applications of Kirchhoff's voltage law (along the closed paths shown) and three applications of Kirchhoff's current law (at the nodes enclosed in squares). This results in six equations which can be solved for the six unknown currents (assuming the value of the voltage source and the values of all resistors are known):

$$V = iR_0 + i_1 R_1 + i_2 R_2$$
$$0 = i_1 R_1 + i_b R_b - i_3 R_3$$
$$0 = i_2 R_2 - i_4 R_4 - i_b R_b$$
$$i = i_1 + i_3$$
$$i_1 = i_b + i_2$$
$$i = i_2 + i_4$$

Clearly, the analysis of general networks can become quite complex. Fortunately, however, much can be accomplished in the analysis and design of electronic networks with simple series and parallel reductions. A detailed study of analysis methods for general networks is not necessary here.

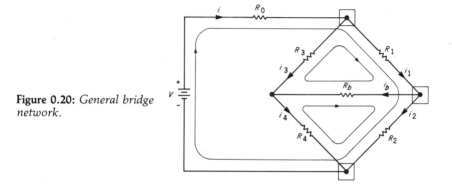

Figure 0.20: *General bridge network.*

0.6.4   Real Voltage Sources

An *ideal voltage source* is a two-terminal device which, regardless of how it is used, provides a specified voltage across its terminals. For example, an ideal automobile battery would provide 12 V across its terminals regardless of the number of automobiles it was simultaneously required to start. Yet, from simply observing an auto's lights dim as it is starting, it is apparent that the voltage across the battery terminals decreases as the battery's load is increased (ie: as more current is drawn from the battery). An automobile battery is not an ideal voltage source. In fact, it is safe to say that there is no ideal voltage source because an ideal voltage source is, in effect, an infinite power source.

A model commonly used for actual voltage sources is shown in figure 0.21. In this model an ideal voltage source is in series with a resistor r. This

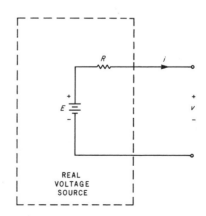

Figure 0.21: *Network model of actual voltage source.*

resistance r is called either the *internal resistance* of the voltage source (particularly when the voltage source is a battery) or the *output impedance* of the voltage source (particularly when the voltage source is an electronic power supply).

Example   0.9

The electric starting motor of an automobile draws 50 amperes from the automobile's 12 V battery. The battery has an internal resistance of 0.1 ohms. What is the battery's terminal voltage during the starting process?

$$v = E - iR$$
$$= 12 - 50 \times 0.1$$
$$= 7 \text{ volts}$$

Thus, operating the starting motor causes the battery's terminal voltage to drop 5 volts.

0.6.5   Potentiometers

In section 0.5.4 it was seen how a potentiometer is used as a variable resistor when only two of its terminals are used. The more general application of a potentiometer is as a *voltage divider*. The most commonly available voltage sources provide specified voltages with no possibility for adjustments. For example, if a 3 V voltage source is required but only a 5 V voltage source is available, it is necessary to design a network which would provide the required 3 volts when connected to the 5 V source. The potentiometer, in a single device, is such a network. Figure 0.22 shows how the potentiometer can be connected to any voltage source V to obtain any fraction of the voltage V.

Frequently when a potentiometer is used as a voltage divider, troublesome loading problems arise, as in the following situation.

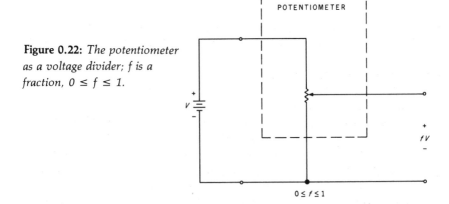

Figure 0.22: *The potentiometer as a voltage divider; f is a fraction, $0 \le f \le 1$.*

Example 0.10

Suppose a 10 kΩ potentiometer is used to obtain 3 V from a 5 V source. In this case the center tap of the potentiometer is positioned so as to obtain the 3 V across a 6 kΩ portion of the 10 kΩ potentiometer resistor. Figure 0.23a shows the equivalent potentiometer circuit for this 3 V setting. To consider the effect of loading, suppose this 3 V source is used to drive a 3 kΩ load as shown in figure 0.23b. The 3 kΩ resistor is in parallel with the 6 kΩ portion of the potentiometer resistor; this parallel combination is equivalent to a 2 kΩ resistor. This 2 kΩ combination is in series with the 4 kΩ portion of the potentiometer resistor. The output voltage of the potentiometer, when loaded with the 3 kΩ resistor, is 1.67 V compared to the 3 V at no load.

If the resistance of the potentiometer load is high compared to the potentiometer resistance, then loading has little effect on the potentiometer output voltage. Figure 0.23c shows that a 1 MΩ load does not significantly affect the voltage division. If a precise 3 V source is required under variable load conditions, then using a potentiometer is not advisable.

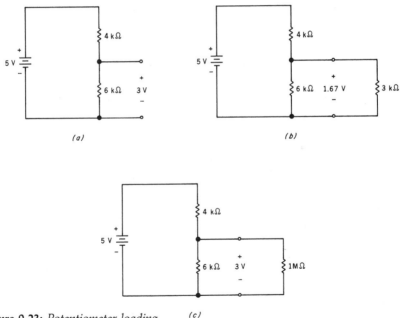

Figure 0.23: Potentiometer loading.

0.6.6 The Solderless Breadboard

Most laboratory construction of test networks (ie: most *breadboarding*) is done on convenient solderless breadboards which are made up of a collection of *socket strips*. Two rather typical socket strips are shown in figure

0.24. Each socket strip is composed of an array of holes (ie: sockets) on 0.1-inch centers. This spacing corresponds to the spacing of standard commercially available *integrated circuits* (ICs). On each socket strip are specified sets of sockets. All the sockets in a set are internally connected to act as a single electrical point. For example, in the socket strip shown in figure 0.24a, each set of five holes in a vertical column on either side of the *gutter* is a single electrical point. The spacing across the gutter, 0.3 inches, is suitable for mounting standard IC dual in-line packages (DIPs). The socket strip shown in figure 0.24b is a *bus* strip; on this socket strip all 25 sockets in each horizontal row are connected as a single electrical point. Thus, this strip has only two electrical points. The bus strip is suitable for establishing the electrical point to which many wires must be connected. Therefore, bus strips are used to distribute standard power-supply voltages, ground (zero-voltage reference), and other common signals.

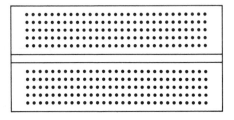

(a) IC SOCKET STRIPS

Figure 0.24: *Socket strips.*

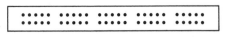

(b) BUS STRIP

Manufacturers generally specify that any solid hookup wire from size AWG No. 20 to No. 26 is suitable for use with the socket strips (stranded hookup wire is not suitable). It has been found that No. 20 wire tends to wear out the sockets prematurely and that No. 26 wire is annoying because of its lack of stiffness, causing it to bend as it is being inserted into the socket. No. 22 wire seems to be the most convenient. If there is special concern about the life of the socket strip, then No. 24 wire makes sense and adds little additional inconvenience. The leads of ¼-watt resistors, disk capacitors, switching transistors, and many other electronic components are easily inserted into the sockets. However, the leads of ½-watt resistors, large filter capacitors, and other components designed to handle large currents are too large for the socket strips and should not be forced into the sockets.

0.7 Simple Electrical Measurements: The VOM

The VOM (volt-ohmmeter) is a relatively inexpensive instrument which is useful in making a variety of electrical measurements. A VOM is a combination of at least two instruments: a *voltmeter* for making voltage measurements and an *ohmmeter* for making resistance measurements. Frequently, a VOM also includes a third instrument: an *ammeter* for making current measurements.

0.7.1 The Meter Element

A *meter element* is defined as any two-terminal electrical device which produces a visual display indicative of either the current through or the voltage across the element. Most inexpensive VOMs employ a d'Arsonval meter movement as the basic meter element. The d'Arsonval meter movement, utilizing the force exerted on a current-carrying conductor in a magnetic field (see section 0.9.1.1), is such that a needle deflection proportional to the current flowing through the meter element is produced. A network model for such an element, useful in the design of ammeters, voltmeters, and ohmmeters, is shown in figure 0.25. In this model the meter element is assumed to be well characterized by a series combination of an *ideal display element* and a meter resistor R_m. The ideal display element, having zero resistance, produces a display indicative of the current flowing through it. For example, a d'Arsonval meter movement, giving a full-scale needle deflection when a current of 100 μA flows through it and having a resistance R_m of 900 Ω, is somewhat typical; such a meter element is referred to as a 100 μA, 900 Ω meter.

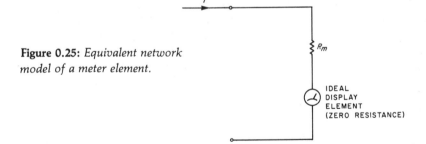

Figure 0.25: *Equivalent network model of a meter element.*

0.7.2 The Ammeter

An *ammeter* is used to measure the current flowing through a component or wire. An *ideal* ammeter presents a *short circuit* (ie: a zero resistance) to the network to which it is connected and therefore does not limit the current flowing in the circuit where current is being measured. However, since the resistance of an actual meter movement is never zero, it is not possible to construct an ammeter having zero resistance. For example, consider the case in which a 100 µA, 900 Ω d'Arsonval meter movement is to be used as the meter element for a 5 mA ammeter (ie: to measure currents up to 5 milliamperes). Such an ammeter can be constructed by *shunting* (ie: paralleling) the meter element with an appropriate resistor R as shown in figure 0.26. The resistance value of this shunt resistor can be easily computed.

When a current of 5 mA flows through the ammeter, a current of 100 µA should flow through the meter element, thereby providing a full-scale meter deflection. With 100 µA flowing through the meter element, a voltage of 0.09 V (900 Ω × 100 µA) is developed across it. In accordance with Kirchhoff's current law, a current of 4.9 mA (ie: 5 mA minus the 100 µA to the meter element) flows through the shunt resistor. The voltage across the shunt resistor is the same as that across the meter element (ie: 0.09 V). Thus, by Ohm's law, the resistance value of the shunt resistor is

$$R = \frac{0.09 \text{ V}}{4.9 \text{ mA}} = 18.37 \text{ } \Omega$$

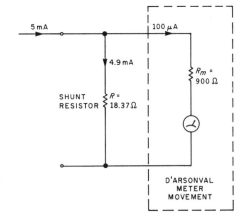

Figure 0.26: *Construction of a 5 mA ammeter.*

Finally, the resistance of this 5 mA ammeter is determined from the parallel combination of the 900 Ω d'Arsonval meter resistance and the 18.37 Ω shunt resistance; thus, the ammeter resistance is 18.0 Ω.

In certain applications, a nonzero ammeter resistance on the order of 18 Ω is negligible. In such cases the ammeter can be considered to be an ideal ammeter having a resistance of 0 Ω. However, there are important situations in which an 18 Ω ammeter resistance can cause erroneous current readings. For example, suppose this 5 mA, 18 Ω ammeter is used to measure the current in the simple circuit of figure 0.27a. Without the ammeter in the circuit, the current is 5 mA. With the ammeter in the circuit, the current is

$$i = \frac{0.1}{20 + 18.0} = 2.6 \text{ mA}$$

The presence of the ammeter in the circuit has the effect of reducing the very current it is intended to measure by approximately 50 percent.

For the circuit of figure 0.27b, the current without the ammeter inserted is 5 mA. With the ammeter in the circuit, the current is

$$i = \frac{5.0}{1000 + 18.0} = 4.9 \text{ mA}$$

The 18 Ω ammeter resistance is small compared with the 1000 Ω circuit resistance, and the current measured is very nearly the correct current.

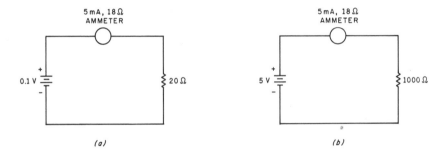

Figure 0.27: *Current measurements.*

0.7.3   The Voltmeter

An ideal *voltmeter*, which measures the potential difference between two points in an electrical network, presents an *open circuit* (ie: an infinite resistance) in the network to which it is connected. Therefore an ideal voltmeter does not create a new current path in the network; such a *parasitic* current path would cause the network to function differently when measurements are being taken. However, a real voltmeter does not have infinite resistance. Certainly, a voltmeter constructed only with a d'Arsonval meter movement and resistors does not have infinite resistance.

Consider using a 100 μA, 900 Ω d'Arsonval meter movement to construct a 5 V voltmeter. This can be done simply by connecting an appropriate resistor R in *series* with the meter element, as shown in figure 0.28. The size of this series resistor can be easily computed. When the voltmeter has 5 V across it, the meter element should deflect fully: the meter element should have 100 μA flowing through it and 0.09 V across it. In accordance with Kirchhoff's voltage law, the voltage across the series resistor is 4.91 V.

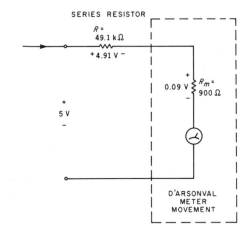

Figure 0.28: *Construction of a 5 V voltmeter.*

Thus, by Ohm's law the value of the series resistor is

$$R = \frac{4.91 \text{ V}}{100 \text{ }\mu\text{A}} = 49.1 \text{ k}\Omega$$

Therefore, the total resistance of the voltmeter is

$$R_{Vm} = 49{,}100 + 900 = 50 \text{ k}\Omega$$

In certain applications a voltmeter resistance of 50 kΩ can be considered to be essentially infinite (an open circuit in which no current flows). However, in other applications such a resistive path cannot be neglected. For example, suppose the 50 kΩ voltmeter is used to measure the voltage across the 20 kΩ resistor of the voltage divider network shown in figure 0.29. The voltage across the 20 kΩ resistor without the voltmeter present is easily computed to be 3.33 V. When the 50 kΩ voltmeter is placed across the 20 kΩ resistor to measure the voltage across it, the parallel combination of the 20 kΩ circuit resistor and the 50 kΩ voltmeter resistance results in an equivalent resistance of 14.29 kΩ. The voltage across this parallel pair is now 2.94 V. Thus, the voltmeter reads 2.94 V instead of 3.33 V. On the other hand, if a *high-resistance* voltmeter having a resistance R_{Vm} of 1 MΩ is used, then the resistance of the parallel pair is 19.6 kΩ (very nearly 20 kΩ), and the voltage across the parallel pair is 3.31 V (very nearly 3.33 V). Obviously, the high-resistance voltmeter is most desirable.

A sensitivity measure commonly used in rating a voltmeter is the *ohms per volt* (ohms/volt) rating, obtained by dividing the voltmeter's resistance by the full-scale voltage. Frequently a voltmeter has several scales available to the user. Thus, if a 20 kilo-ohms/volt voltmeter is used on the 10 V scale, its resistance is 200 kΩ; when this same voltmeter is used on the 3 V scale, its resistance is 60 kΩ.

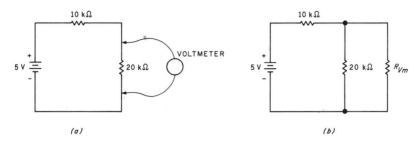

Figure 0.29: *Voltage measurements.*

0.7.4 The Ohmmeter

An *ohmmeter* is a meter used to measure the resistance of *passive** two-terminal devices, usually unknown resistors. The ohmmeter, unlike the ammeter and voltmeter, has its own voltage source. Specifically, a known voltage source V, in series with a known resistor R, is used to cause a current to flow through an unknown resistor R_x. Knowledge of the current through and the voltage across the unknown resistor can be used to determine the unknown resistor. The basic ohmmeter circuit, which includes a voltmeter, is shown in figure 0.30. Assuming that the voltmeter resistance is very large compared to R, $i_V \cong 0$ and

$$i_R = i_x = \frac{v_R}{R}$$

Also,

$$v_x = V - v_R$$

Thus, the unknown resistance R_x can be expressed in terms of the value of the voltage source V, the voltmeter reading v_R, and the value of the known resistor R:

$$R_x = \frac{v_x}{i_x} = \frac{V - v_R}{v_R/R}$$

---

*An electrical device is said to be *passive* when it contains no energy sources. A resistor, or any interconnection of resistors, is passive and cannot supply energy to any device connected to it. There are, however, passive devices such as capacitors (section 0.8) and inductors (section 0.9), which are capable of storing energy and then releasing this stored energy. However, unlike an energy source, such passive energy-storing devices can always be discharged of their stored energy by connecting a resistor across the device's terminals to dissipate this stored energy.

or simply,

$$R_x = R\left(\frac{V}{v_R} - 1\right)$$

This formula can be used as the basis for recalibrating the voltmeter scale, so that the value of the unknown resistance can be read directly in ohms. Figure 0.31 shows how a 1 V voltmeter can be calibrated to read directly in ohms for the case that $V = 1$ V and $R = 1\ \Omega$.

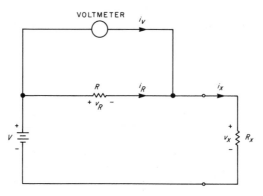

Figure 0.30: *A simple ohmmeter circuit.*

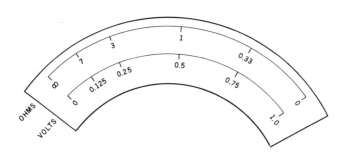

Figure 0.31: *Ohmmeter calibration scale.*

Since the voltage source used in an ohmmeter is generally an inexpensive battery, its value changes with age. To overcome the effects of the variable voltage source on the meter calibration, a variable resistor is used in series with a d'Arsonval meter movement to make an adjustable voltmeter. This adjustable voltmeter is used as part of the ohmmeter circuit shown in figure 0.32. An ohmmeter constructed in this fashion can be adjusted to be independent of the value of the voltage source. Before making measurements with this ohmmeter, a short circuit is placed across its terminals (ie: $R_x = 0$) and resistor R_V is varied until a full-scale deflection is obtained. On most ohmmeters this adjustment is labeled the *Ohms Adjust*.

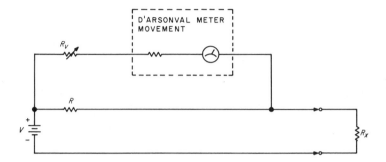

Figure 0.32: *Adjustable ohmmeter.*

0.8   The Capacitor

The *capacitor*, a two-terminal network element, is remarkably different from the resistor. The capacitor, unlike the resistor, consumes no energy. Able to store energy during certain time intervals and release this energy later on, it is the most commonly used energy-storing electrical component.

0.8.1   Dynamic (Energy-Storing) Network Elements

An *energy-storing device* is a device capable of storing energy under certain conditions and releasing the stored energy under other conditions. For example, a mass is an energy-storing device. Energy can be stored in a mass by raising it off the ground (the earth's surface) and can be regained by letting the mass drop back to the ground. The two most common electrical energy-storing devices are the *capacitor* and the *inductor*. Both the capacitor and the inductor are two-terminal devices.

Capacitors store energy in electric fields which are produced by static distributions of charges. The energy stored in a capacitor can be regained by allowing the forces acting on the charges to move those charges. For example, if the charges are allowed to move through a resistor, then the resulting current will act to heat the resistor.

The inductor, unlike the capacitor, does not depend upon an electric field (ie: a static distribution of charges) to store energy; the energy-storing mechanism involves forces which are produced by the interaction of moving charges with each other. This phenomenon, modeled by *Ampere's law*, gives rise to the concept of a *magnetic field* (section 0.9).

0.8.2   The Capacitor

A *capacitor* is defined as any two-terminal device in which the current flowing through it is proportional to the rate of change of the voltage across it. Thus,

$$i = C \frac{dv}{dt}$$

The constant of proportionality C is called the *capacitance* of the capacitor; a unit of capacitance is called a *farad* and is symbolized by F.

A capacitor is usually constructed from two conductors separated by an insulating medium. The conductors are generally called *plates* and the insulating medium is called the *dielectric*. A typical capacitor is constructed from a pair of parallel conducting plates, as shown in figure 0.33a; the network symbol for a capacitor is shown in figure 0.34.

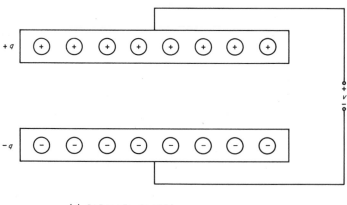

(a) PARALLEL PLATES

Figure 0.33: *Capacitor construction.*

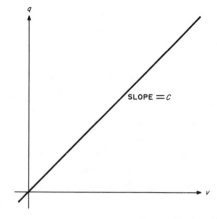

(b) RELATIONSHIP OF CHARGE q AND VOLTAGE v

Figure 0.34: *Network symbol for a capacitor.*

0.8.3   Capacitor Construction: Basic Principles

Consider a two-terminal device such that at any given time v is the voltage across the two terminals, and q is the total net charge that has entered the device through either terminal. It is easy to show that any such device in which voltage is proportional to charge is a capacitor. The proportionality between voltage and charge is expressed by the equation

$$q = Cv$$

Differentiating this equation results in

$$\frac{dq}{dt} = C\frac{dv}{dt}$$

Since $i = \dfrac{dq}{dt}$, it follows that

$$i = C\frac{dv}{dt}$$

which is the defining equation for a capacitor.

The proportional relationship $q = Cv$ is comparable to Ohm's law and is satisfied by any charge-collecting device. Since charge can neither be created nor destroyed, any two-terminal device (eg: the pair of parallel plates in figure 0.33a) that blocks the flow of charge is a charge collector (ie: charge flowing to one of the plates cannot jump across the dielectric gap to the other plate and is, therefore, collected). Although it is economical to construct capacitors using parallel plates, the essence of a capacitor is its charge-collecting property which can be achieved by separating any two conductors by a nonconducting gap. In fact, any two conducting bodies regardless of their shapes satisfy the basic capacitor equation (ie: the ratio of stored charge to voltage is constant):

$$C = \frac{q}{v}$$

The difficulty in constructing real capacitors that satisfy the defining relationship stems from the fact that when a voltage is applied across a capacitor, leakage currents flow through the dielectric, which is not a perfect insulator, and the proportional relationship between charge and voltage does not hold. The quality of a capacitor is determined by the size of these leakage currents.

0.8.4 Series and Parallel Capacitors

The equivalent capacitance of n capacitors in series (as in figure 0.35a) is the reciprocal of the sum of the reciprocals of the n capacitances:

$$C = \frac{1}{\displaystyle\sum_{i=1}^{n} \frac{1}{C_i}}$$

Thus, for example, if two $1 \, \mu F$ capacitors are placed in series, the equivalent capacitance of the series pair is $0.5 \, \mu F$. The equivalent capacitance of a set of series capacitors is always less than the smallest capacitance of the set.

The equivalent capacitance of n capacitors in parallel (as in figure 0.35b) is the sum of the n capacitances:

$$C = \sum_{i=1}^{n} C_i$$

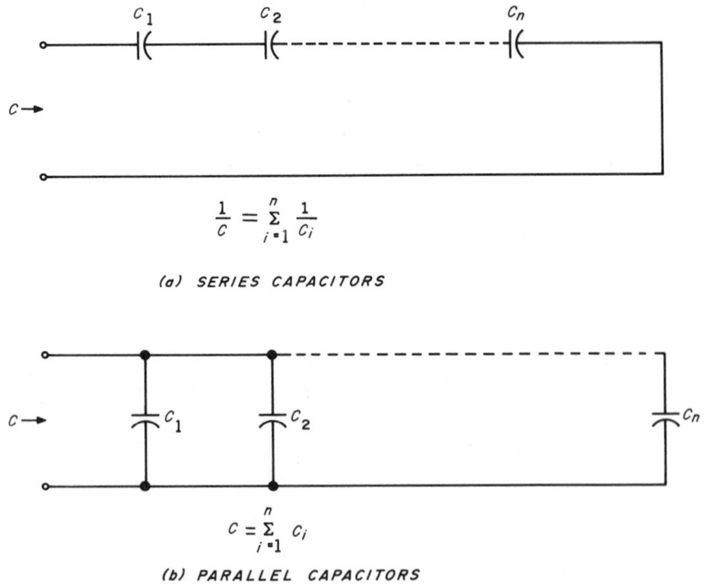

$$\frac{1}{C} = \sum_{i=1}^{n} \frac{1}{C_i}$$

(a) SERIES CAPACITORS

$$C = \sum_{i=1}^{n} C_i$$

(b) PARALLEL CAPACITORS

Figure 0.35: *Series and·parallel capacitors and their equivalents.*

If two 1 μF capacitors are placed in parallel, the equivalent capacitance of the parallel pair is 2 μF. Clearly, the equivalent capacitance of a set of parallel capacitors is always greater than the largest capacitance of the set.

The actual capacitance of a parallel plate capacitor can be determined from the dimensions of the capacitor and the material between the plates:

$$C = \frac{\epsilon A}{d}$$

where A is the area of a plate, d is the distance between the plates, and ϵ is the permittivity of the medium (recall that $\epsilon = 8.854 \times 10^{-12}$ for air).

0.8.5 Stored Energy

A transfer of energy is implicit in any change of voltage across a capacitor. The amount of energy necessary to charge or discharge a capacitor can be easily determined. For a capacitor C having v volts across it, the increment of work dw necessary to transport an increment of charge dq from one plate to the other is, in accordance with the definition of voltage,

$$dw = v \, dq$$

From the capacitor equation, $q = Cv$, it follows that

$$dq = C \, dv$$

Thus,

$$dw = Cv \, dv$$

Therefore, the energy required to change the capacitor voltage from v_1 to v_2 is

$$w = C \int_{v_1}^{v_2} v \, dv$$

$$w = \tfrac{1}{2} C \, (v_2^2 - v_1^2)$$

Recall that the energy supplied to a resistor R is

$$w = i^2 R t$$

where i is the current flowing through the resistor and t is the length of the period during which the current flows. Since R and t are always positive, w is always positive; a resistor is always taking energy from the system to which it is connected, regardless of the direction of the current flow. For the capacitor, however, w can be negative. This occurs when $v_1 > v_2$ (ie: when a capacitor is discharged). Therefore, a capacitor can supply energy to a system to which it is connected, functioning as an energy-storing device.

0.9 The Inductor

An *inductor* is defined as any two-terminal device in which the voltage across it is proportional to the rate of change of current flowing through it. Thus,

$$v = L \frac{di}{dt}$$

The constant of proportionality L is called the *inductance* of the inductor; a unit of inductance is called a *henry* and is **abbreviated H**. An inductor can be constructed from a coil of conducting wire; the network symbol for an inductor appears in figure 0.36.

Figure 0.36: *Network symbol for an inductor.*

0.9.1 Inductor Construction: Basic Principles

The physical phenomena on which the construction of an inductor is based are described by *Ampere's law* and *Faraday's law*. Together, these two laws describe the relationship between electrical and magnetic phenomena: Ampere's law describes the relationship between electric currents and magnetic fields; Faraday's law describes the relationship between varying magnetic fields and voltages.

0.9.1.1 The Magnetic Field: Ampere's Law

Forces not accounted for by Coulomb's law (section 0.2.1) exist between moving charges. Since electric current is defined as the movement of charges, current-carrying conductors experience forces caused by the interaction of the moving charges. Ampere's law provides a model for determining these forces. Consider the situation in figure 0.37a in which a conductor of length D, carrying current i_2, is placed parallel to an infinite-length conductor carrying current i_1. Ampere's law states that a force of attraction exists between these conductors. This force is proportional to the length D and the product of the two currents (i_1 and i_2) and inversely proportional to the perpendicular distance r between the two conductors, ie:

$$f = \mu \frac{i_1 \, i_2}{2\pi r} D$$

where μ is the *permeability* of the medium in which the two wires are placed. A negative f is interpreted as a force of repulsion. The permeability of free space (ie: a vacuum) is $\mu_v = 4\pi \times 10^{-7}$ henry/meter. Most materials (eg: air, wood, aluminum) are *nonmagnetic* materials in that their permeabilities are very nearly equal to that of free space. There are, however, materials having permeabilities many times higher than that of free space. Such materials are said to be *ferromagnetic*. The ferromagnetic elements are iron, nickle, and cobalt. In addition, certain alloys have ferromagnetic properties. Table 0.4 gives the *relative permeability* value of several common ferromagnetic materials. The product of μ_v, the permeability of free space, and the relative permeability of the material is the material's permeability.

Material	Relative Permeability
Cobalt	170
Iron	6000-8000
Nickle	400-1000
Permalloy	25000-100000
Steel	1500-10000

Table 0.4: *The relative permeabilities of several common ferromagnetic materials.*

Example 0.11

Consider two straight parallel wires in air which are 5 centimeters apart, each of infinite length, and each carrying a current of 0.5 amperes. The force exerted by one wire on a 1-cm segment of the other wire can be computed with Ampere's law:

$$f = (4\pi \times 10^{-7}) \times \frac{(0.5)(0.5)}{2\pi \times 0.05} \times 0.01 = 10^{-8} \text{ newtons}$$

This force is roughly equivalent to the force produced at sea level by the earth's gravitational field on a weight of 36×10^{-9} ounces. Clearly, the forces between most current-carrying conductors are negligible.

In the system of parallel current-carrying wires of figure 0.37a, the force

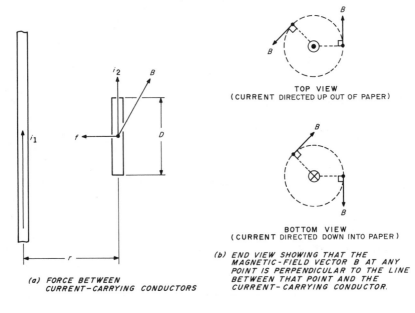

TOP VIEW
(CURRENT DIRECTED UP OUT OF PAPER)

BOTTOM VIEW
(CURRENT DIRECTED DOWN INTO PAPER)

(b) *END VIEW SHOWING THAT THE MAGNETIC-FIELD VECTOR B AT ANY POINT IS PERPENDICULAR TO THE LINE BETWEEN THAT POINT AND THE CURRENT-CARRYING CONDUCTOR.*

(a) *FORCE BETWEEN CURRENT-CARRYING CONDUCTORS*

Figure 0.37: *Ampere's law.*

on current element 2 can be thought of as being caused by the presence of a vector *magnetic field*. Thus,

$$f = BDi_2$$

where the magnitude of the magnetic field vector B is given by

$$B = \frac{\mu}{2\pi r}\, i_1$$

With current i_1 flowing in the direction shown, the direction of the magnetic field vector B at the location of current i_2 is *into* the plane of the paper (see figure 0.37b). The *right-hand rule* is convenient for determining the direction of the magnetic field: if current element 1 is grasped in the right hand with the thumb pointing in the direction of positive current flow, then the fingers will point in the direction of the magnetic field (see figure 0.37c). The force vector f is perpendicular to the plane formed by the vectors B and i_2 and is directed toward current element 1. Figure 0.37d shows the relationship of the current, magnetic field, and force vectors.

A unit of the magnetic field vector B is a newton/ampere-meter. Using the definition of an ampere (coulomb/second), the definition of a joule (newton-meter), and the definition of a volt (joule/coulomb), it is apparent that a unit of B can also be expressed as a volt-second/meter^2. A volt-

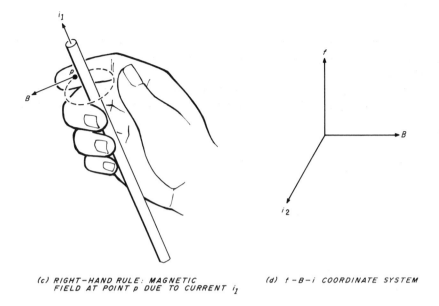

(c) RIGHT-HAND RULE: MAGNETIC
FIELD AT POINT p DUE TO CURRENT i_1

(d) f-B-i COORDINATE SYSTEM

Figure 0.37 cont.

second is called a *weber*. Thus a unit of B is a weber/meter ^{2} (ie: a weber per unit area). Hence the magnetic field vector B is called *magnetic flux density*.

Magnetic flux ϕ is defined over a specified surface area as the integral of the perpendicular components of the magnetic flux density vectors B over that surface, ie:

$$\phi = \int_{\substack{\text{specified} \\ \text{surface}}} B \, dA \cos \theta$$

where θ is the angle between a vector perpendicular to the incremental surface area dA and the magnetic flux density vector B (see figure 0.38). If the area of the surface is A, and if the magnetic flux density B is constant and perpendicular to the surface everywhere on the surface, then

$$\theta = BA$$

Magnetic flux θ has the unit of weber.

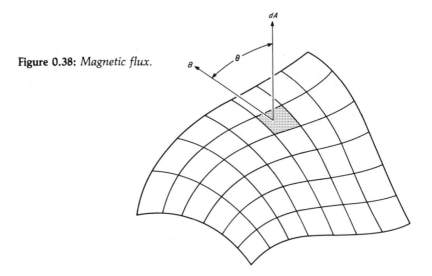

Figure 0.38: *Magnetic flux.*

0.9.1.2 Induced Voltage: Faraday's Law

Faraday's law states that, in any loop of wire (see figure 0.39), a voltage v is induced that is proportional to the rate of change of the flux linking that loop:

$$v = \frac{d\phi}{dt}$$

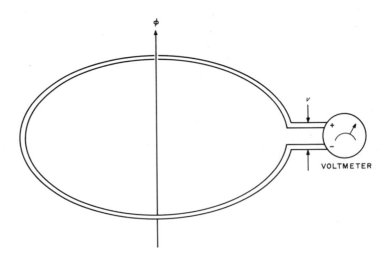

Figure 0.39: *An illustration of Faraday's law.*

The polarity of the induced voltage is such that, if this induced voltage is allowed to produce a current, this current would produce magnetic flux in opposition to the change in flux. For example, in figure 0.39, if ϕ is increasing,

$$\frac{d\phi}{dt} > 0$$

then any current produced by the induced voltage flows clockwise around the loop (ie: the polarity of v is such that the connection to the voltmeter as shown produces a positive deflection); current flowing in a clockwise direction around this loop produces a magnetic field within the loop in opposition to the original flux change (ie: a downward direction determined by the right-hand rule).

If an N-turn coil is constructed, as shown in figure 0.40a, so that the same flux ϕ links each turn, then in accordance with Kirchhoff's voltage law, the voltage induced in the N-turn coil is N times that of a one-turn coil:

$$v = N \frac{d\phi}{dt}$$

The product $N\phi$ is frequently referred to as the total *flux linkages* of a coil. Thus, in terms of flux linkages,

$$v = \frac{d(N\phi)}{dt}$$

or

$$v = \frac{d\left(\frac{N\phi}{i} i\right)}{dt}$$

The material around which the coil is formed is called the *core*. For most core materials, the amount of flux ϕ produced by a coil is proportional to the amount of current i flowing through the coil. This is true of air-core coils; however, for iron-core coils this proportionality exists only when the current levels in the coils are low (see figure 0.40b). When this proportionality exists, the ratio $N\phi/i$ is a constant. In this case,

$$v(t) = \frac{N\phi}{i} \frac{di}{dt}$$

Note that coils for which this proportionality holds satisfy the definition of an inductor,

$$v = L \frac{di}{dt}$$

where the inductance L is given by

$$L = \frac{N\phi}{i}$$

For a given coil, the core material not only determines whether the ratio $N\phi/i$ is constant, but also determines the magnitude of this ratio. Recall that the magnetic flux density produced by a single current-carrying conductor is defined as

$$B = \frac{\mu i}{2\pi r}$$

where μ is the permeability of the region. The permeability of air (and of a vacuum) is $4\pi \times 10^{-7}$; *ferromagnetic* materials in their linear regions have permeability values ranging from 10 to 100,000 times this, and

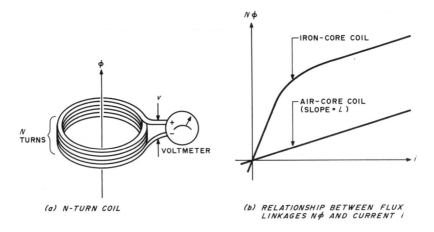

(a) N-TURN COIL

(b) RELATIONSHIP BETWEEN FLUX LINKAGES $N\phi$ AND CURRENT i

Figure 0.40: *Inductor construction.*

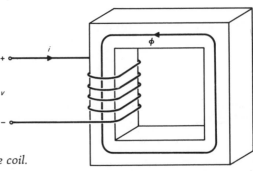

Figure 0.41: *Ferromagnetic-core coil.*

permeabilities of 1000 times that of air are typical. Therefore, the magnetic flux density produced within a ferromagnetic-core coil, as in figure 0.41, is many times greater than that produced within an air-core coil carrying the same current. Because the flux ϕ is determined from the integral of the flux density over the area of the coil, the number of flux linkages of the ferromagnetic-core coil is also many times greater than the number of flux linkages of an air-core coil. Hence, the inductance L of a ferromagnetic-core coil is typically much larger than that of a comparable air-core coil.

0.9.2 Series and Parallel Inductors

The equivalent inductance of n inductors in series (as in figure 0.42a) is determined as the sum of the n inductors:

$$L = \sum_{i=1}^{n} L_i$$

The equivalent inductance of n inductors in parallel (as in figure 0.42b) is

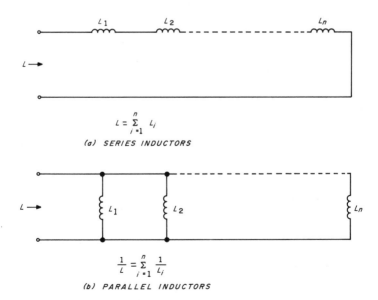

$$L = \sum_{i=1}^{n} L_i$$

(a) SERIES INDUCTORS

$$\frac{1}{L} = \sum_{i=1}^{n} \frac{1}{L_i}$$

(b) PARALLEL INDUCTORS

Figure 0.42: *Series and parallel inductors and their equivalents.*

determined as the reciprocal of the sum of the reciprocal of the n inductors:

$$L = \cfrac{1}{\displaystyle\sum_{i=1}^{n} \cfrac{1}{L_i}}$$

0.9.3 Stored Energy

In the case of a capacitor, a transfer of energy is associated with any change in voltage across the capacitor. In the case of an inductor, a transfer of energy is associated with any change in current through the inductor. The energy required to alter the current flow through an inductor can be easily determined. Consider an inductor L with voltage v across it and current i through it. According to the definition of voltage, the increment of energy dw required to transport an increment of charge dq through the inductor is

$$dw = v \, dq$$

and, since $v = L \dfrac{di}{dt}$,

$$dw = L \frac{di}{dt} dq = L \frac{dq}{dt} di = Li \, di$$

Therefore, the energy required to change the current flowing through the inductor from i_1 to i_2 is

$$w = L \int_{i_1}^{i_2} i \, di = \frac{1}{2} L(i_2^2 - i_1^2)$$

Thus an inductor, like a capacitor, is an energy-storing device: if $i_2 > i_1$, the inductor takes energy from the system to which it is connected; if $i_2 < i_1$, the inductor gives its stored energy to the system to which it is connected.

0.9.4 Transformers

Consider the situation shown in figure 0.43, in which a fraction of the magnetic flux produced by the current in coil 1 links coil 2:

$$\phi_2 = f\phi_1 \qquad 0 \le f \le 1$$

In accordance with Faraday's law,

$$v_1 = N_1 \frac{d\phi_1}{dt}$$

$$v_2 = N_2 \frac{d\phi_2}{dt} = N_2 \frac{d(f\phi_1)}{dt} = fN_2 \frac{d\phi_1}{dt}$$

Thus, the ratio of the two coil voltages is

$$\frac{v_2}{v_1} = f \frac{N_2}{N_1}$$

If a high-permeability ferromagnetic core is used and if the two coils are wound close to each other, then $f = 1$ (ie: the same flux links both coils), and the ratio of the two voltages is completely determined by the ratio of the number of turns in each coil:

$$\frac{v_2}{v_1} = \frac{N_2}{N_1}$$

Such a four-terminal device is called a *transformer*. Remember that voltages v_1 and v_2 are caused by changes in the flux ϕ_1; changes in flux are due to changes in currents i_1 and i_2. Therefore, unless ϕ_1 is increasing at a constant rate, v_1 and v_2 are varying voltages. In a practical sense, it is not possible to increase i_1 and i_2 and, thus, ϕ_1 indefinitely. In fact, if a constant voltage is applied to a transformer coil, which ideally has zero resistance, the current in the coil (and hence, the flux and the energy stored in the coil) will increase continuously and, in general, rapidly until the transformer burns out.

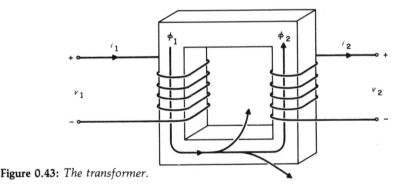

Figure 0.43: *The transformer.*

The network symbol for a transformer is shown in figure 0.44. Because the ideal transformer coils have zero resistance, no energy is consumed by the transformer. For applications in which the energy that is transmitted through a transformer is large compared to the energy that is stored in the magnetic fields of the transformer, it may be assumed that the power input to coil 1 is equal to the power output at coil 2:

$$v_1 i_1 = v_2 i_2$$

Therefore,

$$\frac{v_1}{v_2} = \frac{i_2}{i_1} = \frac{N_1}{N_2}$$

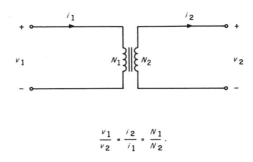

$$\frac{v_1}{v_2} \cdot \frac{i_2}{i_1} \cdot \frac{N_1}{N_2}.$$

Figure 0.44: *Network symbol for a transformer.*

0.10   Dynamic Networks

Electric networks that include dynamic elements (eg: capacitors or inductors) are called *dynamic networks*. The most notable characteristic of a dynamic network is that voltages and currents can exist in the network in the absence of any voltage source or any other energy source. Thus, a passive dynamic network (ie: a network with no energy sources) can store energy. In this section three important dynamic networks are studied. Understanding the behavior of these networks under ordinary switching conditions is fundamental to an understanding of the operation and the limits of operation of many digital computer circuits.

0.10.1   Charging and Discharging a Capacitor (The *RC* Circuit)

Consider the *RC* circuit in figure 0.45a, in which voltage source *V* is used to charge capacitor *C* through resistor *R*. With the switch in position 1, the capacitor is charged; with the switch in position 2, the capacitor is discharged. First examine the charging of the capacitor.

● **Switch in position 1 (capacitor charging)**
Assume that the switch is thrown to position 1 at time $t = 0$ when the voltage across the capacitor is 0 volts (ie: $v_C(0) = 0$). Applying Kirchhoff's voltage law with the switch in position 1 gives

$$V = v_R(t) + v_C(t)$$

Introducing the voltage-current relationship for the resistor and the capacitor gives

$$V = R\,i(t) + \frac{1}{C}\,q(t)$$

where $q(t)$ is the amount of charge stored on each capacitor plate at time t. In accordance with the definition of current,

$$i(t) = \frac{dq(t)}{dt}$$

$$V = R\frac{dq(t)}{dt} + \frac{1}{C}\,q(t) \qquad q(0) = Cv_C(0) = 0 \qquad 0 \le t < \infty$$

This first-order linear differential equation can be solved for $q(t)$ (see appendix A1):

$$q(t) = VC\,(1 - e^{-t/RC}) \qquad 0 \le t < \infty$$

Since $i(t) = \dfrac{dq(t)}{dt}$,

$$i(t) = \frac{V}{R}\,e^{-t/RC} \qquad 0 \le t < \infty$$

The voltage across the capacitor is the difference between the supply voltage V and the voltage across the resistor:

$$v_C(t) = V - i(t)R$$

and thus,

$$v_C(t) = V\,(1 - e^{-t/RC}) \qquad 0 \le t < \infty$$

The graphs in figure 0.45b show the current through and the voltage across the capacitor while it is charging. The product RC has the unit of *seconds* and is called the circuit *time constant*. After one time constant RC, the capacitor is charged to 0.633 V (roughly two-thirds of its final value); after five time constants, the capacitor is essentially fully charged (ie: $V_C = 0.99326$ V).

● **Switch in position 2 (capacitor discharging)**
Assume that the switch is thrown to position 2 at time $t = 0$ when the voltage across the capacitor is V volts (ie: $v_C(0) = V$). An analysis similar to the one above results in

$$i(t) = -\frac{V}{R}\,e^{-t/RC}$$

$$v_C(t) = Ve^{-t/RC}$$

The graphs in figure 0.45c show the current through and the voltage across the capacitor while it is discharging.

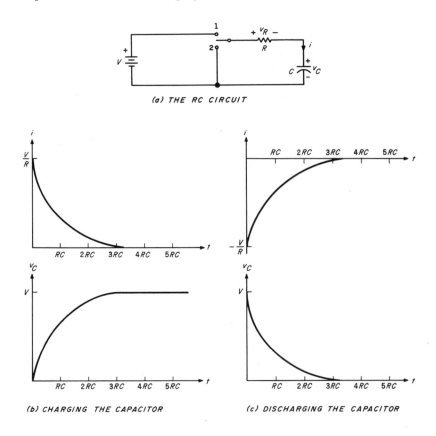

(a) THE RC CIRCUIT

(b) CHARGING THE CAPACITOR

(c) DISCHARGING THE CAPACITOR

Figure 0.45: *RC circuit characteristics.*

0.10.2   Current Through an Inductor (The *RL* Circuit)

Consider the *RL* circuit shown in figure 0.46a, in which the voltage source *V* causes a current to flow through inductor *L* and resistors *r* and *R*.

● **Switch opened (building up current)**

Assume that the switch is thrown open at time $t = 0$ when the current through the inductor is zero (ie: $i(0) = 0$). Applying Kirchhoff's voltage law with the switch open gives

$$V = v_r(t) + v_R(t) + v_L(t)$$

In accordance with the definitions of a resistor and an inductor,

$$V = (r + R)\, i(t) + L\frac{di(t)}{dt}$$

Solving the above first-order linear differential equation for $i(t)$ (see appendix A1) gives

$$i(t) = \frac{V}{r + R}\, (1 - e^{-t\,(r + R)/L})$$

The voltage across the inductor ($v_L(t) = L\,\dfrac{di(t)}{dt}$) is

$$v_L(t) = V e^{-t\,(r + R)/L}$$

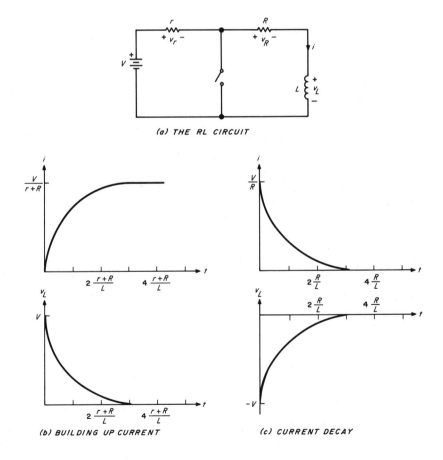

(a) THE RL CIRCUIT

(b) BUILDING UP CURRENT

(c) CURRENT DECAY

Figure 0.46: *RL circuit characteristics.*

Thus, the time constant for building up current in this RL circuit is $(r + R)/L$ seconds. The graphs in figure 0.46b show how the current builds up in an inductor during this process. When the current through the inductor is at a maximum, the voltage is zero since

$$\frac{di}{dt} = 0$$

- **Switch closed (current decay)**

Assume that the switch is closed at time $t = 0$ when the current through the inductor is V/R (ie: $i_L(0) = V/R$):

$$\left. \begin{array}{l} i(t) = \dfrac{V}{R} e^{-tR/L} \\[2em] v_L(t) = -Ve^{-tR/L} \end{array} \right\} \quad 0 \le t < \infty$$

The graphs in figure 0.46c show the current decay in the inductor and the voltage across the inductor during the decay.

0.10.3 RLC Networks

In the RLC network shown in figure 0.47a, energy is to be transferred from the 5 V source to the load-resistor R. Specifically, the switch is closed in order to bring the load-resistor voltage V_R to 5 V or as close to 5 V as possible with the least possible delay. Consider the case that the switch is closed at time $t = 0$ when the current through the inductor and the voltage across the capacitor are zero (ie: $i(0) = 0$ and $v_C(0) = 0$). Applying Kirchhoff's voltage law and Kirchhoff's current law results in

$$V = v_r + v_L + v_R$$

$$i = i_R + i_C$$

Using the defining relationship for a resistor, inductor, and capacitor gives

$$V = ir + L\frac{di}{dt} + v_C$$

$$i = \frac{1}{R}v_C + C\frac{dv_C}{dt}$$

Using the second of the above two equations to eliminate i in the first equation results in

$$\frac{d^2v_R}{dt^2} + \left(\frac{r}{L} + \frac{1}{RC}\right)\frac{dv_R}{dt} + \frac{1}{LC}\left(1 + \frac{r}{R}\right)v_R - \frac{V}{LC} = 0$$

When the initial values $v_R(0)$ and $dv_R(0)/dt$ are given, this equation can be solved for v_R (see appendix A1). The initial value $v_R(0)$ is the voltage across the capacitor at $t = 0$ and is given (ie: $v_R(0) = 0$). Although the initial value $dv_R(0)/dt$ is not given, the current through the inductor at $t = 0$, $i(0)$, is given and $dv_R(0)/dt$ can be expressed in terms of the initial values $v_R(0)$ and $i(0)$:

$$\frac{dv_R(0)}{dt} = \frac{1}{C}i(0) - \frac{1}{RC}v(0)$$

Since both $i(0)$ and $v_R(0)$ are zero,

$$\frac{dv_R(0)}{dt} = 0$$

Proceeding in a standard fashion (see appendix A1), the linear time-invariant, second-order nonhomogeneous equation can be solved for $v_R(t)$.

Importantly, depending upon the combination of values for $V, L, C,$ and R, the voltage $v_R(t)$ can behave in two rather distinct fashions. Specifically, let

$$\alpha = \frac{1}{2}\left(\frac{r}{L} + \frac{1}{RC}\right)$$

$$\beta = \frac{1}{LC}\left(1 + \frac{r}{R}\right)$$

$$k = -\frac{V}{LC}$$

If $\alpha^2 > \beta$, then the exponential response results:

$$v_R(t) = \frac{k}{\beta}\left(-\frac{s_2}{s_1 - s_2}e^{s_1 t} + \frac{s_1}{s_1 - s_2}e^{s_2 t} - 1\right)$$

where

$$s_1 = -\alpha + \sqrt{\alpha^2 - \beta} \qquad s_2 = -\alpha - \sqrt{\alpha^2 - \beta}$$

On the other hand, if $\alpha^2 < \beta$, then the damped harmonic response results:

$$v_R(t) = \frac{k}{\beta}\left[\frac{\sqrt{w^2 + \alpha^2}}{w}e^{-\alpha t}\sin\left(wt - \arctan\frac{w}{\alpha}\right) - 1\right]$$

where

$$w = \sqrt{\beta - \alpha^2}$$

The notably different characteristics of the two types of responses possible in this RLC network are illustrated in the graphs of figure 0.47. In figure 0.47b the response is shown for the case that $V = 5$ V, $r = 100$ Ω, $L = 1$ μH, $C = 1$ μF, and $R = 1$ MΩ; here $\alpha^2 > \beta$. In figure 0.47c the response is shown for $r = 10$ Ω (all other parameters are the same as before); here $\alpha^2 < \beta$. With $r = 100$ Ω and $\alpha^2 > \beta$, the response is rather sluggish; it takes more than 0.2 μ for the response to get to within 10% of its final value of approximately 5 V. On the other hand, with $r = 10$ Ω and $\alpha^2 < \beta$, the system is more responsive; it takes less than 0.05 μ to get within 10% of its final value of approximately 5 V. This is roughly four times faster than the response when $r = 100$ Ω. The price for this improved response is clear. With $r = 10$ Ω (and $\alpha^2 < \beta$), there is considerable *overshoot* and the response is *oscillatory*. If in a given design only the value of r is adjustable, selecting the best value of r can present a difficult problem. A compromise must be made between fast response with overshoot and slow response with no overshoot, with the final choice depending upon the particular application. In digital computer circuits some overshoot with its associated oscillatory behavior is frequently tolerated in order to achieve a fast response.

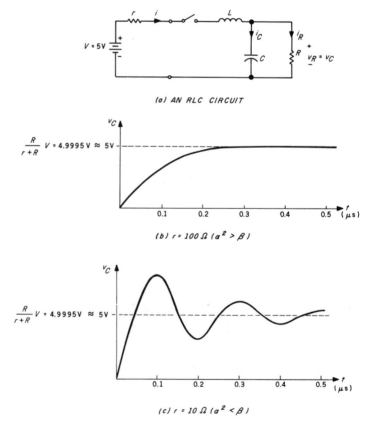

(a) AN RLC CIRCUIT

(b) $r = 100$ Ω $(\alpha^2 > \beta)$

(c) $r = 10$ Ω $(\alpha^2 < \beta)$

Figure 0.47: *RLC circuit characteristics.*

0.11 Dynamic Electrical Measurements

The versatile VOM (section 0.7) is primarily useful in situations in which the voltages and currents are not time-varying. However, the function of virtually all the electronics in a digital computer is to rapidly process, transmit, or store information in the form of electrical signals. Thus, in a digital computer most voltages and currents are changing rapidly (hence the flashing lights on front-panel displays), and instrumentation is necessary to observe these changes. Additionally, in a laboratory situation where digital networks are built and tested, it is useful to have instruments that generate time-varying voltages and currents typical of those time-varying voltages and currents in a digital computer.

0.11.1 The Function Generator

The function generator is an electronic device that typically provides three types of time-varying voltage sources or three *functions*: a *sine wave*, a *square wave*, and a *triangular wave* (see figure 0.48). A switch on the function generator allows a user to select the desired function. In addition, a

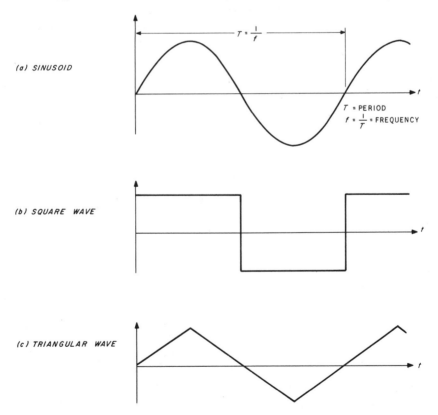

Figure 0.48: *Function-generator signals.*

function generator generally has two adjustable controls: one control selects the frequency of the desired function, while the other control selects the amplitude of the desired function. Rather inexpensive function generators can be purchased with frequency ranges between 1 and 100 kHz and voltage ranges up to 10 V. For digital computer applications, however, frequencies of 1 MHz and higher are not unusual, and a function generator with an upper limit of 5 MHz is appropriate. Although it is desirable for the internal resistance of the function generator to be as low as possible, for many electronic applications a function generator having an internal resistance of 500 Ω is suitable.

0.11.2 The Pulse Generator

Although the three-function generator is a useful all-purpose electronic laboratory instrument, a more specialized function generator is appropriate when working exclusively with digital electronics where the desired voltage variations are simply changes from a high voltage level (eg: 5 V) to a low voltage level (eg: 0 V) and vice versa. The *pulse generator* generates a *pulse train* (ie: a sequence of pulses; see figure 0.49). A *pulse* is, in effect, a burst of high voltage. In a typical pulse generator, the frequency of the pulse train f, the duration D of each pulse, and the amplitude A of each pulse are controlled by the user.

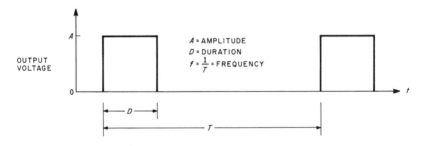

Figure 0.49: *A pulse train.*

0.11.3 The Oscilloscope

The *oscilloscope*, the most useful and versatile of all electronic instruments, provides a visual display of periodically time-varying electrical signals. Although the design and construction of a high-quality oscilloscope is extremely complex and, in total, even well beyond the capabilities of most professionals in electronics, the ideas underlying the operation of an oscilloscope are quite simple. Anyone with a need for an oscilloscope can learn to use one in a short time.

The main electronic device used in the construction of an oscilloscope is the cathode-ray tube (CRT), which converts the electrical test signal to be measured into a visual image. The basic construction of a simple CRT is diagrammed in figure 0.50a. The principles underlying the operation of a CRT are as follows:

1. A voltage is applied across the filament (ie: a wire resistor having a high power rating), causing the filament to get very hot.
2. The hot filament heats the cathode; the hot cathode emits a large number of electrons.
3. High voltage on the anodes, with respect to the cathode, produces an intense electric field in the region between the anodes and the cathode; the intense electric field causes electrons emitted from the cathode to accelerate to high velocities toward the anodes.
4. The anodes are perforated; the momentum of many of these high-velocity electrons carries them through the perforations and past the anodes.
5. Using electric and magnetic fields, the high-velocity electrons are focused into a fine beam, so that when the electron beam strikes the phosphor coating, it registers as a small spot of light on the CRT face (the screen).
6. By applying an appropriate combination of voltages to the horizontal and vertical deflecting plates, the electron beam (and thus the small spot of light) can be deflected to any point on the screen.

The rest of the oscilloscope consists of the electronic circuitry used for generating the various CRT voltages necessary to produce a visual display of periodically time-varying test voltages. The operation of an elementary oscilloscope is depicted in the block diagram in figure 0.50b.

The application of rather high voltages to the horizontal and vertical deflecting plates is required to produce observable deflections. Thus, electronic amplifiers (the vertical and horizontal amplifiers) are used to amplify the voltages being observed before they are applied to the CRT deflecting plates.* The appropriate scale factor for each amplifier setting (generally in volts per centimeter) is used to interpret the deflections on the oscilloscope screen. On most oscilloscopes vertical and horizontal input terminals, which are inputs to the vertical and horizontal amplifiers, are accessible.

To display time-varying voltages, a time-base generator is included in the

---

*To alleviate problems associated with the design of networks having high voltages with respect to ground, the vertical and horizontal amplifiers have *balanced* outputs: Although one of the two input terminals of each amplifier is grounded, neither of the two output terminals is grounded. Instead, the voltages on the two output terminals of the amplifiers are mirror images of each other, with respect to ground (zero voltage). Thus, if the input voltage to an amplifier is V and the amplifier gain is K, then the voltage on one amplifier output terminal is KV, and the voltage on the other amplifier output terminal is $-KV$. Thus, the voltage between the two amplifier output terminals is $2KV$.

oscilloscope. The time-base generator generates a voltage that increases linearly with time (a *ramp* voltage). The ramp voltage is applied to the

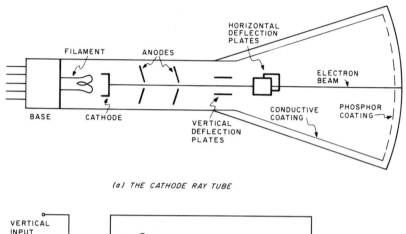

(a) THE CATHODE RAY TUBE

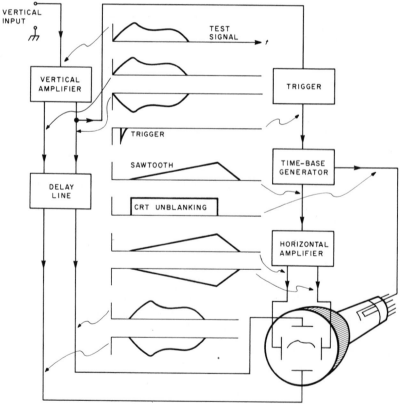

(b) OSCILLOSCOPE BLOCK DIAGRAM

Figure 0.50: *The oscilloscope.*

horizontal amplifier, and the test signal is applied to the vertical amplifier. In this manner, the motion of the CRT electron beam graphs the observed voltage; time is represented as distance along the horizontal axis, and voltage is represented as distance along the vertical axis. Thus, this scheme causes a trace of the test signal to be displayed on the oscilloscope screen. However, when the variations of interest occur in a fraction of a second (or, as is common in digital networks, a fraction of a microsecond), a single trace of the test signal occurs too quickly to be of any practical use. To solve this problem, circuitry included in the oscilloscope allows periodic test signals to be displayed repetitively. Thus, at high repetition rates, the multiple tracings are perceived as a single tracing.

For repetitive operation it is necessary that the time-base generator generate periodic time-base voltages (*sawtooth* voltages). By making the period of the time-base sawtooth signal identical to the period of the test signal, repetitive tracings are achieved. Generating a sawtooth voltage having a period identical to that of the test signal is extremely demanding unless the test signal itself is used to control the time-base generator. The *trigger* achieves the desired controlled synchronization.

The trigger electronics produce a short pulse when the test signal is at a specified voltage level and increasing. Whenever the time-base generator voltage is zero, the trigger pulse is used to initiate one tooth of the sawtooth wave, with the period determined by the user. In this manner synchronization is achieved. However, by the time the trigger circuit senses the specified voltage and initiates the sawtooth, a portion of the test signal is lost. In order not to lose any of the test signal, a delay line delays the test signal before applying it to the vertical deflecting plates. As a result, the test signal is not applied to the vertical deflecting plates until the rising portion of the sawtooth is initiated; thus, the test signal is displayed in its entirety. The CRT unblanking signal generated by the time-base generator is applied to the CRT cathode and serves to extinguish the electron beam during the falling portion of the sawtooth. Without this feature a line would appear on the screen between the point where one tracing terminates and the point where the next tracing begins.

Most oscilloscope probes are provided with interchangeable tips to simplify their connection to a test circuit. Also, scope probes are often designed to attenuate signals by a factor of 10 and are accordingly marked 10 X.

0.12 Practicalities II

In addition to those components placed in a network by design, every network has intrinsic resistors, capacitors, and inductors. The effect of these intrinsic elements upon the operation of a circuit is generally negligible. Under certain conditions, however, these intrinsic elements can alter the operation of a circuit. Hence such intrinsic network elements are frequently referred to as being *parasitic*. Laboratory situations are further complicated by the fact that the parasitic elements associated with each laboratory instrument affect the accuracy of the measurements taken; to offset the effect of these parasitic elements, specially designed instrument probes are frequently used.

0.12.1   Parasitic Elements

Parasitic elements exist in every network. For example, consider the simple network of figure 0.51a, in which a 5 V voltage source is placed across a 1 MΩ load resistor. Figure 0.51b shows what such a network might actually look like if assembled in the laboratory. In this network a parasitic resistor exists having a value equal to the resistance of the connecting wires; the parasitic resistor is in series with the 1 MΩ load resistor. In terms of high-speed digital networks, the existence of parasitic inductors and capacitors is more important than the existence of parasitic resistors.

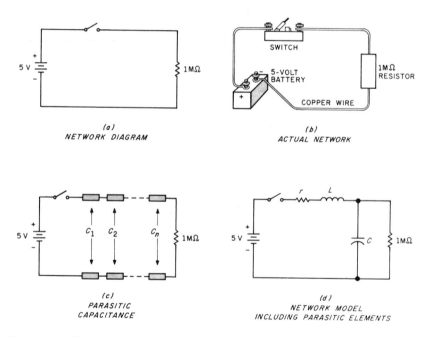

Figure 0.51: *Parasitic elements.*

This network, as wired, is essentially one closed loop of wire. As such, it is an inductor consisting of a one-turn coil. This parasitic inductance is generally small, especially when the two wires connecting the voltage source to the load resistor are placed close to each other so as to minimize the area which the loop encloses. When the switch is opened, the current through the resistor changes in a fraction of a second, and the induced voltage, which in accordance with Faraday's law is proportional to the rate of change of current (ie: $v = L\,di/dt$), can become significant.

The two wires connecting the voltage source to the 1 MΩ load resistor can be thought of as a sequence of tiny capacitors in parallel with each other; each capacitor is made up of a small segment of the wire connecting the positive battery terminal to the load resistor, the positive plate, and a small segment of the wire connecting the negative battery terminal to the load resistor, the negative plate (see figure 0.51c). Since the current through a capacitor is proportional to the rate at which the capacitor voltage varies (ie: $i = C\,dv/dt$), the current through these parasitic capacitors becomes increasingly significant at high switching speeds where rapid voltage variations can occur. Thus, parasitic capacitors play an important role in the design of high-speed digital computers. Parasitic capacitances can be minimized by placing the two wires that connect the voltage source to the load resistor as far from each other as possible (recall that capacitance is inversely proportional to the distance between capacitor plates). Unfortunately this conflicts with the objective of minimizing parasitic inductance which requires placing the wires close to each other.

It is important to note that both parasitic inductances and parasitic capacitances can be minimized by keeping all connecting wires as short as possible. Many difficulties in working with high-speed digital circuits can be avoided by observing this simple rule: *keep your wires short.* This resistor network can be represented by the relatively simple model, shown in figure 0.51d, which takes into account the parasitic elements. In this model the parasitic resistance and inductance are represented by a single parallel component. Note that this network model is the same as the *RLC* network analyzed in section 0.10.3. Because of the parasitic elements, closing the switch connecting a voltage source to a load resistor can produce a rather complex oscillatory voltage response across the resistor. Such complex voltage responses, routinely observed in digital networks, are frequently the source of erratic behavior.

0.12.2   Grounding

In an electrical network, the reference point to which all voltages are measured is called *ground potential* or simply *ground*. Thus, with respect to a particular network, ground and zero volts are synonymous. The term *ground* is traditional because one side of the 120 volt AC power line provided by electric power companies is typically at the same potential as the earth's surface. This is the result of low-resistance connections to rods driven into the earth's surface. In electronics, however, there are many networks in which the main voltage reference is not the earth's surface. Frequently, the metal chassis on which the network is mounted is the zero-voltage reference and is called *ground* even though it is not at earth's potential. The symbol for a ground point is π . Figure 0.52 shows an electric circuit in which the return connection from the load resistor to the voltage source is through ground (either the earth, a metal chassis, or a low-resistance wire).

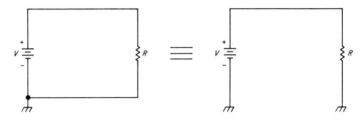

Figure 0.52: *Ground symbols.*

Ground problems can occur when connecting wires are long. For example, the 120 volt AC service provided by electric power companies is generally such that the 120 V source is the secondary of a power transformer out on the street (on a pole or buried underground). The secondary of such a transformer is grounded to earth so as to provide the grounded 120 V source. Wires are run from this transformer to the building being serviced, and within the building wires are run to the various outlets where the electric power is to be used. Figure 0.53 depicts the connection from the grounded 120 V source to a heating appliance. When the distance from the source to the appliance is great, the resistance of the connecting wire r may be significant in that there may be large voltage drops across the connecting

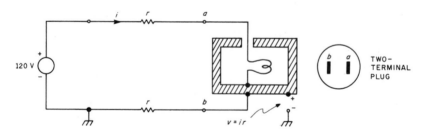

Figure 0.53: *Shock hazard due to improper grounding.*

wires; thus, the voltage across the heating element can be considerably less than 120 V. Specifically, if i amps are drawn there is a drop of $2ir$ volts in the wires and the voltage to the heating element is $V - 2ir$ volts. This reduced voltage is not unusual and most appliances function properly under a fairly wide range of voltages. Important, however, is the creation of a shock hazard which can endanger the person using the appliance. For example the heating appliance of figure 0.53 has one side of the heating element connected to the case of the heating element. Although the case is connected to ground through the return wire, the voltage between the case and ground is not zero; it is ir volts. Depending upon the values of i and r, a serious hazard can be created in which injury or death can occur. Figure 0.54 shows how this hazard is eliminated by redesigning the heating appliance using a three-terminal plug. Here the appliance case is not connected to the heating element at all, but instead is connected to a local ground through the third terminal.

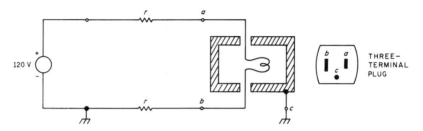

Figure 0.54: *Three-wire system.*

0.12.3 Oscilloscope Probes

In the use of an oscilloscope to measure rapidly time-varying voltages, three major sources of error occur. The first, *inductive noise pickup*, is due to the presence of time-varying magnetic fields (generated by the 60 Hz power lines and other electrical equipment in the vicinity) linking the circuit loops which are formed by the connections between the oscilloscope and the network on which measurements are being taken. The second, *capacitive noise pickup*, is due to the presence of unwanted electric fields. The third, *high-frequency amplifier attenuation*, is due to the parasitic capacitances present across the inputs of the oscilloscope's vertical and horizontal amplifiers; high-frequency amplifier attenuation causes rapidly time-varying signals to be distorted.

Inductive noise pickup, difficult to avoid, is frequently caused when the parasitic inductive loops of a circuit are linked by extraneous magnetic fields which are produced by nearby electrical equipment. Such parasitic inductive loops are often difficult to identify. Especially troublesome are those circuits constructed on a metal chassis and where the chassis itself serves as the common ground. In such circuits, loops exist in which the chassis itself forms a path in the loop. The existence of such loops, called *ground loops*, may not be obvious. In many practical situations where many pieces of electronic equipment and many instruments are interconnected into a single complex network, identification of troublesome ground loops can be especially difficult. However, rearranging equipment and wires is often helpful in reducing inductive noise. Fortunately, inductive noise is not generally a problem in digital electronics.

Both capacitive noise pickup and high-frequency amplifier attenuation can be minimized by using the specially designed input-voltage probes to make connections to the oscilloscope's input amplifiers. These voltage probes are *shielded* to guard against pickup of stray electric fields, thus serving to reduce capacitive noise pickup. In addition, the probes frequently contain RC networks to compensate for unavoidable parasitic capacitance in the oscilloscope's input amplifiers. These probe networks are frequently adjustable; the adjustment typically involves displaying a known high-quality test signal (eg: a pulse) and varying the adjustable component of the network, usually a variable capacitor (see problem P0.13 at the end of this chapter), until the edges of the pulse are as square as possible. In order to be aware of the limitations of the oscilloscope, it is important to understand the theory underlying the operation of the probe's compensation network.

The simplest approach to using an oscilloscope to study digital circuits is to connect the oscilloscope directly to the digital circuit as shown in figure 0.55a. If the oscilloscope is not to load the digital circuit, then its input resistance ought to be high; ideally, the current i drawn by the oscilloscope should be zero. A probe is generally used to minimize the loading effect of the oscilloscope on the digital circuit. A simple probe consists of a current-limiting series resistor as shown in figure 0.55b. For purposes of analysis, this entire system consisting of the digital circuit being studied, the oscilloscope, and the probe can be replaced by a simple equivalent circuit; the digital circuit is replaced by a voltage source v_1 and, assuming the oscilloscope presents a resistive load at its input, the oscilloscope is replaced by a resistor R_2 (see figure 0.55c).

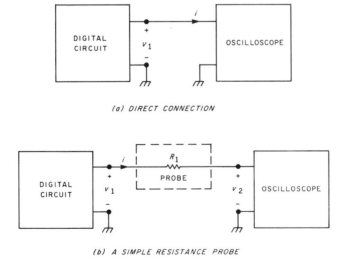

(a) DIRECT CONNECTION

(b) A SIMPLE RESISTANCE PROBE

Figure 0.55: *Oscilloscope probes.*

However, when the oscilloscope is used to observe time-varying signals, the resistor R_2 is not a suitable equivalent for the oscilloscope. Because of the parasitic capacitances in the oscilloscope's input amplifiers, a better representation of the oscilloscope, in terms of its loading effect, is the parallel resistor-capacitor combination shown in figure 0.55d. The effect of the oscilloscope's input capacitance C_2 is to distort the signal v_2 so that it is not simply a fixed fraction of v_1. The voltage v_2 is proportional to the charge stored in C_2 and thus v_2 responds dynamically to changes in v_1; the speed of response depends upon how quickly capacitor C_2 can be charged or discharged. It is possible to compensate for the effect of the oscilloscope input capacitance C_2 by using an oscilloscope probe that is slightly more complex than the single series resistor R_1; a probe consisting of a parallel resistor-capacitor combination is fairly common (see figure 0.55e).

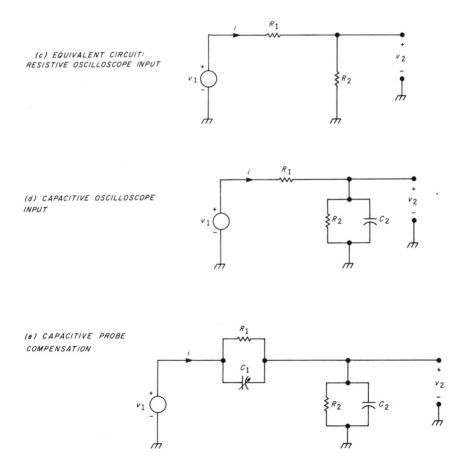

(c) EQUIVALENT CIRCUIT: RESISTIVE OSCILLOSCOPE INPUT

(d) CAPACITIVE OSCILLOSCOPE INPUT

(e) CAPACITIVE PROBE COMPENSATION

Figure 0.55 cont.

In many probes, capacitor C_1 is variable and is adjusted to provide the least distortion for the particular oscilloscope with which it is being used. In using an oscilloscope effectively, it is important to understand how the oscilloscope can distort a signal and how the probe can compensate for this distortion. Toward this end, an understanding of the circuit of figure 0.55e is essential.

Application of Kirchhoff's current law in the circuit of figure 0.55e results in

$$i_{R2} = i_{R1} + i_{C1} - i_{C2}$$

Use of Ohm's law and the defining equations for a capacitor (ie: $i = C \, dv/dt$) in the above equation gives

$$\frac{v_2}{R_2} = \frac{v_1 - v_2}{R_1} + C_1 \frac{d(v_1 - v_2)}{dt} - C_2 \frac{dv_2}{dt}$$

This equation can be rewritten:

$$\frac{dv_2}{dt} = \frac{C_1}{C_1 + C_2} \frac{dv_1}{dt} + \frac{1}{R_1 C_1} \frac{C_1}{C_1 + C_2} v_1 - \frac{1}{R_1 C_1} \frac{R_1 + R_2}{R_2} \frac{C_1}{C_1 + C_2} v_2$$

Something especially interesting occurs when $R_1 C_1 = R_2 C_2$. In this case,

$$\frac{C_1}{C_1 + C_2} = \frac{R_2}{R_1 + R_2}$$

To simplify notation, let

$$K = \frac{C_1}{C_1 + C_2} = \frac{R_2}{R_1 + R_2}$$

$$\tau = R_1 C_1 = R_2 C_2$$

Thus,

$$\frac{dv_2}{dt} = K \frac{dv_1}{dt} + \frac{1}{\tau} (Kv_1 - v_2)$$

This equation is significant in terms of the distortion of the signal v_2. If at any time $v_2 = Kv_1$, then

$$\frac{dv_2}{dt} = K \frac{dv_1}{dt}$$

That is, v_2 changes K times as fast as v_1, and v_2 continues to stay equal to Kv_1 for all time thereafter. Thus, except for a scale factor K, v_2 follows v_1 with no distortion. If, because of initial charges on capacitors C_1 and C_2, v_2 is not equal to Kv_1, then

$$\frac{dv_2}{dt} = K \frac{dv_1}{dt}$$

However, setting v_1 to any constant voltage causes v_2 to approach Kv_1 asymptotically with time constant τ, ie: if $v_1 = $ constant, and if

$$\frac{dv_1}{dt} = 0$$

then

$$\frac{dv_2}{dt} = -\frac{1}{\tau} v_2 + \frac{1}{\tau} Kv_1$$

The solution to this first-order linear nonhomogeneous differential equation is (see appendix A1)

$$v_2(t) = v_2(0)e^{-t/\tau} - Kv_1(e^{-t/\tau} - 1)$$

Thus, as t approaches infinity (in practical applications, five time constants τ is generally a long enough period) a steady-state is reached in which

$$\frac{dv_2}{dt} = 0$$

and $v_2 = Kv_1$; again, v_2 is a constant factor of v_1.

Therefore, if a parallel resistor-capacitor compensating oscilloscope probe is used in which the variable probe capacitor is adjusted so that $R_1C_1 = R_2C_2 = \tau$, and if the time constant τ is small compared to the length of time necessary for significant variations to occur in the voltage v_1 being observed (ie: if over any time interval of duration τ seconds, the voltage v_1 can be considered to be practically constant), then the probe's output voltage v_2, which is applied to the oscilloscope's input amplifiers, will have no discernible distortion; v_2 will be proportional to v_1: $v_2 = Kv_1$ where

$$K = \frac{R_2}{R_1 + R_2}$$

0.12.4 Identifying Capacitors

Capacitors, perhaps even more so than resistors, vary in sizes and shapes.

Identifying capacitors with certainty can be a difficult assignment even for an experienced technician. For this reason a capacitance bridge is extremely helpful. In general the accuracy of capacitors required for use in digital circuits is so low that even a very inexpensive bridge, providing an accuracy of 5 percent, is more than adequate. If there is any doubt about a capacitor's value, its value should be determined on a capacitance bridge.

Most of the capacitors used are either *ceramic* capacitors, in the form of a disk, or *electrolytic* capacitors, in the form of cylindrical tubes. The disk-type ceramic capacitors have the capacitance value written on the body; decimal fractions are microfarads and whole numbers are picofarads. The electrolytic capacitors are also explicitly marked. However, the voltage and polarity ratings of electrolytic capacitors are critical and must not be violated. If either excessive voltage or reverse polarity is applied to an electrolytic capacitor, *leakage current* flows; as a result the capacitor is heated and eventually destroyed.

PROBLEMS

P0.1:   Find the force (magnitude and direction) on charge q_1 in figures P0.1 a, b, and c. In each part, $q_1 = 0.5 \times 10^{-3}$ coulombs, $q_2 = 1.5 \times 10^{-3}$ coulombs, $q_3 = 1.0 \times 10^{-3}$ coulombs, and $q_4 = 1.5 \times 10^{-3}$ coulombs.

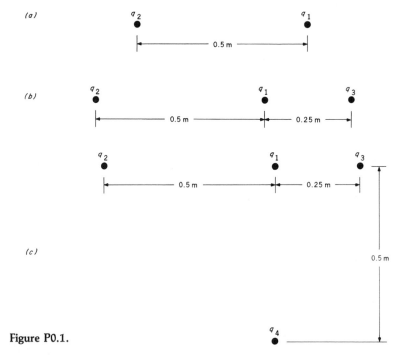

Figure P0.1.

P0.2: There is a distribution of charges surrounding the rectangular area shown in figure P0.2, such that a unit charge placed *anywhere* within this area experiences a force of 1 newton at an angle of 45° to the horizontal (as shown). Determine the potential differences v_{ab}, v_{bc}, v_{cd}, and v_{da}. *Check:* is the conservation of energy satisfied (ie: what is the sum $v_{ab} + v_{bc} + v_{cd} + v_{da}$)?

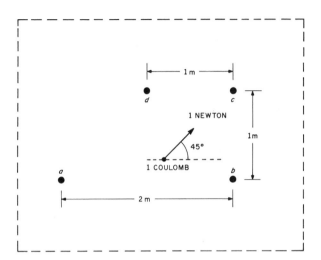

Figure P0.2.

P0.3: In the following problems, refer to table P0.3 to determine the appropriate wire diameters.
(a) The resistivity of standard annealed copper is 1.7241×10^{-8} meter-ohms. What is the resistance of a 6-inch length of No. 26 copper wire?
(b) What is the minimum diameter of a 6-inch length of aluminum wire (resistivity of 2.83×10^{-8} meter-ohms) whose resistance is not to exceed that of a 6-inch length of No. 26 copper wire? Give answer in millimeters (mm).
(c) Repeat (b) for carbon steel (35×10^{-8} meter-ohms).
(d) What is the resistance of a 1-foot length of No. 26 copper wire?
(e) What is the resistance of a 2-foot length of No. 20 copper wire?

Table P0.3.

DIAMETER IN MILS	120	91	81	72	64	57	51	45	40	36
AWG NO.	10	11	12	13	14	15	16	17	18	19

DIAMETER IN MILS	32	28.5	25.3	22.6	20.1	17.9	15.9	14.2	12.6
AWG NO.	20	21	22	23	24	25	26	27	28

P0.4:   A 6-inch length of No. 26 copper wire has 2 amperes of current flowing through it. What is the voltage across the ends of the wire? How much power is the wire dissipating? How much energy does this wire dissipate in 1 minute?

P0.5:   It has been determined that a 6-inch length of No. 26 copper wire is dissipating 0.01 watts. How much current is passing through the wire? What is the voltage across the wire?

P0.6:   For each of the resistor networks shown in figure P0.6, compute the voltage across and the current through each resistor, compute the current i being supplied by the 5 V voltage source, and compute the equivalent resistance R_{AB} between points A and B (with the voltage source disconnected). Record the results of your computation in the appropriate table below each circuit diagram. Note that there is room for two entries for each variable. The results of your computations should be entered in the top blank; the lower blank is reserved for laboratory measurements to be taken in problem P0.11.

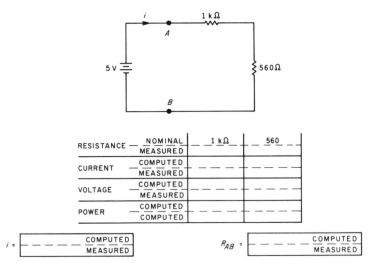

RESISTANCE —	NOMINAL	1 kΩ	560
	MEASURED		
CURRENT	COMPUTED		
	MEASURED		
VOLTAGE	COMPUTED		
	MEASURED		
POWER	COMPUTED		
	COMPUTED		

$i =$ | COMPUTED |
       | MEASURED |

$R_{AB} =$ | COMPUTED |
            | MEASURED |

(a)

Figure   P0.6.

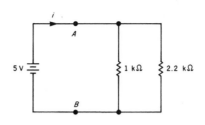

RESISTANCE	NOMINAL	1 kΩ	2.2 kΩ
	MEASURED		
CURRENT	COMPUTED		
	MEASURED		
VOLTAGE	COMPUTED		
	MEASURED		
POWER	COMPUTED		
	COMPUTED		

$i =$	COMPUTED
	MEASURED

$R_{AB} =$	COMPUTED
	MEASURED

(b)

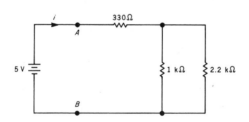

RESISTANCE	NOMINAL	330 Ω	1 kΩ	2.2 kΩ
	MEASURED			
CURRENT	COMPUTED			
	MEASURED			
VOLTAGE	COMPUTED			
	MEASURED			
POWER	COMPUTED			
	COMPUTED			

$i =$	COMPUTED
	MEASURED

$R_{AB} =$	COMPUTED
	MEASURED

(c)

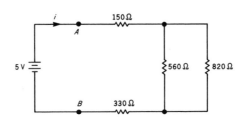

RESISTANCE	NOMINAL	150 Ω	330 Ω	560 Ω	820 Ω
	MEASURED				
CURRENT	COMPUTED				
	MEASURED				
VOLTAGE	COMPUTED				
	MEASURED				
POWER	COMPUTED				
	COMPUTED				

$i =$	COMPUTED
	MEASURED

$R_{AB} =$	COMPUTED
	MEASURED

(d)

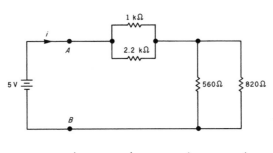

RESISTANCE	NOMINAL	1 kΩ	2.2 kΩ	560 Ω	820 Ω
	MEASURED				
CURRENT	COMPUTED				
	MEASURED				
VOLTAGE	COMPUTED				
	MEASURED				
POWER	COMPUTED				
	COMPUTED				

$i =$	COMPUTED
	MEASURED

$R_{AB} =$	COMPUTED
	MEASURED

(e)

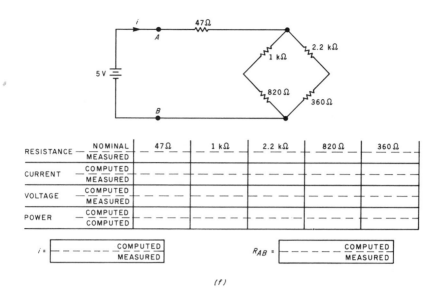

		NOMINAL	47 Ω	1 kΩ	2.2 kΩ	820 Ω	360 Ω
RESISTANCE		MEASURED					
CURRENT		COMPUTED					
		MEASURED					
VOLTAGE		COMPUTED					
		MEASURED					
POWER		COMPUTED					
		COMPUTED					

$i =$
COMPUTED
MEASURED

$R_{AB} =$
COMPUTED
MEASURED

(f)

Figure   P0.6.

P0.7: Consider the loaded voltage source shown in figure P0.7a. The open-circuit terminal voltage v_o of the voltage source (ie: the voltage with $R_L = \infty$ and thus $i = 0$) is measured and found to be 5 V; thus $E = 5$ V. With $R_L = 5\ \Omega$, v_o is again measured and found to be 4.63 V; thus $i = 4.63/5 = 0.926$ A and the internal resistance $r = (E - v_o)/i = (5 - 4.63)/0.926 = 0.4\ \Omega$. On the coordinate systems given in figures P0.7b and P0.7c, graph the terminal voltage v_o versus i and the terminal voltage v_o versus R_L.

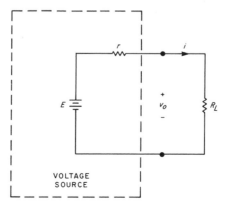

(a)

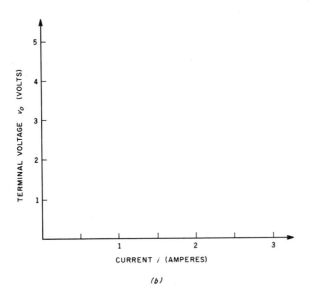

(b)

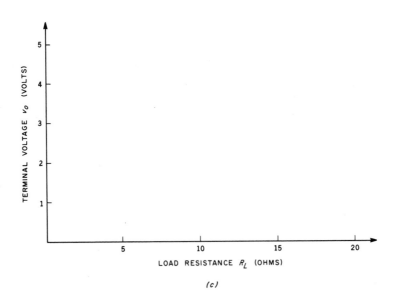

(c)

Figure P0.7: *Loading a voltage source.*

P0.8: For the 25 kΩ potentiometer shown in figure P0.8a, f is the fraction of the 25 kΩ between terminals a and b; $0 \le f \le 1$. Graph v_o versus f for $R_L = \infty$ (no load), $R_L = 1 \text{ M}\Omega$, $R_L = 25 \text{ k}\Omega$, and $R_L = 1 \text{ k}\Omega$ (all on the same coordinate system given in figure P0.8b).

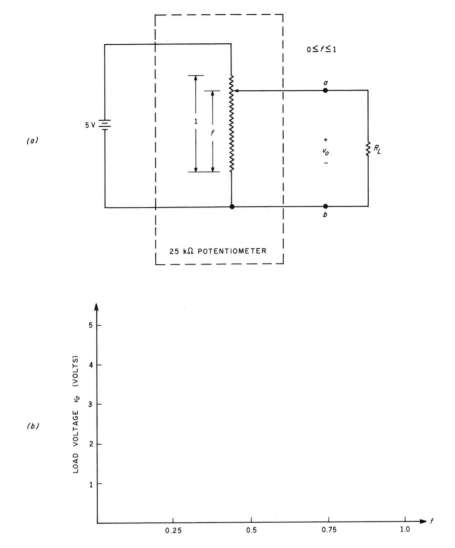

Figure P0.8: *Loading a potentiometer.*

P0.9: You are given a D'Arsonval meter movement which has a resistance R_m of 50 Ω, and which gives a full-scale needle deflection when 2 μA flows through it.

(a) Use this meter movement in the design of the following instruments:

- a 5 mA ammeter: Shunt Resistor = _____ Ω
  Ammeter Resistance = _____ Ω
- a 5 V voltmeter: Series Resistor = _____ Ω
  Voltmeter Resistance = _____ Ω

(b) Compare the effectiveness of the ammeter you designed to the effectiveness of the ammeter designed in section 0.7.2 in terms of the accuracy of current measurements in the two circuits of figure 0.27 (page 35).

(c) Compare the effectiveness of the voltmeter you designed to the effectiveness of the voltmeter designed in section 0.7.3 in terms of the accuracy of voltage measurements in the circuit of figure 0.29 (page 37).

P0.10:   Consider the ohmmeter circuit of figure 0.30 (page 38) for the case that the voltage source $V = 1.5$ volts.

(a) Determine the value of resistor R so that a voltmeter reading of 0.5 V corresponds to a resistance measurement of 1 kΩ (ie: $R_x = 1$ kΩ).

(b) Using a resistor R having the value you just computed and a voltage source V of 1.5 V in the ohmmeter circuit of figure 0.30, calibrate a voltmeter, which gives a full-scale deflection when 1.5 V is applied to it, so it can be used to read directly in ohms. Use the voltmeter scale of figure P0.10 to record your results.

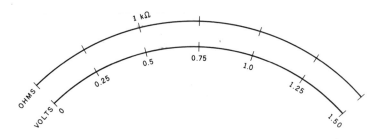

Figure P0.10: *Calibrating a voltmeter to be used in an ohmmeter.*

P0.11:   Check the computations of problem P0.6 in the laboratory. Construct each of the six circuits on your solderless breadboard and make the appropriate measurements using a VOM. Specifically:

(a) Measure the voltage across each resistor and record the value in the appropriate table of figure P0.6.

(b) Measure the current i supplied to each circuit by the 5 V supply. Record the values.

(c) *Disconnect* the 5 V supply and measure the resistance between terminals a and b. Record the values.

(d) Compute the current through each resistor by dividing the voltage measured across the resistor by its nominal resistance value. Record the values.

(e) Compute the resistance between terminals a and b by dividing the measured value of the supply voltage by the measured value of the supply current. Record the values.

(f) Measure the value of each resistor used. Record the values based on your measurements and comment on the differences between the computational results obtained here.

P0.12: The circuit shown in figure P0.12 includes a 12.6 V transformer. A 12.6 V transformer is one that gives a sinusoidal voltage output with a peak value of 17.82 V ($12.6\sqrt{2} = 17.82$) when the input voltage v_s is a sinusoidal voltage with a peak value of 169.7 V (ie: the standard 120 V, 60 Hz AC; $120\sqrt{2} = 169.7$). For this circuit, graph (on the same coordinate system) v_s, i_1, i_2, and v_R against time for the case $R = 100\ \Omega$. Given that there are 2000 turns in the transformer's primary coil, how many turns are in the secondary coil?

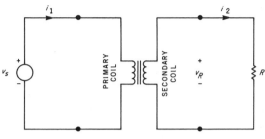

Figure P0.12.   12.6 VOLT TRANSFORMER

P0.13: An analysis in section 0.12.3 shows how a capacitive probe can be used with an oscilloscope to compensate for distortions introduced by the parasitic capacitances of an oscilloscope's input amplifiers. The equivalent circuit of figure 0.55e, in which both the oscilloscope and the probe are represented by a parallel combination of a resistor and a capacitor, forms the basis for this analysis; recall that voltage v_1 is the voltage to be displayed and v_2 is the voltage at the input of the oscilloscope's amplifier. Voltage v_2 is generally a distorted representation of v_1; the purpose of the probe is to minimize this distortion. The relationship between v_1 and v_2 is derived in section 0.12.3 and is given by the following differential equation:

$$\frac{dv_2}{dt} = -\frac{1}{R_1 C_1}\frac{R_1 + R_2}{R_2}\frac{C_1}{C_1 + C_2}v_2 + \frac{1}{R_1 C_1}\frac{C_1}{C_1 + C_2}v_1$$
$$+ \frac{C_1}{C_1 + C_2}\frac{dv_1}{dt}$$

However, if there is to be no distortion, the relationship between v_2 and v_1 should be simply proportional, $v_2 = Kv_1$. The objective of this exercise is to demonstrate *in the laboratory* that a properly designed probe can minimize distortion.

Consider the situation in which voltage v_1 is a step voltage. A step voltage can be obtained by closing a switch connected to a DC voltage source, as shown in figure P0.13a; a sequence of steps occurs with a pulse generator. After the switch is closed,

$$v_1 = V \qquad \text{and} \qquad \frac{dv_1}{dt} = 0$$

Assume C_1 and C_2 (figure P0.13e) are initially uncharged (and therefore the voltage across both capacitors is zero). When the switch is closed, Kirchhoff's voltage law demands that the sum of the voltages across C_1 and C_2 be equal to V. This can occur only if there is charge on the capacitors. An enormous surge of current flows to charge the capacitors in an infinitesimally short time. This instantaneous charging of the capacitors is theoretically possible because the path from voltage source V through the capacitors C_1 and C_2 includes no resistors; in a real situation the internal resistance of voltage source V and the parsitic resistance of the two capacitors would result in a generally small, but finite, charging time. Thus,

$$v_2(0+) = \frac{C_1}{C_1 + C_2} V = \text{the voltage across } C_2 \text{ immediately after the switch is closed.}$$

$$v_{C1}(0+) = \frac{C_2}{C_1 + C_2} V = \text{the voltage across } C_1 \text{ immediately after the switch is closed.}$$

Let

$$x = \frac{1}{R_1 C_1} \frac{R_1 + R_2}{R_2} \frac{C_1}{C_1 + C_2} \quad \text{and} \quad y = \frac{1}{R_1 C_1} \frac{C_1}{C_1 + C_2} V$$

Therefore,

$$\frac{dv_2}{dt} = -xv_2 + y \quad \text{and} \quad v_2(0+) = \frac{C_1}{C_1 + C_2} V$$

The solution to this first order linear homogeneous differential equation is (see appendix A.1)

$$v_2 = \frac{C_1}{C_1 + C_2} V \exp - \left[\left(\frac{1}{R_1 C_1} \frac{R_1 + R_2}{R_2} \frac{C_1}{C_1 + C_2} \right) t \right]$$
$$+ \frac{R_2}{R_1 + R_2} V \left\{ 1 - \exp \left[-\left(\frac{1}{R_1 C_1} \frac{R_1 + R_2}{R_2} \frac{C_1}{C_1 + C_2} \right) t \right] \right\}$$

Consider the case that $R_1 = 10 \text{ k}\Omega$, $R_2 = 47 \text{ k}\Omega$, $C_1 = 0.047 \mu F$, $C_s = 0.01 \mu F$, and $V = 5$ volts.

(a) Using the above equation for v_2, graph v_2 versus t for the circuits of figures P0.13b, c, d, and e, for the case that v_1 is a step voltage. Your graphs should cover the interval from $t = 0$ to $t = 1$ millisecond.

For the following laboratory exercises, v_1 is a 1 kHz pulse generator with an amplitude of 5 V.

(b) Use the pulse-generator and the oscilloscope to verify the analytic results of part (a) of this exercise. Carefully sketch v_1, the pulse-generator square-wave, and the output signals v_2; show the time-base scale and the amplitude scale.

(c) The objective here is to demonstrate how a capacitive load, such as an uncompensated oscilloscope, distorts and attenuates high-frequency signals. Take the necessary measurements on the circuit of figure P0.18c (v_1 is the pulse-generator signal) to graph $v_{2(max)}$ versus f (where f is the pulse-generator frequency in hertz) for the following:

- $R_1 = 10 \text{ k}\Omega$, $R_2 = 47 \text{ k}\Omega$, $C_2 = 0.047 \mu F$
- $R_1 = 10 \text{ k}\Omega$, $R_2 = 47 \text{ k}\Omega$, $C_2 = 0.01 \mu F$

In each case, vary frequency between 100 Hz and 100 kHz. Also in each case, sketch the observed wave forms for the lowest and highest frequencies (ie: for 100 Hz and 100 kHz).

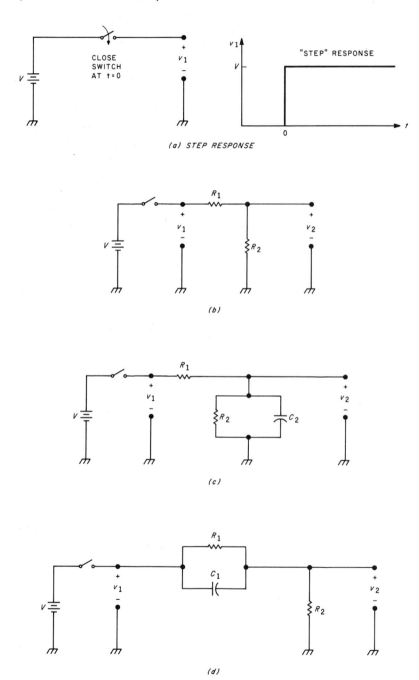

Figure P0.13: *Capacitive compensation for capacitive loads.*

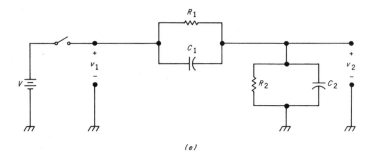

(e)

Figure P0.13 cont.

P0.14: In the circuit shown in figure P0.14, a heating element having a resistance of 10 Ω is to be used at a location 75 feet from the 120 V, 60 Hz AC source that is to power it. Determine the peak value of voltage V_g when the two 75-foot wires used to make the connections are AWG No. 18 annealed copper. Repeat for AWG No. 22 and AWG No. 26 annealed copper wires.

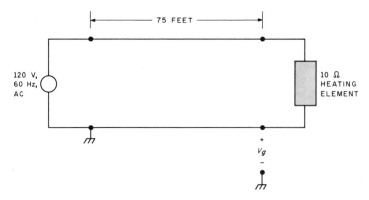

Figure P0.14.

Chapter 1

Introduction to Digital Electronics

A *digital system* is an information processing system in which information is represented by physical quantities (ie: *signals*) constrained to take on only discrete values. A digital computer is the ultimate digital system. Most digital systems are *binary* systems, in that the signals represent only *two* discrete values (eg: 5 V and 0 V). Symbolically, the two values may be represented by HIGH and LOW or by "1" and "0."

The simplest and most fundamental binary device is the *two-position switch*. A two-position switch is defined as a single-input/single-output binary device, such that the output is HIGH when the input is HIGH, and the output is LOW when the input is LOW.

An *inverter* represents an important variation of a switch. The inverter, also a single-input/single-output binary device, produces a HIGH output when the input is LOW and vice versa. Block diagrams of the switch and inverter are shown in figures 1.1a and 1.1b. The *truth table* defining the binary input/output relationship for each device is also given.

The inverter is a more fundamental digital system building block than is the switch, in that a switch can be built by cascading two inverters (see figure 1.1c); no combination of switches can be used to build an inverter. For this reason the emphasis here is on the design and construction of inverters.

1.1 Implementation of Switches

The ideal inverter is defined by the relationship of the two binary variables, v_i and v_o, given in the truth table of figure 1.1b. This binary relationship can also be represented graphically as in figure 1.2a; for convenience, the discrete values are taken to be 0 and 1. An inverter can be implemented with a device in which the input and output variables are con-

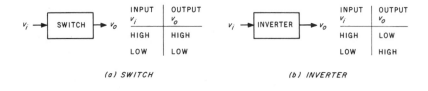

INPUT v_i	OUTPUT v_o
HIGH	HIGH
LOW	LOW

(a) SWITCH

INPUT v_i	OUTPUT v_o
HIGH	LOW
LOW	HIGH

(b) INVERTER

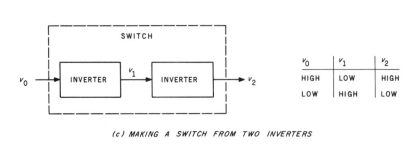

v_0	v_1	v_2
HIGH	LOW	HIGH
LOW	HIGH	LOW

(c) MAKING A SWITCH FROM TWO INVERTERS

Figure 1.1: *Switches and inverters.*

tinuous if the relationship between the variables is correct for both discrete values of the input. An acceptable continuous input/output (I/O) relationship is shown in figure 1.2b. If the output is observed only when the input is 0 or 1, then the inverter relationship is satisfied. Unfortunately, an inverter made from a device with continuous characteristics similar to those of figure 1.2b is generally not suitable in the construction of a digital computer. To achieve the complex functional capabilities typical of modern digital computers, it is not uncommon to use thousands of switching devices. Thus, each switch is imbedded in a complex switching network. Although there are many devices that can function properly as a single switch isolated from other devices, the performance of some of these devices deteriorates when they are made part of a complex switching network. The problems are that:

- It is difficult to mass-produce an inexpensive device so that the two critical points of the I/O characteristics are accurately fixed under all possible operating conditions (eg: temperature, humidity, etc).
- Within a large switching network, it is difficult to guarantee that inputs to a switching device will assume only the two specified discrete values (ie: 0 and 1).

In other words, a device with the characteristics of figure 1.2b is too *sensitive* in terms of both the vagaries of the manufacturing process and the input variations possible. It is essential that a switch which is to be used as a digital system component be insensitive to these variations.

Figure 1.2c shows a set of I/O characteristics providing the proper inverter switching even when the input is in error but "close enough." Within large ranges of $v_i = 0$ and $v_i = 1$, variations in v_i do not produce changes in v_o. Thus, an inverter built from a device having such I/O characteristics is input-insensitive.

If all switching devices used in the construction of a digital system are input-insensitive, the problem of having to precisely specify a switching device's I/O characteristics is eliminated. In such cases, the only requirement is that the input characteristics be "flat" (ie: in the neighborhood of the two discrete defining points),

$$\frac{dv_o}{dv_i} = 0$$

It is not necessary that the states $v_o = 0$ and $v_o = 1$ be achieved exactly because the output of one switch becomes the input to another switch, which is also input-insensitive. Consequently, if the inverters are input-insensitive, they can be manufactured to rather wide tolerances (see figure 1.2d).

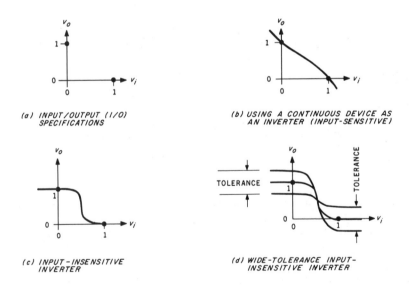

(a) INPUT/OUTPUT (I/O) SPECIFICATIONS

(b) USING A CONTINUOUS DEVICE AS AN INVERTER (INPUT-SENSITIVE)

(c) INPUT-INSENSITIVE INVERTER

(d) WIDE-TOLERANCE INPUT-INSENSITIVE INVERTER

Figure 1.2: *Inverter construction from continuous devices.*

Two examples of input-insensitive switching devices appear in figure 1.3. Figure 1.3a shows the common electrical switch; the input is the force v_i and the output is the voltage v_o. Figure 1.3b shows the electrical relay in which the input is voltage v_i (applied to a ferromagnetic-core coil, the electromagnet) and the output is voltage v_o.

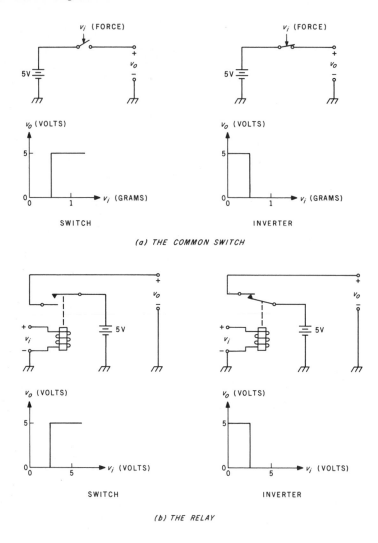

Figure 1.3: *Real switches.*

The input of the common switch is mechanical (a force) and the output is electrical (a voltage). Such a device is suitable for inputting information into a digital computer, and it is the basic device used in the construction of most keyboards. The common switch, however, is not useful as a component in the construction of data processing digital networks; in such networks both the input and the output of all components must be electrical.

In contrast, the relay's input and output are both electrical. The relay is especially suitable for the remote control of large transfers of electrical energy. Although the relay could conceivably be used as a digital network element, it is an electromechanical device (ie: the operation of the relay depends upon moving parts) not suitable for high-speed digital networks. Data processing switching devices used in a digital computer are required to transfer only minute amounts of energy (ie: only enough energy to unambiguously discriminate between a HIGH or a LOW, or one *bit* of information), but they may be called upon to do so several million times per second for 24 hours a day. In such a setting the relay is a relatively slow device and is of limited reliability as contacts, springs, and pivots begin to wear.

The processing of digital data at the high speeds typical of present-day digital computers requires a high-speed, high-reliability, electrical-input, electrical-output switching device. Electromechanical devices such as relays are inappropriate not only because they do not meet the high-speed and high-reliability requirements, but also because they require too much energy and are relatively expensive. Resistor networks are inappropriate because the nonlinear input-insensitive characteristics cannot be attained by networks consisting of only resistors. In fact, electronic switches constructed from *semiconductors* are the only devices presently available that are suitable for high-speed digital data processing. This chapter presents an introduction to semiconductor devices, with emphasis on those semiconductor devices used in present-day digital computers.

1.2 Semiconductors

Semiconductors are essential to the operation of most present-day electronic devices. Recall that a material is called a *semiconductor* if its resistivity is too high to be classified as a conductor, but too low to be classified as an insulator. The most frequently used semiconductors are silicon and germanium. When ordinary voltages are applied to pure silicon or pure germanium, extremely small current flows on the order of 1 nA are typical. Such small currents are insignificant in digital electronic networks; pure semiconductors (ie: *intrinsic* semiconductors) are not useful materials in the construction of digital electronic devices. However, the addition of even minute amounts of certain impurities by a process called *doping* can greatly increase the conduction of a semiconductor. For example, doping germanium with antimony at the rate of 1 antimony atom to every million germanium atoms reduces the resistivity of the germanium by a factor of over 1200.

The reduction of resistivity of an intrinsic semiconductor by doping is based upon the tetrahedral crystal structure of elements having four valence electrons, such as silicon and germanium (see figure 1.4a). In these materials, each of the four valence electrons of each atom forms a covalent bond with an electron of a neighboring atom (see figure 1.4b). Of all the electrons in an atom, the *valence electrons* (ie: the electrons in an atom's outermost orbit) are those that can be freed from the atom with the least energy. They are largely responsible for any current that flows in a material. However, an electron that is bound in a covalent pairing can be freed only by applying a large force to it. Electrically, this requires the application of large voltages across a semiconductor so as to produce an intense electric field within the semiconductor. Hence, intrinsic semiconductors have high resistivity. The addition of certain impurities to an intrinsic semiconductor modifies the tetrahedral crystal structure by freeing valence electrons from covalent bonds, making it easier for electric-field forces to move them.

Doping silicon or germanium with impurities, such as phosphorus, arsenic, or antimony, which have five valence electrons results in an *n-type semiconductor*. In an n-type semiconductor, the tetrahedral structure of the intrinsic semiconductor is altered, in that each atom of the impurity replaces an atom of the intrinsic semiconductor. Since only four of the five valence electrons of the impurity atom are required to complete the covalent bonds, one valence electron of each impurity atom does not form a covalent bond (see figure 1.4c). Such a *free electron* is relatively free to move and does so when relatively small forces (ie: electric fields or voltages) are applied; hence, the resistivity of the n-doped semiconductor is greatly reduced.

Similarly, impurities in the form of elements, such as boron, aluminum, gallium, and indium, which have three valence electrons result in *p-type semiconductors*. Again, the tetrahedral crystal structure of the intrinsic semiconductor is altered when an impurity atom replaces an atom of the intrinsic semiconductor. All three valence electrons of the impurity atom are used in a covalent bond. However, since four valence electrons are required to complete the tetrahedral structure, one valence electron of an atom is not linked to a valence electron of another atom in a bonding pair (see figure 1.4d). The missing electron in the unfilled covalent bond, commonly called a *hole*, produces conditions favorable for the relatively free motion of electrons; an electron from a neighboring atom is easily captured to fill the hole. The capture of an electron from a covalent bond of one atom to fill the hole of another atom can be thought of as the motion of a hole. The motion of a hole is equivalent to the motion of positive charge. Again, the resistivity of the semiconductor is greatly reduced.

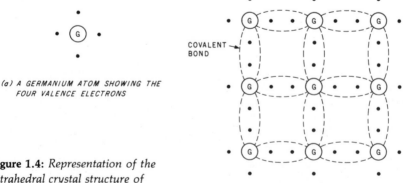

(a) A GERMANIUM ATOM SHOWING THE
    FOUR VALENCE ELECTRONS

Figure 1.4: *Representation of the tetrahedral crystal structure of germanium (or silicon).*

(b) TETRAHEDRAL CRYSTAL STRUCTURE
    OF GERMANIUM (OR SILICON)
    SHOWING THE COVALENT BONDS

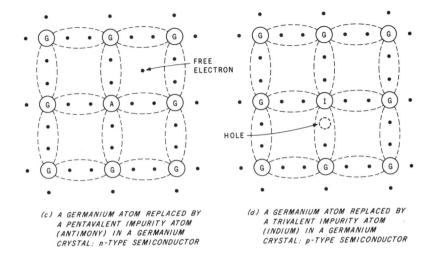

(c) A GERMANIUM ATOM REPLACED BY
   A PENTAVALENT IMPURITY ATOM
   (ANTIMONY) IN A GERMANIUM
   CRYSTAL: n-TYPE SEMICONDUCTOR

(d) A GERMANIUM ATOM REPLACED BY
   A TRIVALENT IMPURITY ATOM
   (INDIUM) IN A GERMANIUM
   CRYSTAL: p-TYPE SEMICONDUCTOR

Figure 1.4 cont.

1.3   The Semiconductor Diode (The pn Junction)

An important phenomenon occurs at a *pn junction*, which is formed when a p-type semiconductor is placed in close contact with an n-type semiconductor. Because of thermal energy, there is a certain amount of electron motion in all materials. In the absence of an electric field, this electron motion is totally random and no net current is produced in any direction. However, in the vicinity of a pn junction, the situation is quite different. On one side of the junction, within the n material, are free electrons not constrained by covalent bonds, and on the other side of the junction, within the p material, are holes ever ready to seize an electron to complete a covalent bond. Any randomly moving electron that happens to cross the pn junction is seized by a hole, producing a covalent bond, and that electron tends not to return. Therefore, there is a net *diffusion current* that flows across the pn junction. The diffusion current results in an accumulation of negative charges on the p side of the junction and an accumulation of positive charges on the n side of the junction (see figure 1.5a). These charge distributions, similar to the charge distributions on a parallel plate capacitor, produce an electric field across the pn junction. The diffusion current flows until the magnitude of the electric field produced by the charge distributions is large enough to inhibit the additional motion of electrons across the pn junction. The flow of diffusion current is extremely sensitive to the magnitude of this electric field. In the absence of an electric field (ie: when there are no charge distributions at the pn junction), the diffusion current is large. Although large currents do not ordinarily flow through semiconductors, a large diffusion current can be sustained by introducing a mechanism for removing electrons from the p material. In this case, no charges would accumulate at the pn junction, and there would be no electric field inhibiting the flow of diffusion current. A *forward bias* voltage applied across the pn junction, as shown in figure 1.5b, provides a mechanism for removing electrons from the p material. As a result a large diffusion current is sustained; the resistance of a forward-biased pn junction is very small. Conversely, a *reverse bias* voltage applied across the pn junction, as shown in figure 1.5c, acts to reinforce the inhibiting electric field; the resistance of a reverse-biased pn junction is very large. Although both p-type and n-type semiconductors are *bilateral*, because current flows through them equally well in either direction, combining these two materials to form a pn junction produces a most unusual *unilateral* device. The pn junction semiconductor is a conductor of *positive* current in the p-to-n direction (ie: from *anode* to *cathode*) and an insulator in the n-to-p direction (ie: from cathode to anode). A pn junction semiconductor is used in the construction of an important electronic device called the *diode*.

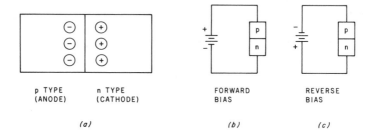

p TYPE   n TYPE   FORWARD   REVERSE
(ANODE)   (CATHODE)   BIAS   BIAS

        (a)   (b)   (c)

Figure 1.5: *The pn junction.*

The network symbol for a diode and the *i-v* characteristics of a typical diode appear in figures 1.6a and 1.6b. When a positive voltage is applied to the p terminal (the anode) with respect to the n terminal (the cathode), the diode is said to be *forward-biased*. Large currents flow through a forward-biased diode even with the application of relatively small voltages. When the polarity of the voltage across the diode is reversed, negligible current flows even with the application of relatively large voltages, and the diode is said to be *reverse-biased*. However, as in figure 1.6b, if the reverse voltage is increased sufficiently, *reverse breakdown* occurs, marked by a sudden increase in reverse current.

Reverse breakdown in a diode is due to the *Zener* effect, in which strong electric fields, produced by voltages applied across the diode, impart large amounts of energy to the electrons, forcing some of the electrons out of their covalent bonds. These electrons can now move freely through the material, gathering energy from the applied electric field as they go. Such high-energy electrons, upon colliding with bonded electrons, knock the bonded electrons out of their covalent bonds in *avalanche fashion*. The amount of voltage necessary to initiate this avalanche effect is called the Zener breakdown voltage V_z and can be varied in manufacture by doping. Diodes with Zener breakdown voltages ranging from a few volts to several hundred volts are commercially available. The breakdown does not destroy the diode unless the current through it is allowed to get large enough to burn it out by overheating. As a result, diodes can safely function at the reverse-breakdown voltage. This is especially useful in applications where voltages must be regulated or limited; diodes intentionally operated at the Zener breakdown voltage are called Zener diodes. The network symbol for a Zener diode is shown in figure 1.6b.

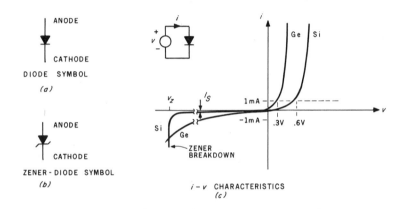

Figure 1.6: *pn junction diode characteristics.*

1.4 A Simple Diode Circuit

A mathematical model often used to characterize a diode's *i-v* relationship is the diode equation (graphed in figure 1.6c):

$$i = I_s(e^{\,kv/T} - 1) \qquad \text{for } v > V_z \qquad (1.1)$$

where I_s is the *reverse saturation current*, T is temperature in °K, and k is a constant which depends upon the particular semiconductor used. Note that the diode equation does not model the phenomenon of Zener breakdown. Table 1.1 gives the values of k and typical values of I_s for germanium and silicon.

	GERMANIUM	SILICON
I_s	1 μA TO 500μA	1nA TO 1μA
k	5800	11600

Table 1.1: *Typical values of k and I_s for germanium and silicon.*

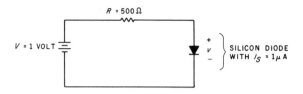

Figure 1.7: *Simple diode circuit.*

Consider the simple resistor-diode circuit of figure 1.7 and the problem of determining the voltage across and the current through the diode. Assume all circuit elements are at room temperature ($T = 300\,^{\circ}$K). By Kirchhoff's voltage law,

$$V = Ri + v \qquad (1.2)$$

Solving the diode equation for v gives

$$v = \frac{T}{k} \ln\left(\frac{i}{I_s} + 1\right) \qquad (1.3)$$

Substituting equation (1.3) into equation (1.2) gives:

$$V = Ri + \frac{T}{k} \ln\left(\frac{i}{I_s} + 1\right)$$

Since $V = 1$ volt, $R = 500\ \Omega$, $T = 300\,^{\circ}$K, $k = 11{,}600$, and $I_s = 1\ \mu$A,

$$1 = 500i + 0.026 \ln(10^6 i + 1) \qquad (1.4)$$

The current through the diode can be obtained by solving the above nonlinear algebraic equation for i.

Obtaining the solution to equation (1.4) is not straightforward. A trial and error process is generally required, in which a sequence of values for i is substituted into the equation in an attempt to converge on the solution. An error function E is defined so that the solution of equation (1.4) is the value of i for which the value of the error, $E(i)$, is zero. For example, the simplest of all such error functions corresponding to equation (1.4) is

$$E(i) = 500i + 0.026 \ln(10^6 i + 1) - 1 \qquad (1.5)$$

By a series of interpolations and extrapolations, one can find a value of i for which $E(i)$ is sufficiently close to zero. To start the process, the values of $E(i)$ are computed for two arbitrary values of i. For example, selecting $i = 0.5$ mA and $i = 5.0$ mA results in $E(0.5\ \text{mA}) = -0.588$, and $E(5.0$

mA) = 1.72. By assuming a linear variation between these two points, it is estimated that the value for which $E(i) = 0$ is $i = 1.646$ mA. This interpolation process is represented graphically in figure 1.8. However,

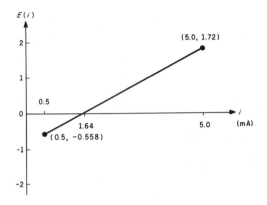

Figure 1.8: *Interpolation in solving for diode current.*

substituting this new value of i in the error function gives $E(1.646$ mA) = 0.0158. At this point in the process, three values of $E(i)$, corresponding to three values of i, have been computed. The interpolation (or extrapolation) process is now repeated by using two of these three values of i: one value of i corresponds to the lowest of the three values of $E(i)$; the other value of i is the value of i closest to this first value. Interpolating between the points $(0.5$ mA, $-0.588)$ and $(1.646$ mA,$0.0158)$ obtains $i = 1.616$ mA with a corresponding $E(i) = -0.142$. The process is continued until the magnitude of $E(i)$ is considered to be close enough to zero. Table 1.2 summarizes the results of the process. Assuming that $E(i) = -0.0000083$ is close enough to zero, the estimated current flowing in this resistor-diode circuit is

$$i = 1.616 \text{ mA}$$

i (milliamps)	$E(i)$
5	1.72
0.5	−0.588
1.646	0.0158
1.616	−0.142
1.631	0.00765
1.625	0.00510
1.616	−0.0000083

Table 1.2: *Computing diode current.*

The voltage v across the diode is determined by using this value of i in equation (1.3). Thus,

$$v = 0.192 \text{ V}$$

When a graph of the diode's i-v characteristics is available, trial and error computational methods can sometimes be avoided. A graphical method can be used to determine the diode's current and voltage in a simple series circuit such as that of figure 1.7. Recall that the diode equation and the equation obtained by application of Kirchhoff's voltage law provide a pair of simultaneous equations that must be solved for the diode current i and the diode voltage v:

$$i = 10^{-6}(e^{38.67v} - 1)$$
$$1 = 500i + v$$

Graphing these equations on the same set of coordinates gives the solution: the intersection of the two graphs (see figure 1.9). The graph of the equation obtained by application of Kirchhoff's voltage law is a straight line and is commonly referred to as the *load line*. Note that the resistor R determines the slope of the line, the voltage source V determines the intercept with the v axis, and the quotient V/R determines the intercept with the i axis. This graphical method is particularly attractive in a design situation where the diode and the voltage source have been specified and where the resistance value necessary to obtain a specified diode current must be determined.

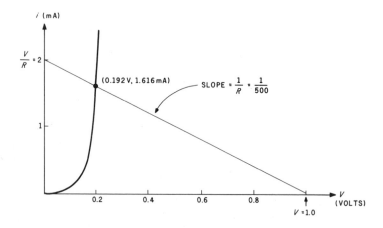

Figure 1.9: *Graphical analysis of a simple diode circuit.*

1.5 Simplified Diode Models

The exact analysis of networks containing more than one diode can be quite difficult. The graphical method used for the simple series circuit is generally not applicable. The alternative is solving rather large sets of nonlinear algebraic equations. Although there are many computer programs based on powerful algorithms for solving such sets of equations, even these methods become unwieldy in a design situation. Fortunately, when diodes are used in digital switching circuits, exact analysis is rarely necessary.

In most digital applications, a diode is employed to act as a simple ON-OFF switch. When forward-biased, the diode should allow current to flow freely; when reverse-biased, the diode should prevent current flow. In a well-designed switching circuit, relatively large variations in the diode's *i-v* characteristics have little effect on the magnitude of the current flowing through the diode. Rather, a resistor placed in series with the diode determines the magnitude of current flowing through the diode. In this way diode circuits can be designed to be highly insensitive to variations in the diode characteristics. Moreover, if a diode circuit is insensitive to variations in the diode characteristics, then the method for designing this circuit is also insensitive to variations in the diode characteristics; the results of a circuit design do not vary significantly with variations in the diode characteristics. Therefore, in designing such circuits, very simple and rather imprecise diode models can be used.

As an example of a diode circuit that is insensitive to diode characteristics, again consider the diode circuit of figure 1.7. Now consider the case that the voltage source V is 5 volts instead of 1 volt. A graphical analysis of this case is shown in figure 1.10. Significantly:

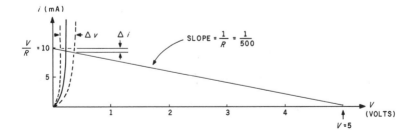

Figure 1.10: *Sensitivity of a diode circuit to variations in diode characteristics.*

- The current through the diode is almost 10 mA, which is the current that would flow if the diode were not in the circuit (ie: $i \cong V/R$).
- The voltage drop across the diode is only a small fraction of the voltage drop across the resistor (ie: $v \cong 0$).
- Even large variations in the diode's i-v characteristics, such as those represented by dotted lines in figure 1.10, have little effect on the validity of the approximations

$$i \cong \frac{V}{R} \text{ and } v \cong 0$$

ie:

$$\Delta i << \frac{V}{R} \text{ and } \Delta v << V$$

- If the voltage source V is negative, $i = 0$ and $v = V$ regardless of the value of the resistor R.

In applications such as this one, exact analysis is seldom necessary, and simple models of the diode can be used effectively.

The concept of an *ideal diode* leads to the simplest diode model. The ideal diode, whose network symbol and i-v characteristics are shown in figure 1.11, is defined as a device having zero resistance when forward-biased and infinite resistance when reverse-biased. Thus, the ideal diode is either a *short circuit* or an *open circuit*, depending on the polarity of the voltage applied to it. In the series circuit of figure 1.7, if $V > 0$, then $i = V/R$ and $v = 0$; if $V < 0$, then $i = 0$ and $v = V$.

Figure 1.11: *The ideal diode.*

In situations where the small voltage drop across the conducting diode is not negligible, other models based on the ideal diode can be used. Two such models and their i-v characteristics are shown in figure 1.12. These models, although more complex than the ideal diode model, are considerably simpler to use than the diode equation. The *pure-offset* diode model in figure 1.12a includes a voltage source $V\gamma_1$ which accounts for the small voltage drop across the diode when it is conducting. This model, however, does not reflect the fact that the diode voltage increases as the current through it increases. The *forward-resistance* diode model of figure 1.12b accounts for this variation by including a series resistor R_f, which is often referred to as the diode's *forward resistance*. Some typical values for $V\gamma_1$,

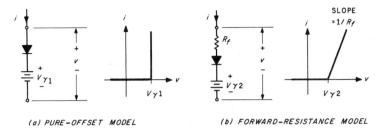

(a) PURE-OFFSET MODEL   (b) FORWARD-RESISTANCE MODEL

Figure 1.12: *Diode models.*

$V\gamma_2$, and R_f for germanium and silicon diodes are shown in table 1.3. Figure 1.13 shows how these values are estimated from actual diode characteristics. The magnitude of current flowing through the diode influences the estimates. For example, if one expects a current of approximately 10 to 30 mA to flow through the silicon 1N3605 diode, one might

	GERMANIUM	SILICON
$V\gamma_1$	0.3 VOLTS	0.7 VOLTS
$V\gamma_2$	0.25 VOLTS	0.65 VOLTS
R_f	6 Ω	5.5 Ω

Table 1.3: *Typical parameter values for diode models.*

properly estimate $V\gamma_2 = 0.6$ V and $R_f = 7$ Ω (figure 1.13a). On the other hand, if one expects a current of 30 to 120 mA, one might estimate $V\gamma_2 = 0.85$ V and $R_f = 0.5$ Ω (figure 1.13b). For most applications, however, the values for $V\gamma_2$ and R_f given in table 1.3 provide suitable estimates.

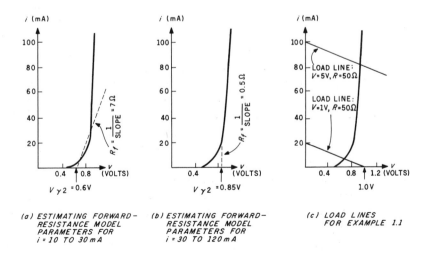

(a) ESTIMATING FORWARD-
    RESISTANCE MODEL
    PARAMETERS FOR
    $i = 10$ TO $30\,mA$

(b) ESTIMATING FORWARD-
    RESISTANCE MODEL
    PARAMETERS FOR
    $i = 30$ TO $120\,mA$

(c) LOAD LINES
    FOR EXAMPLE 1.1

Figure 1.13: *Voltage-current characteristics for silicon diode 1N3605.*

Example 1.1

Determine the current through and the voltage across the diode in the series circuit of figure 1.7 for the case that the diode is a 1N3605 silicon diode and $R = 50\ \Omega$; use the graphical method, the ideal-diode model, the pure-offset model, and the forward-resistance model. Apply each method for both $V = 1$ volt and $V = 5$ volts.

1.   Graphical analysis (see figure 1.13c)
Graphing the load lines ($v = -50i + V$) on the same graph with the 1N3605 characteristics for both $V = 1$ volt and $V = 5$ volts gives:

(a) For $V = 1$ volt,
$$i = 5\text{ mA}$$
$$v = 0.7\text{ V}$$

(b) For $V = 5$ volts,
$$i = 80\text{ mA}$$
$$v = 0.95\text{ V}$$

2.   Ideal-diode model
Figure 1.14a shows the diode circuit with the 1N3605 replaced by the ideal diode. Since the ideal diode is a short circuit (zero resistance) when the diode is forward-biased, the analysis is as follows:

(a) For $V = 1$ volt,

$$i = \frac{V}{R} = 20\text{ mA}$$
$$v = 0$$

(b) For $V = 5$ volts,

$$i = \frac{V}{R} = 100\text{ mA}$$
$$v = 0$$

3.   Pure-offset model
Figure 1.14b shows the diode circuit with the 1N3605 replaced by the pure-offset model of the diode. The value for $V\gamma_1$ used is that given in table 1.3.

(a) For $V = 1$ volt,

$$i = \frac{V - V\gamma_1}{R} = 6\text{ mA}$$
$$v = V\gamma_1 = 0.7\text{ V}$$

(b) For $V = 5$ volts,

$$i = \frac{V - V\gamma_1}{R} = 86 \text{ mA}$$
$$v = 0.7 \text{ V}$$

4.   Forward-resistance model

Figure 1.14c shows the diode circuit with the 1N3605 replaced by the forward-resistance model of the diode. The values for $V\gamma_2$ and R_f are those given in table 1.3.

(a) For $V = 1$ volt,

$$i = \frac{V - V\gamma_2}{R + R_f} = 6.3 \text{ mA}$$
$$v = V - iR = 0.685 \text{ V}$$

(b) For $V = 5$ volts,

$$i = \frac{V - V\gamma_2}{R + R_f} = 78.38 \text{ mA}$$
$$v = V - iR = 1.081 \text{ V}$$

The results are summarized in the table of figure 1.14d. The forward-resistance model is best in the sense that, for both small and large currents, it gives results close to those obtained from the graphical analysis. Note that all three models give better results for large diode currents than for small diode currents.

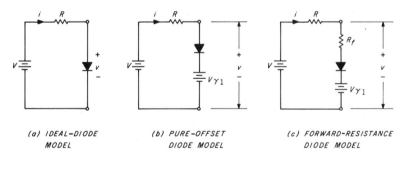

(a) IDEAL-DIODE   (b) PURE-OFFSET   (c) FORWARD-RESISTANCE
   MODEL   DIODE MODEL   DIODE MODEL

DIODE MODEL	V = 1 VOLT		V = 5 VOLTS	
	i (mA)	v (VOLTS)	i (mA)	v (VOLTS)
GRAPHICAL ANALYSIS	5	0.7	80	0.95
IDEAL	20	0	100	0
PURE-OFFSET	6	0.7	86	0.7
FORWARD-RESISTANCE	6.3	0.685	78.38	1.081

(d) TABULATION OF COMPUTATIONAL RESULTS

Figure 1.14: *Example 1.11: Comparison of diode models.*

1.6   Regulated DC Power Supplies

The main source of energy for digital electronic circuits comes from DC voltage sources. All digital electronic circuits require at least one DC voltage source, and many modern digital systems are powered by 5 volt DC power supplies. The cheapest, most reliable, and most convenient source of electrical energy generally available is the 120 volt AC provided to most households by the local electric power companies and accessible by simply plugging into a common wall socket. If the 120 volt AC source is to be used to power a 5 volt DC digital system, a special device is required to convert the 120 volt AC to 5 volt DC. Such a device is called, simply, a 5 V power supply. Although this section specifically deals with the design of 5 V power supplies, the design of DC power supplies of any other voltage is basically the same.

The quickest way to build a 5 volt DC voltage source is to use a 6 V battery as the main energy source and an appropriately adjusted potentiometer (see figure 1.15). There are two distinct problems associated with such a scheme. The first and most serious problem is associated with the limited life of the battery. In effect, the battery's internal resistance r increases as the battery is drained, reducing the battery's terminal voltage v_i for a given load current i_L. As long as the battery's internal resistance r is small, dropping no more than 1 V under the required load conditions, the potentiometer can be adjusted to provide the specified output voltage $v_o = 5$ V. However, with use and age the internal resistance r increases to the point where it drops more than 1 V, making it impossible for the battery to provide the digital system with the necessary 5 V. When this occurs, the battery must be replaced or recharged. The second problem is that the potentiometer setting must be periodically adjusted to compensate for variations in the amount of load current i_L and variations in the battery's terminal voltage v_i. An ideal power supply is one whose output voltage v is independent not only of variations in the energy source (ie: voltage v_i) but also of the varying current demands of the digital system it is powering (ie: variations in i_L). In a typical power-supply design these two problems are resolved separately.

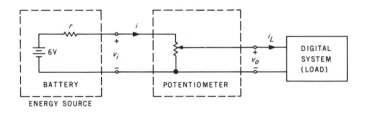

Figure 1.15: *Simple DC power supply.*

The battery can be replaced by an electronic device that is powered by the local power company's readily available 120 volt AC. Such a device, called a *DC power supply*, provides a DC voltage v_i that is independent of the age of the device or the use it has had. The potentiometer can be replaced by an electronic device, a *voltage regulator*, which reduces the output of the DC power supply voltage v_i to the specified output voltage $v_o = 5$ V. The output of the voltage regulator v_o must be independent of the current demands of the digital system being powered (ie: independent of i_L) and independent of any erratic behavior of the DC power supply (ie: independent of v_i), provided that, in this example, $v_i \geq 5$ V. This two-step approach to power-supply design is represented graphically in the block diagram of figure 1.16.

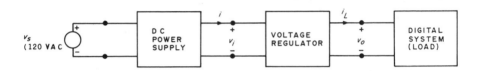

Figure 1.16: *Regulated DC power supply.*

1.6.1   DC Power Supplies (AC to DC)

A DC power supply electronically converts a sinusoidally varying voltage to a constant voltage. The diode is the fundamental electronic component used in the construction of a DC power supply. A *rectifier circuit*, consisting of one or more diodes, is used to convert a positively and negatively varying voltage source to a varying voltage source whose voltage is always positive (or always negative). Figure 1.17 shows three standard rectifier circuits and the resulting output-voltage waveforms when the input voltage to the rectifier is varying sinusoidally; ideal diodes are assumed.

Since the output voltage of a rectifier is always positive, any load being driven by the rectifier always has current flowing through it in the same direction. As a result, a capacitor placed across the rectifier output will charge until its output voltage is equal to the maximum value of the rectified voltage. At this point a DC voltage exists across the capacitor and the capacitor is said to have *filtered* out the variations in the rectifier output voltage. Figure 1.18 shows the use of such a filter capacitor with a full-wave bridge rectifier. In this circuit the output current i of the rectifier is never negative, and any nonzero current i always acts to charge the capacitor: current i flows whenever $|v_s| > v_i$; no current i flows whenever $|v_s| \leq v_i$. The magnitude of current i flowing to charge the capacitor depends upon the difference $|v_s| - v_i$, the forward resistance of the bridge diodes, and the internal resistance of the voltage source v_s. This dependency is clearer when

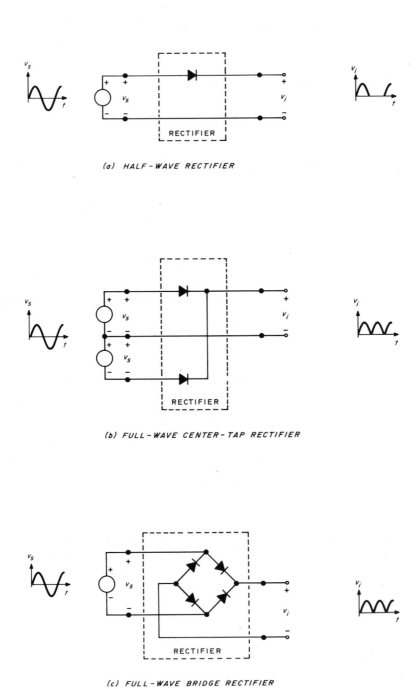

(a) HALF-WAVE RECTIFIER

(b) FULL-WAVE CENTER-TAP RECTIFIER

(c) FULL-WAVE BRIDGE RECTIFIER

Figure 1.17: *Rectifiers.*

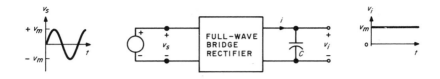

Figure 1.18: DC power supply (a filtered full-wave rectifier).

the power supply circuit of figure 1.18 is replaced by the equivalent circuit of figure 1.19; v_{FW} is a full-wave rectified voltage source (note that $v_{FW} = |v_s|$) and R_s is the sum of the internal resistance of the voltage source and the forward resistance of a bridge diode. This equivalent circuit shows that

$$i = \mathrm{Pos}\left(\frac{|v_s| - v_i}{R_s}\right) \tag{1.6}$$

where the function Pos is defined such that

$$\mathrm{Pos}(x) = \left\{ \begin{matrix} x, & x > 0 \\ 0, & x \leq 0 \end{matrix} \right\}$$

The voltage v_i is proportional to the amount of charge on the plates of the filter capacitor C:

$$v_i = \frac{1}{C} \int_0^t i \, d\tau$$

The evaluation of this integral to determine voltage v_i is not straight-forward because the value of the current i depends on v_i (see equation (1.6)). Thus, v_i must be determined by solving an integral equation:

$$v_i = \frac{1}{C} \int_0^t \mathrm{Pos}\left(\frac{|v_s| - v_i}{R_s}\right) d\tau$$

Although it can be difficult to obtain an analytic solution for the voltage v_i, standard numerical methods are easily applied (see appendix A2) in solving

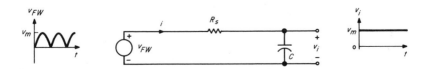

Figure 1.19: Equivalent circuit of DC power supply.

for v_i. The graphs of figure 1.20 show the results of such computations for the case that $R_s = 1\,\Omega$, $C = 4000\,\mu F$, and $v_s = 169.7 \sin 377t$ V (ie: v_s is the standard 120 V, 60 Hz AC). The following observations are made:

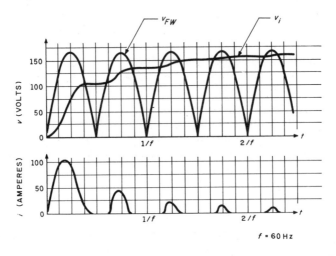

Figure 1.20: *Voltage and current waveforms of a DC power supply under no load.*

- The filtered rectifier voltage v_i achieves a final value of 169.7 V, which is the peak value of the sinusoidal voltage v_s.
- The charging current i flows in spurts (two spurts per cycle when a full-wave rectifier is used) that become increasingly shorter in duration and smaller in magnitude as v_i approaches the peak 169.7 V.
- The length of time that it takes for v_i to come within a specified range of the final value of 169.7 V (eg: within 5 percent of 120 V) depends upon the time constant $R_s C$. Decreasing the value of R_s or C allows the final DC value to be reached in a shorter time. A small value of R_s is generally desirable because it allows more power to be transferred from the source to the load, increasing the effectiveness of the DC power supply; a small value of C is generally undesirable because the effectiveness of the DC power supply depends upon large amounts of energy being stored in the capacitor C.

Thus, a filtered-rectifier circuit converts an AC voltage to a DC voltage. In particular, the circuit of figure 1.18 converts the common 120 volts AC to 169.7 volts DC. It is not advisable to use a sinusoidal voltage source v_s having a peak value of 169.7 V as the rectifier input in designing a 5 V power supply. Reducing a high voltage, such as the resulting 169.7 volts DC, to 5 volts DC by using a voltage divider is wasteful, not only in terms of the energy consumed by the voltage divider itself, but also in terms of the increased cost of voltage dividers rated for operation at the higher voltage and power levels. For this reason, a step-down transformer is used to provide the input to the filtered rectifier circuit (see figure 1.21). In the construction of a 5 volt DC power supply, a 6.3 V transformer* is often used. Using a 6.3 V transformer in the DC power supply circuit of figure 1.21 results in a DC output voltage v_i of 8.9 V (versus 169.7 V without the transformer). The voltage divider is required to drop 3.9 V, at most, to achieve the desired 5 volt DC output.

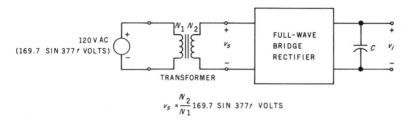

$$v_s = \frac{N_2}{N_1} 169.7 \; \text{SIN} \; 377t \; \text{VOLTS}$$

Figure 1.21: *Use of the transformer in a DC power supply.*

Although the filtered rectifier circuit of figure 1.21 provides a DC voltage v_i as its output, this circuit is not supplying any current to a load. The true test of this circuit as a DC power supply is in terms of its capability to supply DC current to a load. Figure 1.22 shows the equivalent circuit of the DC power supply with resistor R_L connected across its output terminals so as to simulate the loading effect of a digital system. Analysis of this circuit results in the following equations:

$$i = \text{Pos}\left(\frac{|v_s| - v_i}{R_s}\right)$$

$$v_i = \frac{1}{C}\int_0^t i_c \, d\tau$$

$$i_c = i - i_L$$

$$i_L = \frac{v_i}{R_L}$$

These equations can be combined into a single integral equation:

$$v_i = \frac{1}{C}\int_0^t \left[\text{Pos}\left(\frac{|v_s| - v_i}{R_s}\right) - \frac{v_i}{R_L}\right] d\tau$$

---

*A 6.3 volt transformer is one whose secondary voltage is a sinusoid with a peak value of 8.9 V (6.3 × $\sqrt{2}$ = 8.9) when the transformer's primary voltage is a sinusoid with a peak value of 169.7 V (ie: the standard 120 volts AC; 120 × $\sqrt{2}$ = 169.7).

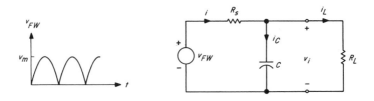

Figure 1.22: *Loading a DC power supply.*

The graphs of figure 1.23 show the results of using a standard numerical method (see appendix A2) to solve the above equation for v_i for the case that $R_s = 1\ \Omega$, $C = 4000\ \mu F$, $R_L = 8.9\ \Omega$, and $v_s = 8.9 \sin 377t$ V. Figure 1.23a shows the *steady-state* behavior of the loaded DC power supply (ie: the cyclic pattern that develops following the initial charge-up period). The table of figure 1.23b summarizes the results of computations for several combinations of circuit parameters. The following general observations can be made:

- When the filtered-rectifier circuit is loaded with a resistor R_L, v_i never achieves a *constant* final value. Rather, the steady-state behavior is oscillatory in nature: ie, the DC voltage has *ripple*. A *ripple factor* r_f is defined as

$$r_f = \frac{v_{i(max)} - v_{i(min)}}{v_{i(avg)}}$$

- The maximum value achieved by v_i is always less than the peak value of the sinusoid v_s (8.9 V in this case).
- As the load current i_L decreases (ie: as the value of resistor R_L increases), the average steady-state value of v_i increases (approaching 8.9 V as R_L approaches infinity) and the ripple factor decreases.
- Increasing the size of the filter capacitor C decreases the ripple factor, but has relatively little effect on the average value of v_i.
- Decreasing the size of resistor R_s increases the average value of v_i, but has relatively little effect on the ripple factor.

1.6.2   Voltage Regulators

Once a DC voltage v_i greater than 5 V has been obtained, this voltage can be used as the input to the voltage regulator circuit. The function of the voltage regulator is to develop a constant 5 V output regardless of the magnitude of the load current i_L. Requiring that the output voltage v_o be well regulated (ie: independent of load current i_L) eliminates the possible use of the potentiometer as a voltage regulator in obtaining the necessary voltage reduction from $v_i > 5$ V to $v_o = 5$ V.

A simple design for constructing a voltage regulator utilizes a 5 V Zener

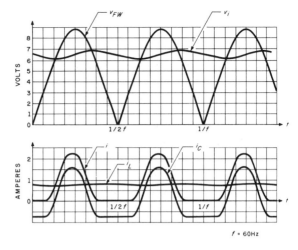

(a) VOLTAGE
AND CURRENT WAVEFORMS

$f = 60\,Hz$

(b) EFFECT OF
PARAMETER VARIATIONS

C_s (ohms)	C (micro-) (farads)	R_L (ohms)	$v_{i(avg)}$ (volts)	$i_{L(avg)}$ (amperes)	Ripple factor
1.0	4000	8.9	6.52	0.73	0.132
1.0	4000	17.8	7.29	0.41	0.070
1.0	4000	4.5	5.54	1.24	0.220
1.0	8000	8.9	6.55	0.73	0.066
1.0	2000	8.9	6.45	0.72	0.245
1.0	2000	4.5	5.30	1.19	0.443
1.0	8000	17.8	7.30	0.41	0.036
0.5	4000	8.9	7.23	0.81	0.147
2.0	4000	8.9	5.56	0.62	0.113

Figure 1.23: *Analysis of a DC power supply under load.*

diode as shown in figure 1.24. The Zener diode connected across the output terminals allows the output voltage to assume any positive voltage up to 5 V. When the voltage across the diode is less than 5 V, the diode acts as an ordinary reverse-biased diode; no current flows through the diode, and $v_i = v_o$. Any attempt to apply a voltage greater than 5 V across the diode causes Zener breakdown. In this case, the Zener diode voltage stays at 5 V; the necessary current flows through the resistor R_v to drop $v_i - 5$ V across resistor R_v.

Figure 1.24:
A simple voltage regulator.

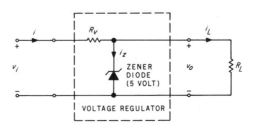

Example 1.2

Consider the problem of designing a simple voltage regulator for a power supply. The voltage regulator output is to be a constant 5 V for load current i_L up to 3 A. Assume that because of the maximum power rating of the DC power supply, which supplies the voltage regulator's DC input voltage v_i, the maximum allowable current i to the regulator is 4 A. Also assume DC power supply characteristics such that v_i is 7.5 V when i is 3 A.

It is important to recognize that, in the design of this simple voltage regulator, regulation is achieved by keeping the input current i constant, regardless of the magnitude of the regulator load current i_L. With current i constant, it is a simple matter to select the value of the resistor R_v so that it drops the voltage necessary to provide the specified output voltage $v_o = 5$ V. R_v is selected so that the maximum load current of $i_L = 3$ A can be obtained with the Zener diode operating in the Zener breakdown region. Since $i = i_z + i_L$ (see figure 1.24), i ought to be greater than the maximum allowable load current of $i_L = 3$ A. Since the energy consumption of the voltage regulator is minimized by making i as small as possible, selecting $i = 3$ A is an obvious design choice. An i somewhat greater than 3 A may be deliberately selected. Although this would make the regulator more wasteful of energy by requiring more cooling, it would provide a safety margin by increasing the regulator's output current rating. In any case, because of the DC power supply rating, it is necessary to keep $i \leq 4$ A. Because the DC power supply voltage v_i is given for $i = 3$ A, and because we require $v_o = 5$ V, R_v can be computed:

$$R_v = \frac{v_i - v_o}{i} = \frac{7.5 - 5}{3} = 0.833 \ \Omega$$

With $R_v = 0.833 \ \Omega$, the output voltage v_o will be a well-regulated 5 V provided that $i_L < 3$ A (or, equivalently, provided that R_L is greater than 1.67 Ω). When $R_L = 1.67 \ \Omega$, $i_L = i = 3$ A, $v_o = 5$ V, and the current through the Zener diode, i_z, is zero. When $R_L > 1.67 \ \Omega$, current flows through the Zener diode; at no load (ie: $R_L = \infty$ and $i_L = 0$), maximum current flows through the diode (ie: $i_z = 3$ A). If $R_L < 1.67 \ \Omega$, the Zener diode, no longer operating in the Zener breakdown region, has the essentially infinite resistance associated with an ordinary reverse-biased diode. In this case, the current $i = i_L > 3$ A, $i_z = 0$, and $v_o < 5$ V. For example, if $R_L = 1.5 \ \Omega$, then,

$$i = i_L = \frac{V_i}{R_v + R_L} = \frac{7.5}{0.833 + 1.5} = 3.2 \ A$$

$$v_o = v_i - iR_v = 7.5 - 3.2 \times 0.833 = 4.8 \ V$$

The outstanding feature of a regulated DC power supply, such as the one considered here and shown in its entirety in figure 1.25, is that the output

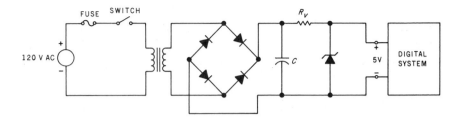

Figure 1.25: *Circuit diagram of a regulated DC power supply.*

voltage v_o is insensitive to most circuit-parameter variations that might occur. Of course, the Zener breakdown voltage is the most critical parameter because it determines the power supply's output voltage; variations in this parameter can be tolerated only to the extent that variations in the output voltage can be tolerated. The effect of variations of most other parameters is to change the maximum power rating of the power supply, rather than to change the value of the output voltage. For example, increases in the resistance values of the transformer windings, the rectifier diodes, or R_v tend to reduce the power rating of the power supply; a decrease in the value of the filter capacitor would also tend to decrease the power rating. Thus, a safety margin can be incorporated by designing the power supply to provide an output current i_L somewhat larger than the maximum current that the power supply will ever be expected to deliver.

Although the voltage regulator circuit suggested here is suitable for many laboratory applications, more efficient voltage regulators are commercially available as single integrated-circuit packages. The LM309, the LM340-5, and the LM7805 are typical of the available 5 V regulators which are capable of converting a DC voltage of 7 to 20 volts to a well-regulated 5 V output that can deliver up to 1 A of load current. The main advantage of the commercial voltage regulators, aside from their great convenience, is that, unlike the simple Zener diode regulator, they draw very little current when there is little or no demand for load current. Under heavier load conditions when more than 1 A of load current is required, these commercial regulators can be used as the main components in rather simple electronic circuits to provide the necessary regulation.

1.7 The Transistor

The bipolar junction transistor, invented in 1948 by William Shockley, is the single device most responsible for the explosive growth of the electronics industry. The transistor, a semiconductor device requiring no hand-assembly in its manufacture, is easily and inexpensively mass-produced, and can be miniaturized to microscopic proportions. The transistor replaced the electronic vacuum tube in every conceivable electronic application. Moreover, because of the transistor's low cost, small size, and negligible energy requirements, it has been possible to use electronics in innumerable new applications where the use of vacuum tubes would be impossible. Integrated circuits (ICs), containing thousands of transistors (some commercially available for under $10), are considerably smaller than the average miniature vacuum tube and require only a tiny fraction of the power.

The transistor is a three-terminal device constructed of three semiconductor layers. There are two main categories of transistors: the npn transistor and the pnp transistor. Diagrams illustrating the construction of these two transistor types with their corresponding network symbols are shown in figure 1.26.

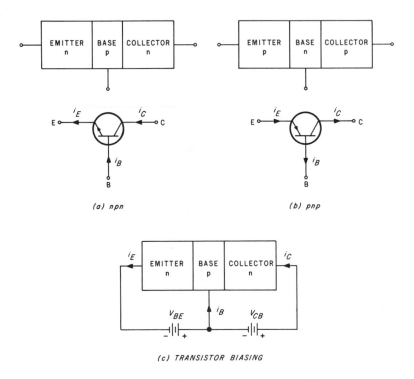

Figure 1.26: *Transistor construction and network symbols.*

Recall (section 1.2) that the diffusion current across a pn junction produces a charge distribution which is responsible for the unilateral conduction properties of the semiconductor diode. A transistor has two pn junctions and can be thought of as two diodes placed back-to-back. Checking a transistor with an ohmmeter between terminals E and B and between terminals C and B establishes that a transistor does contain two back-to-back diodes. Such an ohmmeter check is frequently used to determine whether or not a transistor is minimally functional. However, a transistor is more than two back-to-back diodes. Most importantly, the conduction properties between two terminals of a transistor can be controlled by the current flowing into the third terminal. The third terminal provides control over the charge distributions that normally form across the pn junctions. By forward biasing the base-to-emitter diode with an external voltage source V_{BE}, as shown in figure 1.26c, electrons are removed from the base region. This allows large numbers of electrons to diffuse across the pn junction from emitter to base. The base, however, is made so thin that most of these electrons diffuse across the base toward the base-to-collector pn junction. Reverse biasing the base-to-collector pn junction with an external voltage source V_{CE} (see figure 1.26c) creates a strong electric field across this pn junction. This electric field captures the electrons that have diffused across the base after they have crossed the base-to-emitter pn junction and sweeps them across the base-to-collector pn junction into the collector. As a result, a pn junction, such as the collector-to-base pn junction, which might be expected to have a high resistance because it is wired as a reverse-biased diode, acts as a conductor. The Ebers-Moll transistor model, shown for an npn transistor in figure 1.27, provides valuable insight into the transistor's operation. Although this model does not include the nonlinearities necessary for use in the analysis and design of digital circuits, it graphically illustrates that a transistor is considerably more than just two diodes back-to-back. The *dependent current sources* αi_x and $\alpha_R i_y$ across each of the two diodes make it possible to control the resistivity of the various conduction paths.

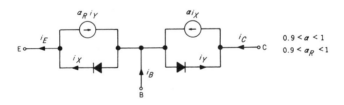

Figure 1.27: *Ebers-Moll npn transistor model.*

For most digital switching applications, the transistor is used in the four-terminal, input-output, *common-emitter* configuration; the emitter terminal is common to both the input and output pairs (see figure 1.28). Although the *common-base* and *common-collector* configurations are also used in various applications, the common-emitter configuration is used most often and is the only configuration studied here. However, the methods for analyzing and designing common-emitter transistor circuits are fundamental and can be extended so as to apply to common-base and

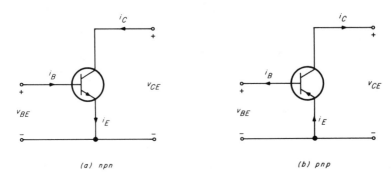

(a) npn   (b) pnp

Figure 1.28: *Transistor in common-emitter configuration.*

common-collector transistor circuits. Figures 1.29a and 1.29b show the current-voltage characteristics used to analyze those transistor circuits in which the transistors are in the common-emitter configuration. These particular graphs represent the nominal characteristics of a 2N1613 silicon npn

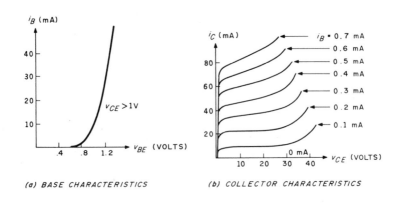

(a) BASE CHARACTERISTICS   (b) COLLECTOR CHARACTERISTICS

Figure 1.29: *Common-emitter characteristic curves for the npn transistor 2N1613 at 25°C.*

transistor at room temperature (25° C); figure 1.30 shows similar characteristics for a comparable pnp transistor. Note that transistors are not generally manufactured to extremely close tolerances and that variations in transistor characteristics of 50 percent or more are not unusual. In addition, transistor characteristics are extremely sensitive to temperature changes. Good transistor-circuit design demands that a circuit's operation be insensitive to these variations.

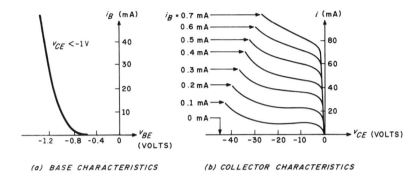

Figure 1.30: *Common-emitter characteristics for a pnp transistor.*

The relationship between the base current i_B and the base-to-emitter voltage v_{BE} for an npn transistor is graphed in figure 1.29a. This graph shows that diode properties exist between the base and emitter when positive current does not flow from the collector to either the base or the emitter (ie: when the base-to-collector diode is not forward-biased). If the collector-to-emitter voltage v_{CE} is greater than 1 V and the base-to-emitter voltage v_{BE} is less than 0.5 V, then no *positive* current will flow from base-to-collector, and the i_B-v_{BE} characteristic of figure 1.29b applies.

The relationship between collector current i_c and collector-to-emitter voltage v_{CE} is represented by the family of curves of figure 1.29b. The value of the base current i_B determines which curve is to be used in any given application. Significant in this set of curves is:

- If base current is flowing, large currents can flow through the collector-to-base diode, even when that diode is reverse-biased. Recall that base current depletes the charge distribution in the collector-to-base pn junction, preventing it from acting as a normal diode.
- Small changes in base current produce relatively large changes in collector current. Thus, the transistor acts as a current *amplifier*.*

The graphs of the base and collector characteristics provide an excellent model for the analysis and design of transistor circuits. Of special concern here is the design of the transistor switch.

---

*Even when the base current is zero, a voltage applied between the collector and the emitter causes a small current to flow. For most digital applications, this current, called the *cutoff current* and denoted by I_{CO}, can be assumed to be zero.

1.8 The Transistor Switch

The most fundamental digital electronic circuit is the simple transistor switch shown in figure 1.31. Although only transistor switches in which npn transistors are used are studied here, there is no loss of generality because the npn and pnp transistor characteristics are identical except for voltage polarities; note that the direction of positive currents in a pnp transistor is assumed to be opposite to the direction of positive currents in an npn transistor (see figure 1.28). The entire discussion can be made to apply to transistor switches utilizing pnp transistors simply by reversing the polarity of all voltages.

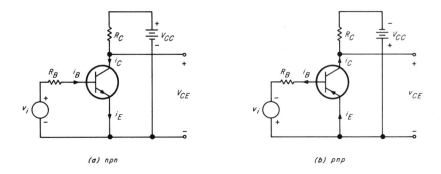

(a) npn   (b) pnp

Figure 1.31: *Transistor switch.*

Consider the analysis of the npn transistor switch for the case that the transistor is a silicon npn 2N68 (characteristics shown in figure 1.32); $R_B = 30$ kΩ, $R_C = 850$ Ω, $V_{CC} = 5$ V and v_i is a pulse generator which generates 5 V pulses of varying durations (ie: sometimes $v_i = 0$ V and sometimes $v_i = 5$ V). A complete analysis of this circuit requires determining all voltage and current values for both $v_i = 0$ V and $v_i = 5$ V.

Regardless of the value of v_i, Kirchhoff's voltage law applied around the collector circuit (figure 1.31a) results in the equation defining the *collector load line*:

$$V_{CC} - R_C i_C - v_{CE} = 0 \qquad (1.7)$$

Solving for i_C and using the actual values of V_{CC} and R_C gives

$$i_C = \frac{-1}{850} v_{CE} + 5.88 \times 10^{-3}$$

This load line is graphed on the collector characteristics of figure 1.32b. If the base current is known, the collector current can be determined from the

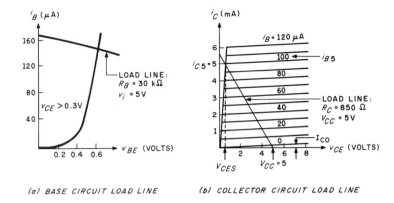

(a) BASE CIRCUIT LOAD LINE   (b) COLLECTOR CIRCUIT LOAD LINE

Figure 1.32: *Load line analysis of a 2N68 (npn) transistor switch.*

intersection of the appropriate i_C-v_{CE} curve and the collector load line. Therefore, it is necessary that base current be determined. This is done from an analysis of the base circuit.

Applying Kirchhoff's voltage law in the base circuit of figure 1.31a gives the equation defining the *base load line*:

$$v_i - R_B i_B - v_{BE} = 0 \qquad (1.8)$$

Solving for i_B and using the actual value of R_B gives

$$i_B = \frac{-1}{30 \times 10^3} v_{BE} + \frac{1}{30 \times 10^3} v_i$$

Now consider each of the two possible values for v_i:

(1) $v_i = 0$ V: For the case that $v_i = 0$ V, the base load line goes through the origin. In this case $i_B = 0$ and $v_{BE} = 0$. The knowledge that $i_B = 0$ allows us to identify the appropriate collector characteristic. The intersection of the collector load line with the collector characteristic corresponding to $i_B = 0$ reveals that:

$$i_C = I_{CO} \cong 0 \text{ mA (hence, the OFF state)}$$

$$v_{CE} \cong V_{CC} = 5 \text{ V}$$

(2) $v_i = 5$ V: For the case that $v_i = 5$ V, the intersection of the base load line with the i_B-v_{BE} characteristics shows that $i_B \cong 145$ μA and $v_{BE} \cong 0.6$ V. Knowledge that $i_B = 145$ μA allows use of the collector load line to determine that $i_C \cong 5$ mA (hence, the ON state) and $v_{CE} \cong 0.3$ V.

The results of this analysis, summarized from table 1.4, show that the transistor circuit of figure 1.31a can be utilized in several ways.

v_i (volts)	i_B (μA)	v_{BE} (volts)	i_C (mA)	v_{CE} (volts)	transistor state
0	0	0	0	5	OFF
5	145	0.6	5	0.3	ON

Table 1.4: *Transistor switch signal levels.*

Considering v_i as the input and i_C as the output, a standard switch is defined: $v_i = 0$ (LOW) results in $i_C = 0$ (LOW), and $v_i = 5$ V (HIGH) results in $i_C = 5$ mA (HIGH). If instead of considering the current i_C to be the output, the voltage v_{CE} were considered to be the output, this transistor circuit would operate as an inverter; $v_i = 0$ (LOW) would result in $v_{CE} = 5$ V (HIGH), and $v_i = 5$ V (HIGH) would result in $v_{CE} = 0.3$ V (LOW).

This transistor circuit can also be used as a *driver*. There are many situations in which a voltage source such as v_i is a *signal source* in the sense that it can supply only tiny amounts of power. Such signal sources are common in digital computers where low power consumption is desirable because of the thousands of switching circuits used in the making of a digital computer. In design the power consumption of each switching circuit is intentionally minimized to the point where a further reduction would cause the information carried by the circuit to be unreliable. Often it is necessary to display the state of a digital logic circuit (ie: output is HIGH or output is LOW) by using an output device (eg: a light-emitting display) that requires large amounts of power. In such situations, a buffer circuit is required to sense the signal from the low-power signal source and *drive* the load device with the necessary power. The transistor switch/inverter circuit of figure 1.31a can be used as a driver.

Recall that when $v_i = 5$ V, $i_B = 145$ μA. The power drain on the source v_i when in the HIGH state is

$$p_i = v_i\, i_B$$

$$= 5 \times 145 \times 10^{-6} = 0.725 \text{ milliwatts}$$

Suppose that the resistor R_C is the load (eg: R_C is an 850 Ω lamp) that is being driven. The power to the load when v_i is in the HIGH state is

$$p_C = i_C^2\, R_C = (5 \times 10^{-3})^2 \times 850 = 21.25 \text{ milliwatts}$$

Therefore, using this transistor circuit, an energy source of 0.725 milliwatts can drive a load requiring 21.25 milliwatts. The driver thus provides a sizable *power gain*:

$$\text{Power gain} = \frac{p_C}{p_i}$$

$$= \frac{21.25}{0.725} = 29.3$$

The transistor itself consumes power which is dissipated as heat. In this case the power dissipated by the transistor is

$$\text{Transistor Power} = v_{CE}i_C + v_{BE}i_B \qquad (1.9)$$
$$= 0.3 \times 5 \times 10^{-3} + 0.6 \times 145 \times 10^{-6}$$
$$= 1.5 \times 10^{-3} + 0.087 \times 10^{-3}$$
$$= 1.587 \text{ milliwatts}$$

Note that base current, i_B, is responsible for only a small fraction (5.5 percent) of the power dissipated by the transistor. The maximum power that a transistor can dissipate is specified by the manufacturer. Such limits should not be exceeded unless special measures are taken to increase the power dissipating capacity of the transistor. Specially designed *heat sinks*, to which the transistors are fastened, and cooling fans are frequently used for such purposes.

Not only is there a gain in power in this transistor circuit, but there is also a gain in current from $i_B = 145$ μA to $i_C = 5$ mA. The actual *current gain* realized by this transistor circuit is:

$$G_i = \frac{i_C}{i_B} = \text{current gain}$$

$$= \frac{5 \text{ mA}}{145 \text{ μA}} = 34.5$$

1.9 Transistor-Circuit Sensitivity

As discussed in section 1.1, a switch that is to be a prototype for switches used in large switching networks must be input-insensitive, in that rather large variations in the input, from the specified nominal LOW and HIGH levels, should have little effect on the output. In a large switching network, the input of one switch is generally provided by the output of another switch. If the switches are input-insensitive, the output tolerances of the switches can be relaxed, and the tolerances in the manufacture of components used in constructing the switches can also be relaxed. Resistor-transistor switching circuits should be designed so as to be insensitive to variations in transistor characteristics, power-supply voltage, resistor values, and input voltage levels. Although properly designed resistor-transistor circuits can be operated as switches, before these switches can be used as prototypes for switches in complex switching networks, these transistor switches must be established as input-insensitive. Toward this end, the input/output (I/O) characteristics of the npn resistor-transistor switch (figure 1.31a) will be generated. For the case that the switch is used as a driver (ie: v_i is the input and i_C is the output), the i_C-v_i characteristic curve will be generated; for the case that the switch is used as an inverter (ie: v_i is the input and v_{CE} is the output), the v_{CE}-v_i characteristic curve will be generated.

The key to designing an input-insensitive transistor switch is to drive the transistor well into *saturation* in the ON state: for the driver, the ON state corresponds to a HIGH output; for the inverter, the ON state corresponds to a LOW output. A transistor is *saturated* when an increase in base current has no effect on the collector circuit; specifically, increases in i_B do not result in increases in i_C or decreases in v_{CE}. The collector saturation current i_{CS} and the collector-to-emitter saturation voltage v_{CES} are determined by the intersection of the collector load line with the rising portion of the i_C-v_{CE} characteristics (figure 1.32b). The minimum value of base current i_{BS} required to saturate the transistor is also determined from this intersection.

Consider a sensitivity analysis of the npn transistor switch studied in section 1.8 in which the transistor is an npn 2N68, R_B = 30 kΩ, R_C = 850 Ω, and V_{CC} = 5 V; the LOW and HIGH voltages are specified as 0 and 5 volts, respectively. Figure 1.32 indicates that at least 100 μA of base current are needed to saturate the 2N68 transistor switch when R_C = 850 Ω and V_{CC} = 5 V. In order to be sure that neither increases nor decreases in base current affect the values of v_{CE} and i_C in the ON state, the transistor switch is designed to operate well into saturation. In this case the transistor is turned ON with a base current of 145 μA instead of the minimum 100 μA required to saturate the resistor. As a result, rather large variations around the nominal value of R_B = 30 kΩ can be tolerated without affecting the basic operation of the switch: variations in R_B from 20 kΩ (or less) to 47 kΩ are tolerable. The lower limit of R_B is determined from the power limitations of the voltage source v_i and the maximum base current that the transistor can handle without overheating. The upper limit of R_B is determined from the i_B-v_{BE} curve and i_{BS}, the least base current that will saturate the transistor (100 μA in this case). Thus, a base load line is drawn intersecting the i_B-v_{BE} curve at 100 μA and intersecting the v_{BE} axis at 5 V. The slope of this line gives the maximum R_B. Equation (1.9) shows the effect of base current on transistor power; the transistor's power rating should not be exceeded.

The minimum base current required to saturate a transistor determines the maximum current gain of the transistor. Thus, the *maximum current gain*, denoted by h_{FE}, is

$$h_{FE} = \frac{i_{CS}}{i_{BS}} \qquad (1.10)$$

For the silicon 2N68 npn transistor,

$$h_{FE} = \frac{5 \text{ ma}}{100 \ \mu\text{A}} = 50$$

The i_C-v_{CE} characteristics of Figure 1.32 illustrate that the value of h_{FE} is relatively independent of the particular load line used (ie: h_{FE} is independent of V_{CC} and R_C). For example, when $V_{CC} = 2$ V and $R_C = 400$ Ω, the collector current at saturation is $i_{CS} = 4$ mA. The minimum base current to saturate the transistor in this case is 80 μA. Thus,

$$h_{FE} = \frac{4 \text{ mA}}{80 \text{ μA}} = 50$$

This *linear region* of operation extends to operating points *below* saturation. For example, in the original example ($V_{CC} = 5$ V, $R_C = 850$ Ω) if i_B is 20 μA, then $i_C = 1$ mA and the maximum current gain, $h_{FE} = 50$, is realized.

The maximum current gain h_{FE} of a transistor is generally the main identifying parameter for that transistor. As is shown in the next section, this parameter and the transistor's power rating provide sufficient information for the design of most switching circuits. The manufacturer of a transistor, however, will seldom guarantee the accuracy of the value of h_{FE} except to within rather broad tolerances. Instead, the manufacturer will guarantee the minimum value of h_{FE}; the actual value of h_{FE} may, in fact, be several hundred percent higher. For example, the *GE Transistor Manual* indicates that for npn transistor 2N709 the value of h_{FE} can range from 20 to 120. The designer must design his circuit so that variations of this magnitude do not affect the operation of the circuit.

The progression of graphs in figure 1.33 shows how the transistor's base and collector characteristics are used to generate the I/O characteristics of the npn transistor switch. Graphing a family of base load lines (R_B is fixed and v_i is the parameter identifying each load line) on the same coordinate system with the graph of the transistor's base characteristics (figure 1.33a) provides the data for graphing i_B versus v_i (figure 1.33b); each intersection of a load line with the base characteristic gives an ordered pair (v_i, i_B). Similarly, graphing the collector load line on the same coordinate system with the family of collector characteristics (R_C is fixed and i_B is the parameter identifying each collector characteristic: see figure 1.32c) provides the data for graphing i_C versus i_B (figure 1.33d); each intersection of a collector characteristic with the collector load line gives an ordered pair (i_B, i_C). The i_B-v_i graph (figure 1.33b) and the i_C-i_B graph (figure 1.33d) are used to generate the i_C-v_i graph (figure 1.33e). This is done simply by entering the i_B-v_i graph with a value for v_i to obtain the corresponding value of i_B; this value of i_B is used to enter the i_C-i_B graph to obtain the corresponding value of i_C. Thus, a value of i_C can be determined for every value of v_i, and the i_C-v_i curve can be graphed. The v_{CE}-v_i graph (figure 1.33f) is easily generated from the i_C-v_i graph (figure 1.33e) using the equation $v_{CE} = v_{CC} - i_C R_C$.

The I/O characteristic curve for the npn transistor switch when used as a driver is the i_C-v_i graph of figure 1.33e; the I/O characteristic curve for the npn transistor switch when used as an inverter is the v_{CE}-v_i graph of figure

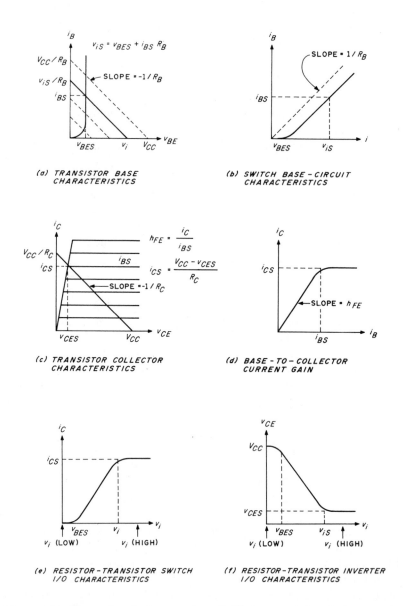

Figure 1.33: *Generating the input/output (I/O) characteristics of an npn resistor-transistor switch.*

1.33f. The transistor switch, whether used as a driver or as an inverter, is input-insensitive if two conditions are satisfied:

- The LOW input is defined so that

$$v_{i(LOW)} < v_{BES}$$

In other words, it is necessary for the specified nominal LOW voltage to be less than the base-to-emitter conducting voltage v_{BES}; for input voltages less than v_{BES}, both the driver and the inverter are insensitive to input voltage variations. Note that the collector-to-emitter saturation voltage v_{CES} is the LOW output voltage of the inverter. Therefore, if v_{CES} is interpreted as a LOW by another transistor switch which receives v_{CES} as an input, it is necessary that v_{CES} be within the LOW insensitive region (ie: $v_{CES} < v_{BES}$). Selecting a nominal $v_{i(LOW)} = 0$ is safe since generally $v_{BES} = 0.6$ V and $v_{CES} = 0.3$ V, and the inequality assuring input insensitivity for LOW inputs is satisfied.

- The HIGH input is defined so that

$$v_{i(HIGH)} > v_{iS} = v_{BES} + i_{BS}R_B$$

In other words, it is necessary for the specified nominal HIGH voltage to be large enough to drive the transistor well into *saturation*. The saturation base current i_{BS} is determined from the intersection of the collector load line with the rising edge of the collector characteristics (figure 1.33c). Thus, in order to operate in the insensitive region, input voltage v_i must be large enough to drive the series combination of the base-to-emitter diode and the base resistor R_B with more current than i_{BS}, the minimum current necessary to saturate the transistor. Since $i_{BS} = i_{CS}/h_{FE}$ and since, in saturation, $i_{CS} = (V_{CC} - v_{CES})/R_C$, the inequality assuring input insensitivity for HIGH inputs can be rewritten as

$$v_{i(HIGH)} > v_{iS} = v_{BES} + \frac{V_{CC} - v_{CES}}{h_{FE}} \frac{R_B}{R_C}$$

The selection of the two resistors R_B and R_C is critical in assuring input insensitivity for HIGH inputs.

1.10   Simplified Transistor-Switch Analysis and Design

Because of the wide tolerances in the manufacture of transistors and because of the sensitivity of transistor parameters to temperature changes, it is necessary to design transistor circuits that are insensitive to large parameter variations. From the standpoint of design, a circuit that is insensitive to large component variations is also insensitive to the design method by which it is created. It would be difficult to justify the use of exacting design methods in situations where specifications require the switching circuit to remain operational even when the most important transistor parameter, h_{FE}, is allowed to vary 500 percent above its minimum value. A circuit's insensitivity to large parameter variations allows the design method itself to be rather coarse. The design of a transistor switch can be carried out knowing only the minimum value of the transistor's h_{FE} and the transistor's power rating. Transistor junction voltages can be estimated for most design purposes using table 1.5.

		Germanium (volts)	Silicon (volts)
V_{BET}	v_{BE} threshold voltage below which little conduction occurs	0.1	0.5
V_{BES}	v_{BE} saturation voltage	0.3	0.5 to 0.7
V_{CES}	v_{CE} saturation voltage	1.0	0.1 to 0.3
V_{BE}	v_{BE} typical conducting voltage	0.2	0.6

Table 1.5: *Typical transistor junction voltages.*

As a preliminary to a simplified transistor-switch design, consider a simplified analysis of the npn silicon transistor switch circuit of figure 1.31a for the case that $V_{CC} = 5$ V, $R_B = 30$ kΩ, and $R_C = 850$ Ω.

- Transistor OFF ($v_i = 0$): If $v_{BE} < v_{BET}$, no base current flows. Since $v_i > v_{BE}$, it follows that if $v_i < v_{BET}$, no base current flows. From table 1.5 it is estimated that $v_{BET} = 0.5$ V. Thus, no base current flows if $v_i < 0.5$ V; equivalently, this transistor is OFF if $v_i < 0.5$ V. In terms of the operation of this circuit, any input voltage v_i less than 0.5 V is perceived as a LOW input. The collector current and collector-to-emitter voltage can be easily determined:

$$i_C \leq h_{FE} \, i_B = 0$$

$$v_{CE} = V_{CC} - R_C i_C = 5 \text{ V}$$

- Transistor ON ($v_i = 5$ V): Assuming a standard transistor switch design, it follows that the transistor is saturated when the input is HIGH. From table 1.5 it is estimated that $v_{CES} = 0.3$ V and $v_{BES} = 0.6$ V. The collector current is computed:

$$i_C = \frac{V_C - v_{CES}}{R_L} = \frac{5 - 0.3}{850} = 5.53 \text{ mA}$$

This compares well with the 5 mA collector current determined by the graphical analysis of this circuit. The base current is computed:

$$i_B = \frac{v_i - v_{BES}}{R_B} = \frac{5 - 0.6}{30K} = 146.7 \ \mu A$$

This also compares well with the 145 μA base current determined by the graphical analysis. The current gain of the transistor in this circuit can be easily computed:

$$G_i = \text{current gain} = \frac{i_C}{i_B} = \frac{5.53 \text{ mA}}{146.7 \ \mu A} = 37.6$$

Again, this compares well with the 34.5 current gain computed by the graphical analysis. However, a word of caution is in order. If the computed transistor current gain G_i is greater than h_{FE} (50 in this case), it means that the transistor is not saturated, as assumed, and the above simplified analysis is not valid.

Now considering design, evaluate the problem in which the silicon npn transistor 2N68 ($h_{FE(min)}$ = 50) is to be used to construct a transistor driver for a 5 V system (ie: V_{CC} = 5 V and a HIGH input is equivalent to v_i = 5 V). The driver is to drive a 50 Ω load with 5 mA. The basic driver circuit of figure 1.31a is modified by replacing the resistor R_C with the series combination of the specified 50 Ω load resistor and a resistor R_x to be selected in the design process (see figure 1.34). The resistor R_x serves to limit the collector current to the required 5 mA whenever the transistor is saturated. The values of both R_B and R_x are determined from considerations applicable only when the transistor is in the ON state.

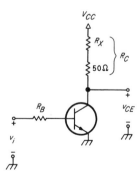

Figure 1.34: *Transistor driver.*

The value of R_C is determined from an application of Kirchhoff's voltage law in the collector circuit with the transistor in saturation:

$$R_C = \frac{V_{CC} - v_{CES}}{i_C} \tag{1.11}$$

$$= \frac{5 - 0.3}{5 \text{ mA}} = 940 \ \Omega$$

Since $R_C = 50 + R_x$, $R_x = 890 \ \Omega$.

Because the 5 mA of collector current flows only if the transistor is in saturation, the resistor R_B must now be selected to insure transistor saturation. Applying Kirchhoff's voltage law in the base current gives

$$R_B = \frac{v_i - v_{BES}}{i_B} \tag{1.12}$$

In the ON state $v_i = 5$ V and $v_{BES} = 0.6$ V. Although the base current i_B is not known, i_{BS}, the minimum value of i_B for saturation, can be determined from i_C and h_{FE}. Since $i_C \leq h_{FE} \ i_B$, the minimum value i_{BS} of i_B that saturates the transistor is

$$i_{BS} = \frac{i_C}{h_{FE}}$$

$$= \frac{5 \text{ mA}}{50} = 100 \ \mu A$$

Thus, the maximum value of R_B is

$$R_B = \frac{5 - 0.6}{100 \ \mu A} = 44 \text{ k}\Omega$$

Using a 44 kΩ resistor for R_B is somewhat risky if there is the possibility that either a HIGH v_i might be less than 5 V or h_{FE} might be less than 50. To be certain that the transistor will turn ON even when a HIGH v_i is only 4.5 V and h_{FE} is only 40, the computation is repeated using these extreme values, and it is determined that an R_B of 31.2 kΩ is safe. In constructing the circuit, select the highest standard resistor value that is less than 31.2 kΩ, using an R_B of 30 kΩ. If the circuit must remain operational under even greater adversity, such as when a HIGH v_i is only 2.5 V and h_{FE} is only 20, an R_B of 7.5 kΩ could be used. In this latter case, the power supplied by the input voltage source, with $v_i = 5$ V, is 2.9 milliwatts compared with the 0.733 milliwatts supplied when an R_B of 30 kΩ is used.

1.11 Inverter Design

The design specifications for an inverter, unlike those for a driver, do not generally specify the amount of collector current i_C that is to flow; this current must be determined by the designer. The value of the collector resistor R_C determines the amount of collector current that flows in the ON state. The collector current, generally many times greater than the base current, is responsible for a large fraction of the power consumption of the circuit. The value of the collector resistor R_C almost solely determines the amount of power that is used by the entire circuit. Since the power $v_i i_B$ drawn from the input source is generally negligible (ie: $v_i i_B << V_{CC} i_C$), a reasonable estimate of the power consumed by the transistor switch is given by the product $V_{CC} i_C$.

From the standpoint of power consumption, it is sensible to make R_C as large as possible, thus making the collector current as small as possible. Consequently, the energy source V_{CC} can be kept relatively small and inexpensive. There is another side to this argument: a strong case can be made for making R_C small even though more power is consumed in doing so.

An inverter is an I/O device. Certainly, there is no point to inverting a signal if the inverted signal is not to be used as an input to some other electronic device (eg: another switching circuit or an output device). An inverter's output is normally loaded by another circuit. For purposes of analysis and design, the loading circuit can often be represented by a single resistor. In high-speed switching applications the loading circuit may require a more complex representation involving capacitors and sometimes inductors (see section 0.12.1). For the present, however, consider the simplest situation in which a single resistor is sufficient to characterize the loading circuit at its input terminals. Figure 1.35a shows an inverter driving another switching circuit whose input resistance is R_L; figure 1.35b shows how, for purposes of analysis and design, the loading circuit can be represented by resistor R_L. Note that the current i_{CC} through the collector resistor R_C is no longer equal to the collector current i_C, as in the case when the transistor is not loaded. The implications of the loading resistor R_L on the selection of R_C in the design of an inverter are now examined.

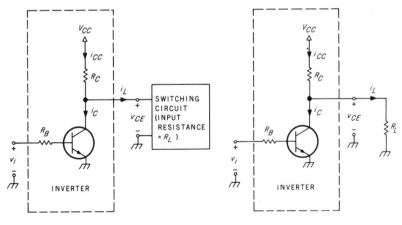

(a) INVERTER AND LOADING CIRCUIT

(b) INVERTER AND RESISTOR EQUIVALENT
OF LOADING CIRCUIT

Figure 1.35: *Inverter design.*

When the transistor is ON, the inverter's output voltage v_{CE} is relatively insensitive to the resistor R_L. The effect of the loading resistor R_L is to reduce the saturation voltage v_{CES} from what it would be without the resistor. This is evident from the following analysis. Applying Kirchhoff's current law at the collector node gives

$$i_{CC} = i_C + i_L \tag{1.13}$$

Application of Kirchhoff's voltage law around a loop including resistor R_C, voltage source V_{CC}, and the transistor (collector-to-emitter path) gives

$$V_{CC} - R_C i_{CC} - v_{CE} = 0 \tag{1.14}$$

Application of Ohm's law to the loading resistor R_L gives

$$v_{CE} = R_L i_L \tag{1.15}$$

Equations (1.13), (1.14), and (1.15) can be combined into the single equation relating v_{CE} and i_C:

$$i_C = -\left(\frac{1}{R_L} + \frac{1}{R_C}\right)v_{CE} + \frac{1}{R_C}V_{CC} \tag{1.16}$$

This equation defines a load line which can be graphed on the i_C-v_{CE} transistor characteristics. Figure 1.36 shows the graph of such a load line; also shown is the collector load line that would apply in the absence of the loading resistor R_L. This graph indicates that the load resistor R_L causes the transistor to saturate with less base current. This increases the safety margin

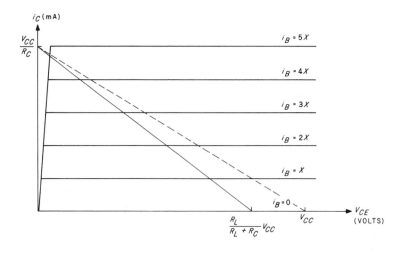

Figure 1.36: *Effect of the loading resistor on inverter output in the ON state.*

with respect to possible drops in the transistor current gain h_{FE} and the HIGH input voltage $v_{i(HIGH)}$. Also, the output voltage v_{CE} is slightly less than what it would be in the absence of R_L. Because this voltage should be as close to zero as possible in the ON state (the output is LOW when the input is HIGH), this reduction of v_{CE} is also desirable. Thus, the presence of the loading resistor R_L improves the operation of the inverter when the transistor is in the ON state. This is not the case, however, when the transistor is in the OFF state.

When the input to the inverter is LOW (ie: $v_i = 0$ V), the inverter output should be HIGH (ie: $v_{CE} = V_{CC}$). When v_i is zero, the base current i_B is zero, and the transistor is turned OFF. The load lines of figure 1.36 show that in the absence of the loading resistor R_L, the output voltage v_{CE} is equal to V_{CC}, providing the necessary HIGH output voltage. When the inverter is loaded with R_L, only a fraction of V_{CC} appears as the output voltage v_{CE}:

$$v_{CE} = \frac{R_L}{R_L + R_C} V_{CC} \qquad (1.17)$$

As R_L approaches infinity (which is equivalent to removing the resistor R_L) the output voltage v_{CE} approaches the desired V_{CC}. The condition that must be satisfied if v_{CE} is to be nearly V_{CC} volts, with the transistor in the OFF state, is

$$R_C << R_L$$

As is typically the case in a design process, there are conflicting objectives in the selection of resistor R_C: to minimize power consumption, R_C should be made as large as possible; to maximize the inverter's HIGH output, R_C should be made as small as possible. Obviously, a compromise must be made based upon which needs are most pressing in a particular application.

Example 1.3

An inverter is required for a 5 V system. The output of this inverter is to be used to drive another switching circuit having an input resistance of 7 kΩ; the HIGH output of the inverter should be at least 4.5 V; the HIGH input to the inverter may be as low as 4.5 V. The miscellaneous components box is examined and a 2N3013 transistor is found. Examination of the *TI Transistor and Diode Data Book* reveals that this transistor is no longer being manufactured. As a result, the listing is brief, only one line. The data given is transcribed here:

2N3013:   npn switching transistor

Maximum power dissipation = 360 milliwatts

$v_{CB(max)}$ = 40 V

$v_{CE(max)}$ = 15 V

$30 \le h_{FE} \le 120$

v_{CES} = 0.18 V (@i_C = 30 mA)

R_C is determined from an analysis of the inverter circuit in the OFF state. By using the minimum tolerable value of v_{CE} in equation (1.17), the maximum allowable value of R_C is determined:

$$R_{C(max)} = \frac{R_L}{v_{CE(min)}}(V_{CC} - v_{CE(min)})$$

Thus,

$$R_{C(max)} = \frac{7\ K}{4.5}(5 - 4.5) = 778\ \Omega$$

To simplify construction and increase the margin of safety, the largest standard resistor value less than 778 Ω is selected: R_C = 680 Ω.

R_B is determined from an analysis of the inverter circuit in the ON state. Assuming that the transistor is saturated in the ON state, the value of the collector current is computed:

$$i_C = \frac{V_{CC} - v_{CES}}{R_C} = \frac{5 - 0.18}{680} = 7.1\ mA$$

The minimum base current required to guarantee transistor saturation is determined by assuming that the transistor has the minimum current gain h_{FE}:

$$i_{BS(min)} = \frac{i_C}{h_{FE(min)}} = \frac{7.1\ mA}{30} = 237\ \mu A$$

The maximum value of R_B that guarantees transistor saturation is computed by using $i_{BS(min)}$ and $v_{i(min)}$ (ie: the minimum value of v_i that is interpreted as a HIGH):

$$R_{B(max)} = \frac{v_{i(min)} - v_{BES}}{i_{BS(min)}} = \frac{4.5 - 0.6}{237\ \mu A} = 16.5\ k\Omega$$

A standard resistor value that is approximately 25 percent smaller than $R_{B(max)}$ is selected for R_B to assure saturation even under relatively adverse conditions: R_B = 12 kΩ. The power consumed by this inverter circuit in the HIGH state is

$$P_{HIGH} = \frac{v_i^2}{R_B} + V_{CC}i_C = \frac{5^2}{12K} + 5 \times 7.1\ mA = 37.6\ milliwatts$$

1.12 The Resistor-Transistor NOR Circuit

The resistor-transistor inverter studied in section 1.11 provides the basis for the design of an endless variety of digital-logic circuits. For example, figure 1.37 shows how the basic inverter is used as the basis for a fundamental logic circuit, the *NOR circuit*. The NOR circuit has two inputs and one output and is designed so that the output voltage is LOW if either of the two input voltages is HIGH. In comparison, an OR circuit is one in which the output voltage is HIGH if either of the two input voltages is HIGH. The output of a NOR circuit, then, is the inverse of the output of an OR circuit.

The operation of the resistor-transistor NOR circuit is essentially the same as the operation of the resistor-transistor inverter. The value of R_B is selected so that if either input voltage v_1 or v_2 is HIGH (say, greater than 4.5 V), then sufficient base current flows to saturate the transistor. With the transistor saturated, the output voltage v_o is LOW ($v_o = v_{CES} \cong 0.3$ V). However, when both v_1 and v_2 are LOW (say, less than 0.5 V), virtually no base current flows, the transistor is OFF, and the output voltage v_o is HIGH ($v_o = 5$ V).

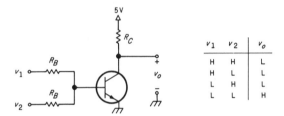

v_1	v_2	v_o
H	H	L
H	L	L
L	H	L
L	L	H

Figure 1.37: *The resistor-transistor NOR circuit.*

An inverter is trivially obtained from a resistor-transistor NOR circuit by grounding one of the two inputs and then using the ungrounded input as the inverter input. An OR circuit can be obtained by appropriately *cascading* two resistor-transistor NOR circuits (ie: using the output of one NOR circuit as an input to the other) as shown in figure 1.38: the first NOR circuit is used as a NOR circuit; the second NOR circuit, with an input grounded, is used as an inverter. The output voltage v_o is the inverse of the NOR's output v_x, and the OR function is achieved.

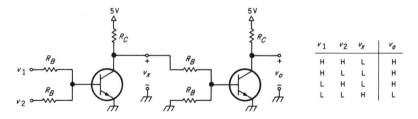

v_1	v_2	v_x	v_o
H	H	L	H
H	L	L	H
L	H	L	H
L	L	H	L

Figure 1.38: *A resistor-transistor OR circuit.*

Proceeding in this manner, it is possible to use nothing but interconnections of the fundamental resistor-transistor NOR circuits to obtain a circuit for any logic function (see section 2.1). For example, figure 1.39 shows how the AND function is achieved by using three resistor-transistor NOR circuits: an AND circuit's output is HIGH if and only if both inputs are HIGH. All logic circuits designed by interconnecting resistor-transistor NOR circuits belong to the resistor-transistor logic (RTL) family.

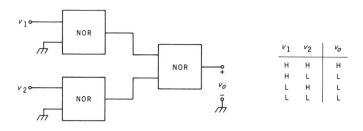

Figure 1.39: *An AND circuit obtained from three resistor-transistor NOR circuits.*

1.13   The Building-Block Approach to the Design of Complex Digital Logic Networks

In designing large and complex digital-logic networks, there is an enormous advantage in using a fundamental digital-logic circuit (such as the NOR circuit) as a universal building block. The alternative is to design totally at the electric circuit level and to specify every electric circuit component for every logic circuit in the design. There is, however, an important issue to be considered before a digital-logic circuit can be used as a universal building block in the design of other digital-logic circuits. One must be absolutely certain that the operation of the fundamental circuit does not deteriorate when it becomes part of an interconnection which includes many other identical circuits. To illustrate the problem, consider the possibility of using the resistor-transistor NOR circuit, based upon the inverter design of example 1.3, as the fundamental building block in the design of other digital-logic circuits. Figure 1.40 shows such a NOR circuit and summarizes the important design characteristics of the circuit. This circuit has been designed to provide a HIGH output of at least 4.5 V even if the output is loaded with a resistor as low as 7 kΩ.

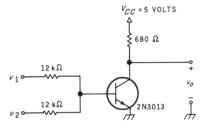

Figure 1.40: *An actual resistor-transistor NOR circuit.*

1.13.1   Cascading

Recall that two digital circuits are said to be *cascaded* when the output of one is the input of the other. Figure 1.41 shows the cascading of n NOR circuits. The minimum resistance with which a digital logic circuit can be loaded becomes an important factor in the reliable operation of a cascaded interconnection of identical circuits. For example, consider cascading two resistor-transistor NOR circuits, each identical to the one of figure 1.40. Examination of this NOR circuit reveals that it functions within specifications when it is loaded with another identical NOR circuit. Because the input resistance of the NOR circuit (ie: the resistance between an input terminal and ground) consists of the series combination of the 12 kΩ base resistor R_B and the base-to-emitter resistance of the transistor R_{BE} (ie: the forward resistance of the base-to-emitter diode), the resistive load that the loading NOR circuit puts on the driving NOR circuit is always at least 12 kΩ. Because this NOR circuit is designed to operate within specifications with a load resistance of 7 kΩ or more, the output voltage of the driving NOR circuit, when in the HIGH state, is greater than the minimum 4.5 V required to turn ON the loading NOR circuit. Thus, the output circuit of one NOR unit is *matched* to the input circuit of the next NOR unit in the cascade. There is *no limit* to the number of resistor-transistor NOR circuits of this type that can be cascaded.

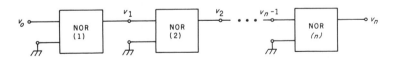

Figure 1.41: *Cascading n NOR circuits.*

The transistor is the important component in achieving the high degree of *isolation* between the inputs and the output of the resistor-transistor NOR circuits. Although the values of the input voltages determine whether or not the transistor is turned ON, the input voltage sources themselves only supply a fraction of the power necessary to turn the transistor ON. The power that turns the transistor ON is provided almost entirely by V_{CC}, the 5 volt DC power supply in the collector circuit. For a particular resistor-transistor NOR circuit, the value of the output voltage v_o is determined only by the state of the transistor (ie: either OFF or ON and saturated) and the magnitude of the loading resistor (ie: the input resistance of the next NOR circuit in the cascade). Variations in the input voltages, and thus in the base current, that do not take the transistor out of the saturated state, do not affect the output voltage v_o. This great isolation between the input and output circuits allows NOR circuits to be cascaded endlessly with no deterioration in operation. In figure 1.41, if each NOR is a resistor-transistor NOR circuit equivalent to that of figure 1.40 and if the first input v_o is within specifications (ie: $v_o \le 0.5$ V for a LOW and $v_o \ge 4.5$ V for a HIGH), then all n NOR circuits will operate within specifications. The number of NOR circuits in the cascade, n, is unimportant as long as the 5 volt DC power supply is large enough to power all circuits in the cascade.

Now consider a NOR circuit which has been designed using the 2N3013 transistor to drive a 7 kΩ load while maintaining a HIGH output voltage of at least 4.9 V. Such a design results in a NOR circuit in which $R_C = 150\ \Omega$ and $R_B = 3$ kΩ. If two of these NOR circuits are cascaded, the HIGH output voltage of the first NOR circuit, which is loaded by the base circuit of the second NOR circuit, is

$$v_{o\,(HIGH)} = 5 - \frac{V_{CC} - v_{BES}}{R_C + R_B} R_C$$

$$= 5 - \frac{5 - 0.6}{150 + 3000} 150$$

$$= 4.79 \text{ volts}$$

In this case the required minimal HIGH of 4.9 volts is not achieved. Since one of these NOR circuits cannot be used to drive another similar NOR circuit, it should not be used as a fundamental building block.

1.13.2 Fan-out

A more severe demand on the design of a digital-logic circuit that is to be used as a universal building block is encountered when the output of one digital circuit must provide the inputs for *several* other digital circuits. This is called *fan-out*. Figure 1.42a shows the output of a resistor-transistor NOR circuit providing the input to n other identical NOR circuits (ie: a fan-out of n). By replacing each of the n loading NOR circuits by its equivalent input circuit (ie: a resistor R_B in series with the base-to-emitter diodes as shown in figure 1.42b), the effective load on the one NOR circuit can be determined. Using the offset diode model, the n input NOR circuits are equivalent to a single loading resistance of R_B/n in series with a voltage source v_{BES}, ac-

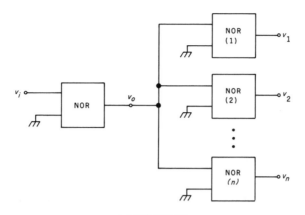

(a) FAN-OUT OF n

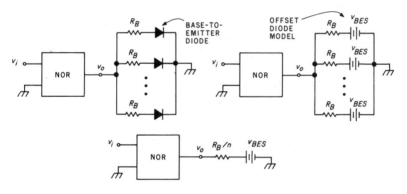

(b) EQUIVALENT FAN-OUT LOAD

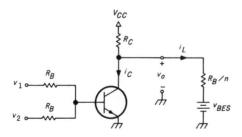

(c) RESISTOR-TRANSISTOR NOR WITH EQUIVALENT FAN-OUT LOAD

Figure 1.42: *Fan-out.*

counting for the voltage drop across the base-to-emitter diodes. For the case that the transistor is OFF (ie: $i_C = 0$), the HIGH output voltage $v_{o\,(HIGH)}$ of a resistor-transistor NOR circuit with fan-out n can be obtained from analysis of figure 1.42c:

$$v_{o\,(HIGH)} = i_L \frac{R_B}{n} + v_{BES}$$

$$= \left(\frac{v_{CC} - v_{BES}}{R_C + R_B/n} \right) \frac{R_B}{n} + v_{BES}$$

or, equivalently,

$$v_{o\,(HIGH)} = \frac{V_{CC} - v_{BES}}{n\,R_C/R_B + 1} + v_{BES}$$

Increasing the fan-out n decreases $v_{o(HIGH)}$; fan-out can be increased to the point that $v_{o(HIGH)}$ cannot be distinguished from $v_{o(LOW)}$. In the design of a resistor-transistor NOR circuit to be used as a universal building block, it is desirable to select the values of R_B and R_C so as to obtain a maximum fan-out for a specified minimum $v_{o(HIGH)}$. From the above equation for $v_{o(HIGH)}$, it is clear that either decreasing the value of R_C or increasing the value of R_B (or, equivalently, increasing the ratio of R_B/R_C) increases the value of $v_{o(HIGH)}$, thus compensating for the effect of increasing fan-out. To maintain the minimum specified HIGH output voltage $v_{H(min)}$, it is necessary that

$$v_{H(min)} \leq v_{o(HIGH)} = \frac{V_{CC} - v_{BES}}{n\,R_C/R_B + 1} + v_{BES}$$

or, equivalently,

$$\frac{R_B}{R_C} \geq \frac{v_{H(min)} - v_{BES}}{n\,(V_{CC} - v_{H(min)})}$$

Note that the ratio R_B/R_C also determines whether or not the transistor saturates when one of the input voltages, v_1 or v_2, is HIGH. Fan-out cannot be increased by increasing the ratio R_B/R_C indefinitely. Increasing the ratio R_B/R_C beyond a certain point results in a situation where a HIGH input voltage, $v_{1(HIGH)}$ or $v_{2(HIGH)}$ does not saturate the transistor. In this case, $v_{o(LOW)} > v_{CES}$ and the maximum LOW output voltage may be exceeded.

Recall that the transistor is saturated if the current gain

$$G_i = \frac{i_C}{i_B}$$

is less than the maximum current gain h_{FE} (ie: the transistor is saturated if $G_i \leq h_{FE}$). Analysis of the resistor-transistor NOR circuit in the ON state (assuming $i_L = 0$) gives

$$G_i = \frac{i_C}{i_B} = \frac{V_{CC} - v_{CES}/R_C}{v_{i(HIGH)} - v_{BES}/R_B}$$

$$= \frac{R_B}{R_C} \frac{V_{CC} - v_{CES}}{v_{i(HIGH)} - v_{BES}}$$

Because this NOR circuit is to be used as a fundamental building block, the minimum HIGH *input* voltage and the minimum HIGH *output* voltage are specified to be the same. To insure saturation with a minimum HIGH input voltage $v_{H(min)}$, it is necessary that

$$\frac{R_B}{R_C} \frac{V_{CC} - v_{CES}}{v_{H(min)} - v_{BES}} \leq h_{FE}$$

or, equivalently,

$$\frac{R_B}{R_C} \leq h_{FE} \frac{v_{H(min)} - v_{BES}}{V_{CC} - v_{CES}}$$

Therefore, to insure saturation and to insure that the output voltage v_o is greater than the minimum HIGH output voltage $v_{H(min)}$, it is necessary that

$$n \frac{v_{H(min)} - v_{BES}}{V_{CC} - v_{H(min)}} \leq \frac{R_B}{R_C} \leq h_{FE} \frac{v_{H(min)} - v_{BES}}{V_{CC} - v_{CES}} \tag{1.18}$$

The situation is clear: for a given transistor (ie: for a given h_{FE} and v_{CES}), a given voltage source V_{CC}, and a specified minimum HIGH voltage $v_{H(min)}$, there is a maximum fan-out that can be achieved without risking the possibility of not saturating the transistor in the ON state:

$$n \leq h_{FE} \frac{V_{CC} - v_{H(min)}}{V_{CC} - v_{CES}} \tag{1.19}$$

Note that the maximum fan-out possible is not affected by v_{BES}. Any increases in fan-out can come only at the expense of the safety margin used to insure saturation.

Example 1.4

Consider the design of a NOR circuit using the 2N3013 transistor (ie: $h_{FE} = 30$, $v_{CES} = 0.18$ V, $v_{BES} = 0.6$ V) and a 5 V voltage source (ie: $V_{CC} = 5$ V), in which the minimum HIGH voltage is specified to be 4.5 V (ie: $v_{H(min)} = 4.5$ V). Using equation (1.18), the limits on the ratio R_B/R_C

can be determined:

$$7.8n \leq \frac{R_B}{R_C} \leq 24.27$$

Thus, the absolute maximum fan-out possible is 3. In the NOR circuit of figure 1.39, $R_B = 12$ kΩ and $R_C = 680$ Ω. For this circuit $R_B/R_C = 17.6$ and the maximum fan-out is 2. In situations where lower minimum HIGH voltages $v_{H(min)}$ can be tolerated, larger fan-out is possible. For example, suppose $v_{H(min)} = 3.5$. Then,

$$1.9n \leq \frac{R_B}{R_C} \leq 18.0$$

In this case, the absolute maximum fan-out is 9.

1.14 Transistor Switching Speed

Switching speed is a measure of the time that it takes for a digital circuit to change its output state (ie: the time to go from LOW to HIGH or vice versa). Determination of a circuit's switching speed requires a transient analysis of that circuit in which the important parasitic dynamic elements are included. Most important in the determination of switching speed are the transistor's parasitic capacitors associated with the charge distributions at the pn junctions of the transistor. The most significant of these parasitic capacitors are associated with the charge that accumulates in the base of the transistor. They are the base-to-emitter junction capacitor C_{BE} and the base-to-collector junction capacitor C_{BC} (see figure 1.43a). The transistor models used thus far have not included these parasitic capacitors and, therefore, are not suitable for determining the switching speeds of transistor switching circuits such as the resistor-transistor NOR. In addition, it has been assumed that the digital circuits are loaded with purely resistive loads. However, because unavoidable parasitic capacitances exist between wires that connect the output of a digital circuit to its load and because most loads are digital circuits which use transistors (with their inherent pn junction parasitic capacitors), a more realistic model of the load is provided by adding a capacitor in parallel with the equivalent output resistor. This equivalent loading capacitor can rarely be neglected in the computation of switching speed.

In the design of digital computers, the switching speeds of the digital circuits used are extremely important. These switching speeds determine the maximum computing speed at which the digital computer can operate. Since computing speed often represents the most important figure of merit of a computer, considerable research continues in the development of new electronic devices and ingenious circuitry, resulting in digital-logic circuits with faster switching speeds. In general, many other digital-circuit features are willingly compromised for improvements in switching speed. Nevertheless, because most switching delays are associated with unwanted capacitances (either the transistor's parasitic capacitances or the parasitic capacitance of the loading circuit), significant reductions in switching times can often be realized by reducing the resistance values of R_C and R_B. This allows for faster charging and discharging of the parasitic capacitances through these resistors. The problem with this strategy is that the power dissipated by a switch increases as the values of R_C and R_B decrease; the value of R_C is especially critical because, often, the power dissipated by the switch is approximately inversely proportional to R_C. Improving switching speed comes at the expense of greater power dissipation.

Thus far, the analysis of the common-emitter resistor-transistor switch has been a static analysis in the assumption that the output is in either the HIGH state or the LOW state. Attention is now turned to the switching speed of the resistor-transistor switch by focusing on the transition periods when the digital switch is in neither the HIGH state nor the LOW state, but is in the process of changing from HIGH to LOW or vice versa. The length of time taken to make the HIGH-to-LOW, or the LOW-to-HIGH, transition is called the *switching time*.

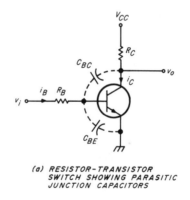

(a) RESISTOR-TRANSISTOR
SWITCH SHOWING PARASITIC
JUNCTION CAPACITORS

Figure 1.43: *Switching times for resistor-transistor switch.*

1.14.1 Switching Delays Caused by Transistor Parameters

Consider the application of the rectangular input voltage to the resistor-transistor switch (see figure 1.43a); V_1 is a positive voltage large enough to saturate the transistor; V_2 is a negative voltage which drives the transistor OFF. Because of the transistor's parasitic capacitances, the transistor's collector current i_C and collector-to-emitter voltage v_{BE} do not respond instantaneously to changes in input v_{BE} or i_B. With respect to the transistor-resistor switch, this means that the collector current i_C and the output voltage v_o ($v_o = V_{CC} - i_C R_C$) respond to changes in v_i only with some delay. Figure 1.43b shows a typical collector-current waveform in response to the rectangular input voltage which is varying between V_1 and $-V_2$ volts, where $V_1 > 0$ and $V_2 > 0$. The important switching-time parameters are:

- *delay time t_d*: This is the time required for the collector current to rise to 10 percent of its final value (approximately V_{CC}/R_C) from the time the input signal is applied. The delay t_d is due to the time required to discharge and charge the transistor's parasitic junction capacitors C_{BE} and C_{BC} and the time required for the holes to propagate from the emitter across the entire base to the collector and be initially identified as collector current. Although it is possible to obtain a rather precise mathematical expression for delay time t_d, such a derivation requires a transistor model which is significantly more complex than is generally required for our purposes. However, it is important that for a given R_B and R_C, the delay time t_d can be decreased by either increasing V_1 or decreasing V_2.

- *rise time t_r*: This is the time required for the collector current to rise from 10 percent of its final value to 90 percent of its final value. The rise time is influenced primarily by the two parasitic junction capacitors C_{BE} and C_{BC}. Increasing V_1 decreases t_r.

- *storage time t_s*: This is the time required for the collector current to drop to 90 percent of its saturated value (ie: approximately 90 percent of V_{CC}/R_C) from the time the input signal is removed. A saturated transistor has excess holes in the base region and cannot respond until this excess charge is removed. The time required to remove this charge, as reverse base current through R_B, makes up the largest component of the storage time. The transistor's parasitic junction capacitors C_{BE} and C_{BC} also contribute to the storage time. Storage time t_s can be decreased by decreasing V_1 or increasing V_2.

- *fall time t_f*: This is the time required for the collector current to drop from 90 percent to 10 percent of its saturated value. The main transistor parameters in determining fall time are the parasitic junction capacitors C_{BE} and C_{BC}. Fall time can be decreased by increasing V_2.

In a high-speed computer, the circuit designer tries to design a circuit with the smallest possible turn-on and turn-off times. The dilemma is that by increasing V_1 and decreasing V_2, turn-on time is decreased, but these same variations in V_1 and V_2 increase turn-off time. Shortening the turn-on time comes at the expense of lengthening the turn-off time. Therefore, although faster switching speeds can be achieved by proper circuit design, the fastest average switching speed of a digital system made up of transistor switching circuits, in which the number of transistor turn-ons is approximately equal to the number of turn-offs, is limited. At a certain point, increased switching speed can be obtained only by using a "faster" transistor.

Especially notable, in terms of many digital circuits where the input voltage is a positive pulse (ie: $V_1 > 0$ and $V_2 = 0$) rather than a rectangular wave with $V_2 > 0$, is that transistor turn-on is considerably faster than transistor turn-off. Clever output designs for resistor-transistor switches can be used to obtain high speeds for the LOW-to-HIGH transition (ie: transistor turn-on) as well as the HIGH-to-LOW transition (ie: transistor turn-off). Designs such as the totem-pole output (section 2.2.3) involve the use of additional transistors in ingenious circuits so as to take advantage of a transistor's faster turn-on speed in both output transitions.

The important transistor switching-time parameters usually given by the manufacturer on the transistor data sheets are the turn-on time t_{ON}, the turn-off time t_{OFF}, and the storage time t_s. Knowledge of these switching times is generally all that is required for most digital design applications.

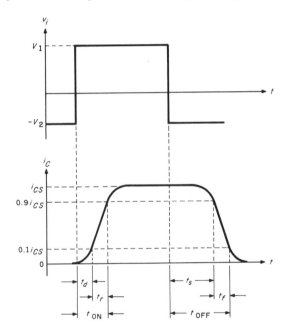

(b) INPUT AND OUTPUT WAVEFORMS

Figure 1.43 cont.

1.14.2 Switching Delays Caused by Loading

Although the lower limits of a transistor switch's switching times are determined by the transistor's parameters, in most applications the circuit within which the transistor is used is primarily responsible for excessive switching times. For example, because the parasitic junction capacitors C_{BE} and C_{BC} are charged and discharged through resistors R_B and R_C, respectively, the size of these resistors influences the switching times; decreasing the size of these resistors decreases switching times. Higher power consumption is also associated with decreases in R_B and R_C. Higher speed is often obtained by increasing power consumption.

A particularly important circuit parameter influencing the switching time of a resistor-transistor switch is the capacitive load generally existing at the output of a transistor switch (ie: between the collector and emitter terminals of the transistor) as shown in figure 1.44a. Most often, this loading capacitance is not the result of a discrete capacitor intentionally placed in the circuit. Rather, the capacitive load is made up of the parasitic capacitance of the connecting wires and the capacitive input of the loading circuit (eg: input of the resistor-transistor switch itself is not purely resistive). The effect of a loading capacitor C on the switching times of the resistor-transistor switch of figure 1.44a is best understood if the transistor itself is considered to be ideal in that its turn-on and turn-off times, t_{ON} and t_{OFF}, are assumed to be zero (ie: assume $C_{BE} = C_{BC} = 0$). In this way, the effect of the loading capacitor C can be isolated.

Application of Kirchhoff's current law at the output junction results in

$$i_{CC} = i_C + i_L$$

Assuming the transistor is *not* saturated and that $t_{ON} = t_{OFF} = 0$ results in

$$i_C = h_{FE} i_B \qquad v_o > v_{CES}$$

In accordance with the definition of a capacitor,

$$i_L = C \frac{dv_o}{dt}$$

Thus,

$$i_{CC} = h_{FE} i_B + C \frac{dv_o}{dt} \qquad v_o > v_{CES}$$

Application of Kirchhoff's voltage law in the collector circuit gives

$$v_o = V_{CC} - i_{CC} R_C$$

Therefore,

$$v_o = V_{CC} - (h_{FE} i_B + C \frac{dv_o}{dt}) R_C \qquad v_o > v_{CES}$$

or,

$$\frac{dv_o}{dt} = - \frac{1}{R_C C} v_o + \frac{1}{R_C C} (V_{CC} - h_{FE} R_C i_B) \qquad v_o > v_{CES}$$

(a) CAPACITIVELY LOADED
    RESISTOR-TRANSISTOR SWITCH

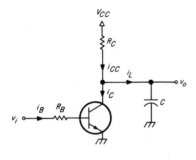

(b) RESPONSE DURING
    TRANSISTOR TURN-ON

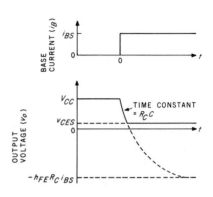

(c) RESPONSE DURING
    TRANSISTOR·TURN-OFF

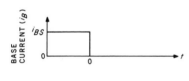

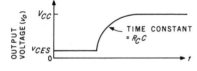

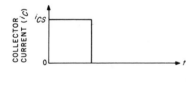

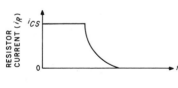

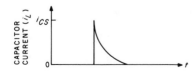

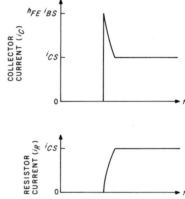

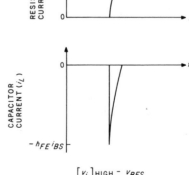

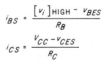

$$i_{BS} = \frac{[v_i]_{HIGH} - v_{BES}}{R_B}$$

$$i_{CS} = \frac{V_{CC} - v_{CES}}{R_C}$$

Figure 1.44: *Capacitive loading of a resistor-transistor switch.*

Consider the case that i_B is switched from $i_B = 0$ to $i_B = i_{BS}$ at $t = 0$ as shown in figure 1.44b. Prior to switching at $t = 0$, $i_C(0) = 0$, and $v_o(0) = V_{CC}$. Thus, the output voltage response is given by (see appendix A1.1)

$$v_o(t) = (V_{CC} + h_{FE} R_C i_{BS})\, e^{-t/R_C C} - h_{FE} R_C i_{BS} \qquad v_o > v_{CES}$$

The response of v_o to the step change in i_B is graphed in figure 1.44b. The output voltage decreases exponentially with time constant $R_C C$ and approaches $-h_{FE} R_C i_{BS}$ (not zero) until the transistor saturates. Clearly, the time required for v_o to reach the LOW state from the HIGH state (ie: for the collector current to go from $i_C = 0$ to $i_C \cong V_{CC}/R_C$, or for the transistor to turn ON) depends upon the transistor gain h_{FE} as well as the time constant $R_C C$. The currents i_C, i_{CC}, and i_L are also graphed during this period. Note the sharp pulse of current i_L discharging capacitor C. This rapid discharge current flows through the low-resistance path provided by the collector of the turned-on transistor.

Now, consider switching i_B from $i_B = i_{BS}$ to $i_B = 0$ (ie: turning the transistor OFF) at $t = 0$ as shown in figure 1.44c. In this case, $v_o(0) = v_{CES}$ and

$$v_o(t) = (V_{CC} - v_{CES})\,(1 - e^{-t\,R_C C}) + v_{CES} \qquad v_o > v_{CES}$$

This response is graphed in figure 1.44c. Again, the time constant is $R_C C$. However, in this case, where the transistor is being turned OFF, the voltage v_o approaches its final value exponentially. This trajectory is not truncated by the saturation of the transistor, as was the case when the transistor was being turned ON. As a result, the time for transistor turn-on is considerably less than the time for turn-off. The delays caused by the loading capacitor C are similar to those caused by the transistor's parasitic junction capacitors in that the transistor turn-off delays are greater than the transistor turn-on delays.

PROBLEMS

P1.1:   For the series resistor-diode circuit of figure P1.1a, use three methods of analysis to graph current i versus resistance R (vary R from 10 Ω to 50 kΩ) for both the case that the diode is a germanium 1N270 diode and the case that the diode is a silicon 1N3605 diode:
(a) Use the diode characteristics of figure P1.1b in a graphical analysis.
(b) Use the pure-offset model (figure 1.12a) for the diode.
(c) Use the forward-resistance model (figure 1.12b) for the diode.

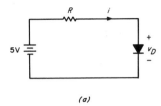

Figure P1.1.

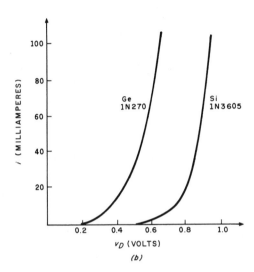

(b)

P1.2:   There exists a special class of diodes that give off light when conducting current in the forward direction. Such diodes are called *light-emitting diodes* or *LEDs*. In this exercise, a laboratory study of an LED will be conducted in which the necessary measurements are taken on the resistor-diode circuit of figure P1.2 to determine the parameters of the forward-resistance model of the LED.

(a) Take the necessary voltage measurements (*do not take any current measurements*) and make the necessary computations to complete table P1.2. Be sure to note the relative brightness of the LED for each current value.

(b) Graph the LED's volt-current characteristics (v_D versus i) on the coordinate system given in figure P1.2b.

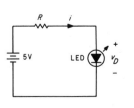

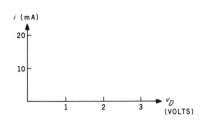

Figure P1.2.   (a)   (b)

R (OHMS)	150	330	680	1 kΩ	5.1 kΩ	10 kΩ	51 kΩ
v_D (VOLTS) (MEASURED)							
i (mA) (COMPUTED)							

Table P1.2

(c) From the graph of part (b), develop a suitable forward-resistance model for the LED. This model is to be used to determine the value of the series resistance R required to operate the LED at current levels of 10 mA to 20 mA.

(d) Use the forward-resistance model developed in part (c) to determine the value of the series resistor R, so that

1. i = 10 mA
2. i = 15 mA
3. i = 20 mA

(e) Check the results of part (d) in the laboratory.

P1.3: (a) Analytically determine the waveforms of the voltage across and the current through the 10 kΩ resistor for the diode rectifier circuits of figures P1.3a and P1.3b (note that ideal diodes are assumed in these circuits) for each of the following cases:

1. v_i is a 1 kHz square wave with an amplitude of 5 V.
2. v_i is a 1 kHz triangular wave with a peak value of 5 V.
3. v_i is a 1 kHz sinusoid with a peak value of 5 V.

In each case, graph the voltage across the 10 kΩ resistor against time for a 2-millisecond interval.

(b) Verify the results of your analysis in the laboratory; use a function generator, an oscilloscope, and 1N4148 diodes. Carefully sketch the oscilloscope displays to show the proper voltage and time scale factors.

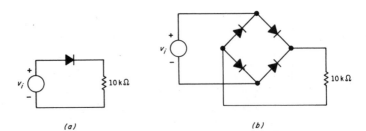

Figure P1.3.   *(a)*   *(b)*

P1.4: The diode rectifier-filter circuit shown in figure P1.4 is to be studied for various combinations of R and C. Use the oscilloscope to take the measurements necessary to fill table P1.4. A function generator can be used for the 1 kHz sinusoidal voltage source. However, remember that a function generator is generally a low-power source having a relatively high internal resistance (eg: 600 Ω is not unusual) and should not be used in the above circuit if R is small or C is large.

Use the above results to *estimate* the value of C required to obtain $v_{(avg)} = 3$ V for the case that $R = 100$ Ω. Assume that the 1 kHz sinusoidal voltage source is an ideal voltage source (ie: that its internal resistance is zero). *DO NOT TRY THIS IN THE LABORATORY.*

Figure P1.4.

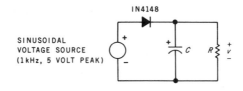

Table P1.4.

C	10 kΩ		47 kΩ		100 kΩ	
	r_f	$v_{(avg)}$	r_f	$v_{(avg)}$	r_f	$v_{(avg)}$
0.01 μF						
0.047 μF						
0.1 μF						
1.0 μF						

r_f = RIPPLE FACTOR $v_{(avg)}$ = AVERAGE OF VOLTAGE v

P1.5: The diode rectifier-filter circuit of figure P1.4 is now to be studied with respect to the effects of frequency variations of the sinusoidal voltage source. Fill in table P1.5 for the case that $R = 100$ kΩ, and $C = 0.047$ μF.

Table P1.5.

FREQUENCY	0.1 kHz	1 kHz	10 kHz
r_f			
$v_{(avg)}$			

P1.6: The zener-diode regulator circuit shown in figure P1.6 is to be used as a voltage regulator to transform the 9 V, 5 A, DC voltage source into a 5 V, 5 A DC voltage source. Analytically determine the resistance value and power rating of resistor R_v. Graph i_z versus i_L and v_o versus i_L in the range $i_L = 0$ to $i_L = 6$ A. What is the minimum power rating of the zener diode used in this circuit?

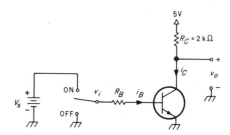

Figure P1.6.

P1.7:   Perform a *graphical analysis* of the npn 2N68 transistor switch shown in figure P1.7. Use the transistor characteristics graphed in figure 1.32. Summarize your results in the tables P1.7a, P1.7b, and P1.7c. Compare the results obtained for table P1.7c to those obtained for tables P1.7a and P1.7b.

Figure P1.7.

NOMINAL PARAMETER VALUES: R_B =91 kΩ, V_S = 5 VOLTS

Table P1.7a.

SWITCH POSITION	i_B (μA)	i_C (mA)	v_{BE} (VOLTS)	v_0 (VOLTS)
OFF				
ON				

VARIATIONS IN R_B; SWITCH POSITION IS ON, V_S = 5 VOLTS

Table P1.7b.

R_B (Ω)	i_B (μA)	i_C (mA)	v_{BE} (VOLTS)	v_0 (VOLTS)
43 kΩ				
220 kΩ				

VARIATIONS IN V_S; SWITCH POSITION IS ON

Table P1.7c.

	V_S (VOLTS)	R_B (Ω)	i_B (μA)	i_C (mA)	v_{BE} (VOLTS)	v_0 (VOLTS)
V_S IS 20% LOW	4	220K				
	4	91K				
	4	43K				
V_S IS 20% HIGH	6	220K				
	6	91K				
	6	43K				

P1.8:   Consider the 2N1613 transistor switch shown in figure P1.8.
(a) For the case that $V_B = 2$ V, $V_{CC} = 20$ V, $R_B = 3.9$ kΩ, and
$R_C = 680$ Ω, determine h_{FE}, $v_{CE(OFF)}$, $v_{CE(ON)}$, $i_{C(ON)}$, $i_{B(ON)}$, the power from
source V_B when ON, the power dissipated in R_C when ON, and the power
dissipated by the transistor when ON. Use the transistor characteristic
curves given in figure 1.29.
(b) Repeat part (a) by using a simplified design method based only upon the
following data:

$$h_{FE} = 100 \ (@ \ i_C = 50 \text{ mA})$$
$$V_{CE} = 0.5 \text{ V} \ (@ \ i_C = 50 \text{ mA})$$
$$V_{BE} = 0.6 \text{ V} \ (@ \ i_B = 1 \text{ mA})$$

(c) Suppose R_C is a lamp which draws 70 mA when 40 V is applied to it
(therefore, $R_C = ?$) and $V_C = V_B = 40$ V. Find the value of R_B which per-
mits the proper switching. Do this first graphically and then using only the
transistor data given in part (b).

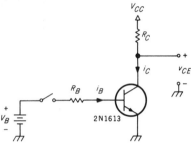

Figure P1.8.

P1.9:   The following data for the 2N3393 transistor is transcribed here from two
transistor manuals:

GE Transistor Manual:
$$h_{FE} = 90 \text{ to } 180 \ (i_C = 2 \text{ mA})$$
$$v_{CE(max)} = 25 \text{ V}$$
$$i_{C(max)} = 100 \text{ mA}$$
$$P_{T(max)} = 200 \text{ milliwatts.}$$

TI's Transistor and Diode Data Book (data for TI595, which is TI's nearest
equivalent to the 2N3393):
$$h_{FE} = 100 \text{ to } 300 \ (i_C = 1 \text{ mA})$$
$$v_{CE(max)} = 60 \text{ V}$$
$$i_{C(max)} = 200 \text{ mA}$$
$$P_{T(max)} = 625 \text{ milliwatts}$$
$$v_{BES} = 0.5 \text{ to } 0.7 \text{ volts } (i_B = 1 \text{ mA})$$
$$v_{CES} \leq 0.5 \text{ V} \ (i_B = 5 \text{ mA, } i_C = 100 \text{ mA})$$

(a) Determine the values of R_C and R_B so that the transistor switch shown in
figure P1.9 operates as a driver; in the ON state, 20 mA of current should
pass through R_C.
(b) Determine the value of R_B ($R_C = 1$ kΩ) so that the transistor switch
shown in figure P1.9 operates as an inverter with a fan-out of 5
($v_{o(min)} = 4.5$ V).
(c) Build and test the circuits designed in parts (a) and (b). Fill in tables
P1.9a and P1.9b with both theoretical computed data and actual test data.

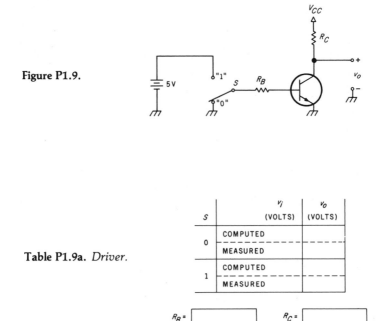

Figure P1.9.

Table P1.9a. *Driver.*

	v_i (VOLTS)	v_o (VOLTS)
0 — COMPUTED		
0 — MEASURED		
1 — COMPUTED		
1 — MEASURED		

$R_B =$ [   ] $R_C =$ [   ]

S		v_i (VOLTS)	v_o (VOLTS)
0	COMPUTED		
0	MEASURED		
1	COMPUTED		
1	MEASURED		

$R_B =$ [   ] $R_C =$ [   ]

$S = 0$

LOAD (OHMS)	FAN-OUT		v_o (VOLTS)
∞	0	COMPUTED	
∞	0	MEASURED	
R_B	1	COMPUTED	
R_B	1	MEASURED	
$1/2\ R_B$	2	COMPUTED	
$1/2\ R_B$	2	MEASURED	
$1/5\ R_B$	5	COMPUTED	
$1/5\ R_B$	5	MEASURED	

Table P1.9b. *Inverter.*

P1.10: Assuming that an LED drops 1.7 V when it is conducting 20 mA, design, build, and test the two logic circuits shown in figures P1.10a and P1.10b. Be sure that the LEDs, when ON, are conducting 20 mA ± 10 percent. Fill in tables P1.10a and P1.10b with both theoretical computed data and actual test data. *Take voltage measurements only;* determine all required values from voltage measurements and from known resistance values.

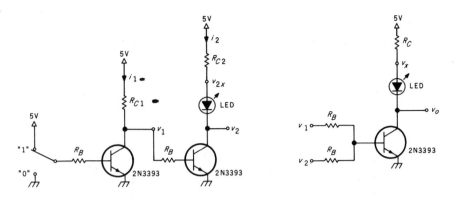

Figure P1.10a.   Figure P1.10b.

Table P1.10a.

SWITCH POSITION	LED		v_1 (VOLTS)	v_2 (VOLTS)	v_{2x} (VOLTS)	i_1 (mA)	i_2 (mA)
0	ON	COMPUTED					
		MEASURED					
1	OFF	COMPUTED					
		MEASURED					

$R_B =$ [　　　] $R_{C1} =$ [　　　] $R_{C2} =$ [　　　]

Table P1.10b.

v_1 (VOLTS)	v_2 (VOLTS)		v_0 (VOLTS)	v_x (VOLTS)	LED	i (mA)
5	5	COMPUTED			ON	
		MEASURED				
5	0	COMPUTED			ON	
		MEASURED				
0	5	COMPUTED			ON	
		MEASURED				
0	0	COMPUTED			OFF	
		MEASURED				

$R_B =$ [　　　] $R_C =$ [　　　]

P1.11:   Using your inverter design from problem P1.11b, observe the effect of capacitive loading (figure P1.11) on transistor turn-on and turn-off times. Record your results in table P1.11.

Figure P1.11.

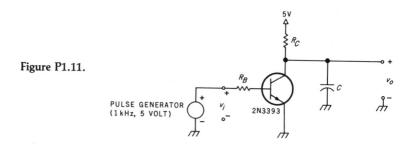

Table P1.11.

C	t_{ON}	t_{OFF}
0		
0.01 μF		
0.1 μF		

$R_C = \boxed{\quad 1\,k\Omega \quad}$ $R_B = \boxed{\qquad\qquad}$

Chapter 2

Digital-Logic Networks

A fundamental digital-logic circuit, such as the resistor-transistor NOR circuit, can be used as a universal building block in constructing digital-logic networks which realize complex digital functions. For a digital-logic circuit to be eligible for use as a universal building block, the following conditions are essential:

1. The digital-logic circuit must be fundamental in that any digital-logic function should be realizable by an interconnection of a finite number of identical versions of the fundamental digital-logic circuit.
2. The fundamental digital-logic circuit must operate within specifications with a fan-out of at least two.

In this chapter a basis is established for the analysis and design of digital-logic networks, which are made up of interconnections of fundamental building blocks. Several fundamental digital-logic circuits commonly used as building blocks are introduced. Switching algebra, a valuable tool in the analysis and design of digital-logic networks, provides an excellent framework within which to model complex digital-logic networks. Importantly, within the framework of switching algebra, one can ascertain the suitability of a particular digital-logic circuit as a universal building block from which all other logic functions can be synthesized.

A *logic family* of digital circuits evolves from a single, fundamental digital-logic circuit. Thus, a logic family consists of a collection of digital-logic circuits, realizing a variety of logic functions, in which each digital circuit is constructed by interconnecting identical fundamental digital-logic circuits. For example, the *resistor-transistor logic* (RTL) family is based upon the resistor-transistor NOR circuit. Several of the important logic families are introduced in this chapter.

2.1   Switching Algebra

Switching algebra, developed for the modeling of large switching systems, is a special case of *Boolean algebra*. Specifically, switching algebra is a Boolean algebra with only two basic elements (eg: HIGH and LOW, true and false, 1 and 0, etc). In the analysis and design of digital computers, however, the binary number system traditionally plays an important role; thus, the two basic switching-algebra elements are taken to be 0 and 1. The variables of switching algebra are denoted by capital letters (eg: V, X, etc). A switching variable can assume a value corresponding to one of the two elements of switching algebra. For example, we may write $V = 0$ or $X = 1$. However, because there are only two switching-variable elements, it follows that

$$\text{If } V \neq 0, \text{ then } V = 1$$
$$\text{If } V \neq 1, \text{ then } V = 0$$

In other words, because of the *binary* nature of switching algebra, the *negation* or *complement* of a switching variable corresponds to only a single element and can also be represented by a switching variable. By denoting $\overline{V}$ to be the negation of V, it follows that

$$\text{If } V = 0, \text{ then } \overline{V} = 1$$
$$\text{If } V = 1, \text{ then } \overline{V} = 0$$

The bar over a switching variable, representing the negation of the switching variable, denotes one of the three *primitive operators* defined in switching algebra. It is called the NOT operator. The other two primitive operators are the AND and the OR operators. The AND and OR operators, symbolized by • and + respectively, represent operations defined on a pair

	$Z = \overline{X}$			$Z = X \cdot Y$				$Z = X + Y$	

X	Z		X	Y	Z		X	Y	Z
0	1		0	0	0		0	0	0
1	0		0	1	0		0	1	1
			1	0	0		1	0	1
			1	1	1		1	1	1

(a) NOT	(b) AND	(c) OR

Figure 2.1: *The three primitive operators of switching algebra.*

of variables. The AND operator is defined such that if $Z = X \cdot Y$, then $Z = 1$ if and only if both X *and* Y are 1. The OR operator is defined such that if $Z = X + Y$, then $Z = 1$ if and only if X *or* Y is 1. The definitions of the three primitive operators of switching algebra are summarized in the *truth tables* of figure 2.1. From the definitions of the NOT, AND, and OR operators, the identities of figure 2.2 follow.

$$\overline{1} = 0 \qquad\qquad 0 \cdot 0 = 0 \qquad\qquad 0 + 0 = 0$$
$$\overline{0} = 1 \qquad\qquad 0 \cdot 1 = 0 \qquad\qquad 0 + 1 = 1$$
$$1 \cdot 0 = 0 \qquad\qquad 1 + 0 = 1$$
$$1 \cdot 1 = 1 \qquad\qquad 1 + 1 = 1$$

$$\text{(a) NOT} \qquad\qquad \text{(b) AND} \qquad\qquad \text{(c) OR}$$

Figure 2.2: *Identities of switching elements.*

The variables and operators of switching algebra can be combined into *well-formed formulas* to describe complex logical processes; a well-formed formula is formally defined as any of the following:

- a switching-algebra constant (ie: 1 or 0)
- a switching-algebra variable
- the negation of any well-formed formula
- the AND of any two well-formed formulas
- the OR of any two well-formed formulas

The following are five examples of well-formed formulas of switching algebra:

$$0, \quad 1 + \overline{A}, \quad \overline{X \cdot Y}, \quad A \cdot (B + C) + \overline{A} \cdot (B \cdot C),$$
$$X \cdot (\overline{Y \cdot (Z + W) + \overline{X + W \cdot Z}})$$

The relationship of switching algebra to actual switching networks becomes apparent if one associates a switching variable (eg: V) either with a switch that is *normally open* or with the voltage of a point with respect to a ground reference. If the switching variable represents a normally open switch, then the value of the switching variable indicates whether or not the switch is closed. $V = 0$ implies that switch V is open (ie: in its normal position), and $V = 1$ implies that switch V is closed. If the switching variable represents the voltage of a point, then the value of the variable indicates whether or not a nonzero voltage exists at that point. $V = 0$ implies that point V is at ground voltage (ie: 0 V or the LOW state), and $V = 1$ implies that point V has a nonzero voltage (eg: 5 V or the HIGH state). Figure 2.3

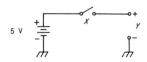

Figure 2.3: *Switching circuits and switching variables.*

shows a simple switching system in which the position of switch X determines the state of point Y. In this system $Y = X$: when $X = 1$ (ie: when switch X is closed), then $Y = 1$ (ie: point Y is 5 V with respect to ground); when $X = 0$, then $Y = 0$. Figures 2.4a and 2.4b show that the fundamental operator AND models a pair of series switches and that the fundamental operator OR models a pair of parallel switches. The NOT operator can be realized by a switch that is *normally closed*. If the switching variable X represents a switch that is normally closed, then $X = 0$ implies that the

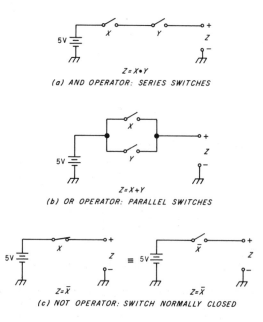

Figure 2.4: *Realization of switching algebra operators.*

switch is closed (the normal position), and $X = 1$ implies that the switch is open. Rather than drawing switching diagrams with two types of switches, it is generally more convenient to represent a normally closed switch X with a normally open switch that is labeled $\overline{X}$. This equivalence is shown in figure 2.4c.

The important properties of switching algebra are the following:

1. *Commutative Properties*
   (a) $X \cdot Y = Y \cdot X$
   (b) $X + Y = Y + X$
2. *Associative Properties*
   (a) $X \cdot (Y \cdot Z) = (X \cdot Y) \cdot Z$
   (b) $X + (Y + Z) = (X + Y) + Z$
3. *Distributive Properties*
   (a) $X \cdot (Y + Z) = (X \cdot Y) + (X \cdot Z)$
   (b) $X + (Y \cdot Z) = (X + Y) \cdot (X + Z)$

The commutative and associative properties of switching algebra correspond to the familiar properties of ordinary algebra as does the first distributive property of switching algebra. However, the second distributive property of switching algebra, not true in ordinary algebra, may appear strange.

The proofs of these properties are easily established by using *proof by perfect induction*, in which the appropriate truth tables are constructed to exhaust all possibilities. For example, the truth table of figure 2.5 proves the first distributive property. Specifically, comparing columns (5) and (8) shows that $X \cdot (Y + Z) = (X \cdot Y) + (X \cdot Z)$ for all the possible combinations of values for X, Y, and Z.

(1)	(2)	(3)	(4)	(5)	(6)	(7)	(8)
X	Y	Z	$Y + Z$	$X \cdot (Y + Z)$	$X \cdot Y$	$X \cdot Z$	$(X \cdot Y) + (X \cdot Z)$
1	1	1	1	1	1	1	1
1	1	0	1	1	1	0	1
1	0	1	1	1	0	1	1
1	0	0	0	0	0	0	0
0	1	1	1	0	0	0	0
0	1	0	1	0	0	0	0
0	0	1	1	0	0	0	0
0	0	0	0	0	0	0	0

Figure 2.5: *Truth table proving first distributive property.*

Some useful identities in switching algebra, easily proven by perfect induction, are given in figure 2.6.

$$X + X = X$$
$$X \cdot X = X$$
$$X + \overline{X} = 1$$
$$X \cdot \overline{X} = 0$$
$$X + 1 = 1$$
$$X \cdot 1 = X$$
$$X + 0 = X$$
$$X \cdot 0 = 0$$
$$X \cdot (X + Y) = X$$
$$X + (X \cdot Y) = X$$

Figure 2.6: *Some useful identities of switching algebra.*

Two important theorems of switching algebra, known as *De Morgan's theorems*, are

$$\overline{X \cdot Y} = \overline{X} + \overline{Y}$$
$$\overline{X + Y} = \overline{X} \cdot \overline{Y}$$

Again, De Morgan's theorems are easily established by perfect induction.

Each property, identity, or theorem of switching algebra has a *dual*. Duality means that from any property, identity, or theorem of switching algebra, another dual property, identity, or theorem can be obtained by carrying out the following four steps:

1. Replace all 0s by 1s and vice versa.
2. Replace all ORs by ANDs and vice versa.
3. Leave the variables unchanged.
4. Leave the NOTs unchanged.

As an example of this duality, observe that De Morgan's theorems are duals of each other. Also, the commutative, associative, and distributive properties given are dual pairs in each case.

Switching algebra was originally derived by Claude Shannon in 1938 from George Boole's Boolean algebra (1854) to simplify the analysis and design of telephone switching networks. Switching algebra now provides a powerful tool in the analysis and design of electronic digital-logic networks. In using switching algebra to model digital-logic networks, it is common to speak of *logic functions* rather than *switching functions, logic variables* rather than *switching variables,* and to graphically represent the *switching functions* (ie: the *logic functions*) with input/output (I/O) *logic-block diagrams* rather than with *switching-circuit diagrams*. For example, the logic-block diagram of figure 2.7 shows that logic variable Z is a function of logic variables W, X, and Y. This diagram does not in itself define the function relating variables W, X, and Y to Z; in order to be useful, an explicit definition of the function F must be provided. As a result, another I/O representation of logic functions, in which the geometric shape of the I/O logic block uniquely defines the block's logic function, has gained wide acceptance.

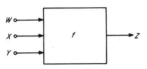

Figure 2.7: *A logic block representing the funciton $Z = F(W,X,Y)$.*

Figure 2.8 defines a generally accepted set of standard symbols for the basic logic *gates*; a gate is a logic device with one output and one or more inputs — it is often implied that a logic gate is the realization of a primitive or simple logic function such as NOT, AND, OR, NOR, etc. A small circle on an input or output line denotes the negating of the signal on that line. Symbols for the NAND and NOR gates are obtained simply by negating (using the NOT logic function) the outputs of the AND and OR gates, respectively.

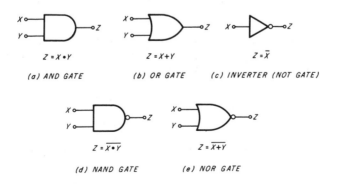

Figure 2.8: *Standard symbols for logic gates.*

By the definition of switching algebra, the primitive operators AND, OR, and NOT provide a complete set of operators with which all logic functions can be expressed. There are, however, single logic functions which can provide a basis from which all other logic functions can be expressed. A given logic function is a *basic logic function* if all three primitive operators (AND, OR, and NOT) can be derived from the proposed basic function. For example, in section 1.12 it is suggested that the NOR gate might form the basis for an entire logic family. This is certainly the case if the primitive operators can be derived from interconnections of only NOR gates. Figure 2.9 shows that the primitive operators are so derivable, making the NOR gate a suitable device around which a family of digital-logic devices can be developed. Of course, there are many other devices that would be similarly suitable; among these the NAND gate is perhaps the most important.

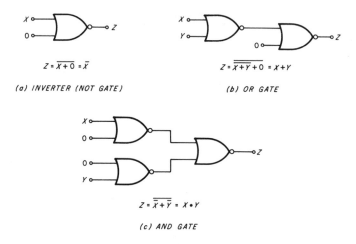

$$Z = \overline{X+0} = \overline{X}$$

(a) INVERTER (NOT GATE)

$$Z = \overline{\overline{X+Y}+0} = X+Y$$

(b) OR GATE

$$Z = \overline{\overline{X}+\overline{Y}} = X \cdot Y$$

(c) AND GATE

Figure 2.9: *Primitive operators AND, OR, and NOT obtained from interconnections of NOR gates.*

A truth table can be obtained from a logic function simply by evaluating the logic function for all possible combinations of values of the variables in the logic function. A truth table for a logic function of n variables has 2^n rows corresponding to the 2^n combinations of n logic variables. Therefore, the truth table represents a complete I/O description of the logic function. There are, of course, many logic functions which have identical truth tables (eg: $F = \overline{X \cdot Y}$ and $F = \overline{X} + \overline{Y}$ have identical truth tables, as established by De Morgan's theorem). The problem of finding a logic function corresponding to a particular truth table does not have a unique solution; nevertheless, it is a simple matter. Two processes for deriving logic functions from truth tables are described below.

Consider the truth table shown in figure 2.10a. Examination of this table reveals that the logic variable F, which is a function of the logic variables X, Y, and Z, is 1 if and only if X AND Z are 0 AND Y is 1. In terms of switching algebra, this is expressed as

$$F = \overline{X} \cdot Y \cdot \overline{Z} \tag{2.1}$$

It is easily verified that the truth table of figure 2.10a is valid for this logic function.

Consider now the truth table of figure 2.10b. Here, F is 1 if and only if X AND Y are 1 AND Z is 0, OR X is 0 AND Y AND Z are 1. In terms of switching algebra, this is expressed as

$$F = (X \cdot Y \cdot \overline{Z}) + (\overline{X} \cdot Y \cdot Z) \tag{2.2}$$

Again, it is easily verified that this logic function results in the truth table of figure 2.10b. Realizations of the logic functions given by equations (2.1) and (2.2) are shown in figure 2.10; only logic gates corresponding to the three fundamental logic operators are used.

A method emerges in which only the *true* rows of the truth table (ie: the rows for which the logic functions $F = 1$) are examined in deriving a logic function from a truth table. In summary, each *true* row of the truth table is used to identify what is called a *true minterm* (eg: the terms of $X \cdot Y \cdot \overline{Z}$ and $\overline{X} \cdot Y \cdot Z$ are the true minterms corresponding to the truth table of figure 2.10b), and all these true minterms are ORed to obtain a logic function for the truth table. The resulting logic function is the canonical *sum-of-products* form.

INPUTS			OUTPUT	MINTERMS		INPUTS			OUTPUT	TRUE MINTERMS
X	Y	Z	F			X	Y	Z	F	
1	1	1	0	$X \cdot Y \cdot Z$		1	1	1	0	—
1	1	0	0	$X \cdot Y \cdot \overline{Z}$		1	1	0	1	$X \cdot Y \cdot \overline{Z}$
1	0	1	0	$X \cdot \overline{Y} \cdot Z$		1	0	1	0	—
1	0	0	0	$X \cdot \overline{Y} \cdot \overline{Z}$		1	0	0	0	—
0	1	1	0	$\overline{X} \cdot Y \cdot Z$		0	1	1	1	$\overline{X} \cdot Y \cdot Z$
0	1	0	1	$\overline{X} \cdot Y \cdot \overline{Z}$ (TRUE MINTERM)		0	1	0	0	—
0	0	1	0	$\overline{X} \cdot \overline{Y} \cdot Z$		0	0	1	0	—
0	0	0	0	$\overline{X} \cdot \overline{Y} \cdot \overline{Z}$		0	0	0	0	—

TRUTH TABLE   *TRUTH TABLE*

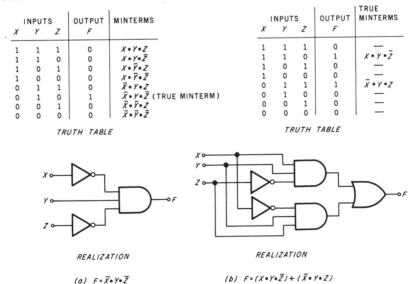

REALIZATION   *REALIZATION*

(a) $F = \overline{X} \cdot Y \cdot \overline{Z}$ (b) $F = (X \cdot Y \cdot \overline{Z}) + (\overline{X} \cdot Y \cdot Z)$

Figure 2.10: *Logic functions from truth tables. Each function is derived by using the minterms of the truth tables.*

Because there are many logic functions having identical truth tables, the logic function obtained from a truth table by summing true minterms is not necessarily the simplest. In the design of digital-logic circuits, the complexity of the resulting digital circuit is closely related to the complexity of the logic function being implemented. Considerable savings in design time and implementation costs may be realized by finding a simpler logic function corresponding to the truth table of interest. There is no known algorithmic procedure for finding the least complex logic function equivalent to a truth table. Nevertheless, skill can be developed in applying the properties, identities, and theorems of switching algebra to obtain simplified logic functions. An examination of the truth table could indicate that an alternate approach to that of identifying true minterms can result in a simpler logic function. For example, consider the truth table of figure 2.11a. The logic function obtained by summing true minterms results in seven minterms. In this case, a simpler logic function can be obtained by using an alternate derivation.

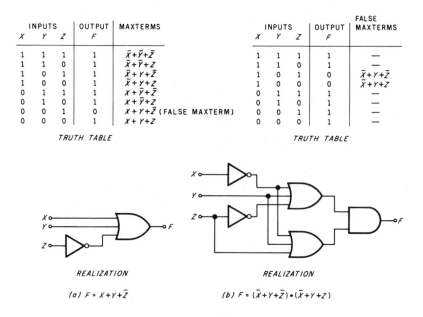

Figure 2.11: *Logic functions from truth tables. The functions are derived by using the maxterms of the truth tables.*

The truth table of figure 2.11a shows that the output switching variable F is 1 for seven combinations of the input switching variables X, Y, and Z. In contrast, F is 0 for only one combination of X, Y, and Z. This suggests that attention ought to be given to the conditions for *falsity* (ie: $F = 0$) rather than truth (ie: $F = 1$). Note that F is 0 when X AND Y are 0 AND when Z is

1. In terms of switching algebra this is written as

$$\overline{F} = \overline{X} \cdot \overline{Y} \cdot Z$$

Negating both sides of the above switching equation results in

$$F = \overline{\overline{X} \cdot \overline{Y} \cdot Z}$$

Application of De Morgan's theorem gives

$$F = X + Y + \overline{Z}$$

It is easily verified that the above switching function results in the truth table of figure 2.11a.

Similarly, examining truth table 2.11b results in

$$\overline{F} = (X \cdot \overline{Y} \cdot Z) + (X \cdot \overline{Y} \cdot \overline{Z})$$

Repeated applications of De Morgan's theorem give

$$F = \overline{(X \cdot \overline{Y} \cdot Z) + (X \cdot \overline{Y} \cdot \overline{Z})}$$

$$F = \overline{(X \cdot \overline{Y} \cdot Z)} \cdot \overline{(X \cdot \overline{Y} \cdot Z)}$$

$$F = (\overline{X} + Y + \overline{Z}) \cdot (\overline{X} + Y + Z)$$

A dual method emerges in which a logic function is derived from a truth table by examining only the *false* rows of the truth table (ie: the rows for which the function F is 0). In summary, each *false* row of the truth table is used to derive what is called a *false maxterm*; the terms $(\overline{X} + Y + \overline{Z})$ and $(\overline{X} + Y + Z)$ are the maxterms corresponding to the truth table of figure 2.11b. All the false maxterms are ANDed to obtain a logic function for the truth table. The resulting logic function is the canonical *product-of-sums* form.

The concept of a *conditional truth table* is often useful in simplifying representations of logic systems. For example, the three-input, one-output logic system shown in figure 2.12a is defined by the truth table given in figure 2.12b. Close examination of this truth table reveals that the output Z is either the NAND or NOR of inputs X and Y, depending upon the value of Q: if Q = 1 then Z = $\overline{X \cdot Y}$, and if Q = 0 then Z = $\overline{X + Y}$. This particular viewpoint of the system is better characterized by the conditional truth table of figure 2.12c.

The logic function can be derived from the conditional truth table by using either the minterm or maxterm approach. Because there are minterms and maxterms that are true or false depending upon the value of Q, such terms must be included to reflect this dependency. In this case, summing minterms gives

$$Z = Q \cdot X \cdot \overline{Y} + Q \cdot \overline{X} \cdot Y + \overline{X} \cdot Y$$

The product of maxterms gives

$$Z = (X + Y) \cdot (X + \overline{Y} + Q) \cdot (\overline{X} + Y + Q)$$

In the summing of minterms, the factor Q in a minterm causes that minterm to vanish when $A = 0$. Similarly "adding" Q to a maxterm causes that factor to be 1 when $Q = 1$. Applying the theorems and identities of switching algebra shows that both forms are identical, and that they can be put into the form

$$Z = Q \cdot (\overline{X \cdot Y}) + \overline{Q} \cdot (\overline{X + Y})$$

Some of the functions that can be represented with switching algebra have been described in this section. The following section shows how they can be realized electronically.

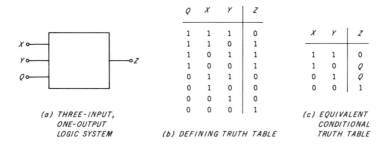

(a) THREE-INPUT,
ONE-OUTPUT
LOGIC SYSTEM

Q	X	Y	Z
1	1	1	0
1	1	0	1
1	0	1	1
1	0	0	1
0	1	1	0
0	1	0	0
0	0	1	0
0	0	0	1

(b) DEFINING TRUTH TABLE

X	Y	Z
1	1	0
1	0	Q
0	1	Q
0	0	1

(c) EQUIVALENT
CONDITIONAL
TRUTH TABLE

Figure 2.12: *A conditional truth table. Note that the output function Z has a value equal to the input variable Q when the values of X and Y differ.*

2.2   Fundamental Digital-Logic Circuits and IC Logic Families

With the development of the *integrated circuit* (IC), the building-block approach to digital-logic networks became the basis for the construction of practically all digital-logic networks. An integrated circuit is a single monolithic chip of semiconductor in which electric circuit elements and their connections are fabricated by the same processes used to fabricate diodes and transistors. These processes consist primarily of a series of precisely controlled material depositions and impurity diffusions. Highly developed photolithographic technology makes it possible to mass-produce enormously complex electronic networks of exceedingly high reliability and of microscopic proportions. For example, Intel Corporation's 8085 microprocessor chip, a general-purpose central processing unit for a microcomputer which can execute 770,000 instructions per second, consists of a network of digital-logic gates in a design using 6200 transistors. The entire 8085 chip is fabricated on a thin rectangular chip of silicon measuring 0.164 inch by 0.222 inch (ie: less than 0.04 square inches in area).

An integrated circuit such as the 8085 microprocessor is an example of a large-scale integrated (LSI) circuit. The technology used in its manufacture approaches the limits of the present state-of-the-art. There are, however, many commercially available medium-scale integrated (MSI) circuits implementing a myriad of digital-logic functions. The broad selection available and the low cost of these MSI circuits make them indispensable in the design and construction of digital-logic networks. In the following section, some fundamental digital-logic circuits, each of which is the basis of an important IC logic family, are studied.

2.2.1 Resistor-Transistor Logic (RTL)

The fundamental logic gate of the resistor-transistor logic (RTL) family is the NOR gate shown in figure 2.13. The NOR circuit is shown loaded with a network equivalent to n identical turned-ON NOR gates; this load is the equivalent of n parallel base resistors R_B in series with the voltage source v_{BES} which corresponds to the base-to-emitter voltage of the turned-ON loading transistors (ie: the offset model of the base-to-emitter diode of the loading transistors).

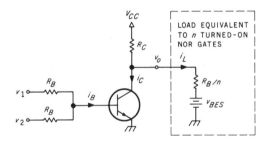

Figure 2.13: *The RTL NOR gate shown with a load equivalent to n turned-ON NOR gates.*

The MC803 NOR gate shown in figure 2.14 is a typical commercial IC RTL NOR gate. It is somewhat different from the RTL NOR gate studied thus far, in that a separate transistor is used for each input. Nevertheless, the analysis of the multitransistor NOR gate is similar to the analysis of the single-transistor NOR gate. Importantly, a HIGH on any input will produce a LOW output. In terms of additional expense, there is little disadvantage in adding the extra transistors; they are inexpensive in an integrated circuit (IC). The advantage of including the extra transistors is in the achievement of *input decoupling* — this is particularly significant when the number of inputs being NORed is large.

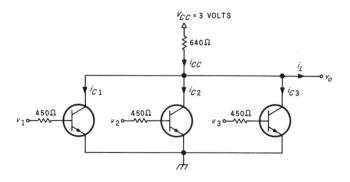

Figure 2.14: *The MC803 RTL NOR gate.*

To illustrate the input coupling problem, consider the k-input NOR gate in figure 2.15a. In particular, observe that if input 1 is HIGH (ie: $v_1 = v_H$ volts) and all remaining inputs are LOW (eg: $v_2 = v_3 = \ldots = v_k = 0$ volts), then the input voltage source v_H is supplying current not only to the transistor base circuit, but also to all the remaining input resistors:

$$i_1 = i_B + \sum_{j=2}^{k} i_j$$

The effect of the additional current paths is to reduce the base-to-emitter voltage v_{BE}, thus reducing the base current i_B. Under marginal conditions, a reduction in base current can prevent the transistor from turning ON.

A simplified analysis of the input circuit is obtained from a study of figure 2.15b, where the transistor is replaced by the forward-resistance model of the base-to-emitter diode; the $k - 1$ grounded inputs result in a path from base terminal to ground having a resistance of $R_B/(k - 1)$ ohms. Analysis of this equivalent circuit results in the following expression for the base-to-emitter voltage v_{BE}:

$$v_{BE} = \frac{R_f}{R_B + kR_f} v_H + \frac{R_B}{R_B + kR_f} V_{\gamma 2}$$

The base current can now be determined:

$$i_B = \frac{v_{BE} - V_{\gamma 2}}{R_f}$$

Table 2.1 shows how the base-to-emitter voltage v_{BE} and, importantly, base current i_B are reduced as the number of inputs k is increased for the case that $R_B = 450\ \Omega$, $R_f = 30\ \Omega$, and $V_{\gamma 2} = 0.7$ V. Remember that the forward-resistance diode model used for the base-to-emitter diode is not valid for all current values. As the current i_B decreases, R_f increases and $V_{\gamma 2}$ decreases. If the diode model were changed for each computation to reflect the changes in R_f and $V_{\gamma 2}$ which result from changes in i_B, table 2.1 would show that i_B decreases much more rapidly with increasing k than is presently indicated.

k	v_{BE} (VOLTS)	i_B (mA)
1	0.84	4.79
2	0.79	3.14
3	0.75	1.67
4	0.71	0.33

Table 2.1: *Effect of input coupling on base current in RTL NOR circuit.*

Clearly, the safety margin used in the design of the RTL inverter to assure transistor turn-ON can vanish because of the effects of input coupling. With a transistor placed in each input path, there is no conducting path from one input terminal to another, and the input coupling problem is eliminated.

The critical operating values of the MC803 RTL NOR gate can be easily computed. Assuming the NOR gate is properly designed (ie: v_1, v_2, or v_3 greater than $v_{H(min)}$ turns the corresponding transistor ON; v_1, v_2, and v_3 less than $v_{L(max)}$ turns the corresponding transistor OFF), then the maximum collector current in a transistor j, which occurs when only transistor j is ON, is given by

$$i_{CSj} = i_{cc} = \frac{V_{CC} - v_{CES}}{R_C}$$

If more than one transistor is ON, then the current i_{cc} is divided equally among these transistors, and less base current is required to turn each transistor ON. The minimum base current that can always turn the transistor i ON is determined from the case that only one transistor is turned ON:

$$i_{B(min)j} = \frac{i_{CSj}}{h_{FE(min)}}$$

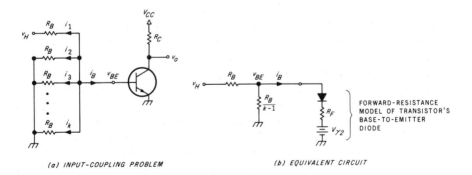

(a) INPUT-COUPLING PROBLEM   (b) EQUIVALENT CIRCUIT

Figure 2.15: *Input coupling in an RTL NOR gate.*

The minimum HIGH input voltage necessary to turn the transistor j ON is

$$v_{H(min)j} = i_{B(min)j} R_B + v_{BES}$$

The maximum current to the load when all the transistors are turned OFF $(i_{Cj} = 0, j = 1, 2, 3)$ is

$$i_{L\ OFF(max)} = \frac{V_{CC} - v_{H(min)}}{R_C}$$

Therefore, assuming $V_{CC} = 3$ V, $h_{FE(min)} = 30$, $v_{CES} = 0.1$ V, and $v_{BES} = 0.7$ V gives

$$i_{CS} = \frac{3 - 0.1}{640} = 4.5 \text{ mA}$$

$$i_{B(min)} = \frac{4.5}{30} = 0.15 \text{ mA}$$

$$v_{H(min)} = 0.15 \times 450 + 0.7 = 0.768 \text{ V}$$

$$i_{L\ OFF(max)} = \frac{3 - 0.768}{640} = 3.48 \text{ mA}$$

The maximum fan-out can be determined by application of equation (1.18):

$$n\, \frac{v_{H(min)} - v_{BES}}{V_{CC} - v_{H(min)}} \le \frac{R_B}{R_C} \le h_{FE}\, \frac{v_{H(min)} - v_{BES}}{V_{CC} - v_{CES}}$$

Thus,

$$0.03\, n \le 0.703 \le 0.703$$

and

$$n_{(max)} = \text{Integer}\left[\frac{0.703}{0.03}\right] = 23$$

The values of R_B and R_C in the MC803 have been selected to maximize fan-out. However, the computed allowable fanout of 23 is the maximum attainable and depends upon using the least base current necessary to turn ON an input transistor. Using this NOR gate with a fan-out of 23 leaves no safety margin to compensate for possible variations in circuit parameters. It is especially risky to assume that transistor saturation can be guaranteed even when the input voltage is only 0.768 V. A safety margin can be introduced by defining $v_{H(min)}$ to be roughly 40 to 50 percent greater than the computed minimum. For example, define

$$v_{H(min)} = 1.1 \text{ V}$$

In this case

$$i_B = \frac{v_{H(min)} - v_{BES}}{R_B} = \frac{1.1 - .7}{450} = 0.89 \text{ mA} > i_{B(min)} = 0.15 \text{ mA}$$

$$i_{L \text{ OFF}} = \frac{V_{CC} - v_{H(min)}}{R_C} = \frac{3 - 1.1}{640} = 2.97 \text{ mA} < i_{L \text{ OFF(max)}} = 3.48 \text{ mA}$$

With a higher specified $v_{H(min)}$, the allowable base current is increased (assuring turn-ON), and the allowable output current is decreased (decreasing fan-out). Application of equation (1.18) results in

$$0.21 \, n \leq 0.703 \leq 4.13$$

and

$$n_{(max)} = \text{Integer} \left[\frac{0.703}{0.21} \right] = 3$$

To maintain a 0.332 V safety margin on the HIGH-voltage threshold, the actual fan-out should not exceed 3. The fan-out specified for the MC803 is 5.

2.2.2 Diode-Transistor Logic (DTL)

A simple two-input AND gate can be constructed from two diodes and a transistor, as shown in figure 2.16a. The operation of the diode-resistor AND gate is such that if either input v_1 or v_2 is LOW, then the diode in that input circuit conducts, and the output voltage v_o is LOW. This circuit has little potential for use as a universal building block in a complex digital network because its operation deteriorates when it is cascaded. Notice that the LOW output voltage is v_D (typically 0.7 V) when the LOW input voltage is 0 V. If a low of 0.7 V is used as an input to this diode-resistor AND gate, the corresponding LOW output is 1.4 V. In every stage of a cascade, the LOW voltage threshold increases by 0.7 V, a situation that could not be tolerated in a large digital-logic network.

Placing a transistor inverter stage on the output of the diode-resistor AND gate, as shown in figure 2.16b, produces a NAND gate. More importantly, however, the transistor stage isolates the input from the output so that identical NAND gates can be cascaded endlessly. Note that two diodes are included in the base circuits of the transistor. Without these diodes, a voltage v_D, corresponding to the voltage drop across the conducting input diode (typically 0.7 V), would appear at the base terminal when v_1 or v_2 is zero. To eliminate the possibility of this 0.7 V turning the transistor ON, the two extra diodes are included in the base circuit. These two diodes are in series with the transistor base-to-emitter diode. Thus, three diodes divide the 0.7 V drop across the conducting input diode, and each of these three diodes drops approximately 0.23 V. Importantly, 0.23 V applied to the base is not sufficient to turn the transistor ON. An extra safety margin is often obtained by placing a resistor R_S from the base to ground (figure 2.16c). The resistance of R_S is selected to be relatively large compared to the resistance of a conducting diode (ie: R_S is negligible when the transistor is ON) and relatively small compared to the resistance of a nonconducting diode (ie: the base-to-emitter resistance is negligible when the transistor is OFF). As a result R_S insures that the transistor is OFF even in cases where the input voltages are not quite zero. The diode-transistor NAND gate is the fundamental digital-logic circuit for a logic family: the *diode-transistor logic* (DTL) family. Because of the input diodes, there is no input coupling problem associated with the diode-transistor NAND gate.

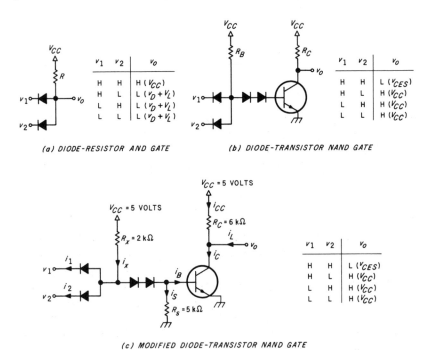

(a) DIODE-RESISTOR AND GATE   (b) DIODE-TRANSISTOR NAND GATE

(c) MODIFIED DIODE-TRANSISTOR NAND GATE

Figure 2.16: *Diode logic gates.*

The method for determining the allowable fan-out of a DTL NAND gate is considerably different from that used for an RTL NOR gate. Because of the polarity of the input diodes in the DTL NAND gate, current only flows *out* of the input terminal and then only when the input voltage is LOW. Compare this with the RTL NOR gate where current flows *into* the input terminal, but only when the input voltage is HIGH. In the DTL NAND gate, the source of the input current is the DC voltage source V_{CC}; the gate's transistor is turned OFF by providing a current path to ground (ie: a *sink*) through the input terminal. Conversely, removing the sinks from the input terminals (ie: leaving them disconnected) will cause the transistor to be turned ON. In other words, although applying HIGH's to both input terminals will turn the transistor ON, the HIGH input voltage sources are not necessary; breaking the input current path to ground is sufficient to turn the transistor ON. Hence, DTL is an example of *current sinking logic*.

When two DTL NAND gates are cascaded, as in figure 2.17, it is the second gate (NAND gate 2) which supplies current to the first gate (NAND gate 1); NAND gate 1 must supply a low-voltage sink (ideally ground) to the circuit to which it is connected. Because the transistor's collector-to-emitter saturation voltage v_{CES} is typically 0.1 to 0.3 volts, NAND gates with a LOW output provide an excellent sink. Thus, it is necessary for the gate transistor to stay saturated even when it is sinking the input currents of the other NAND gates to which it is connected.

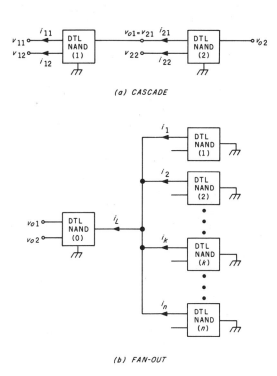

(a) CASCADE

(b) FAN-OUT

Figure 2.17: *Loading DTL NAND circuits.*

The allowable fan-out for the DTL NAND gate (figure 2.17b) is determined when the transistor of the driving NAND gate (ie: the transistor of NAND gate 0) is ON. This transistor, when ON, must be able to sink the necessary current from all the NAND gates to which it is connected (ie: NAND gates 1,2....,n), and it must still stay saturated. The amount of current that this transistor may be required to sink is determined by the fan-out n and the maximum current that a DTL NAND gate input will try to sink. Therefore, determining fan-out requires two computations:

1. The maximum current $i_{L(max)}$ that the transistor can sink in the ON state and still stay saturated.
2. The maximum current $i_{k(max)}$ that any input terminal k, $k = 1,2,...,n$, may have to sink in order to turn OFF transistor k.

Fan-out is determined as the ratio of these two currents:

$$n_{(max)} = \text{Integer} \left[\frac{i_{L(max)}}{i_{k(max)}} \right]$$

The following equations are derived for the DTL NAND gate of figure 2.16c. In the OFF state (eg: $v_1 = v_L$, $v_2 = v_H$),

$$i_x = \frac{V_{CC} - v_D - v_L}{R_x}$$

$$i_S \cong 0$$

$$i_{k(max)} = i_{x \, OFF(max)} = \frac{V_{CC} - v_D - v_{L(min)}}{R_x}$$

In the ON state (eg: $v_1 = v_2 = v_H$),

$$i_x = \frac{V_{CC} - 2v_D - v_{BES}}{R_x}$$

$$i_S = \frac{v_{BES}}{R_S}$$

$$i_B = i_x - i_S$$

$$i_{CC} = \frac{V_{CC} - v_{CES}}{R_C}$$

$$i_{C(max)} = h_{FE(min)}i_B = \left\{ \begin{array}{l} \text{maximum collector current} \\ \text{that can flow while the} \\ \text{transistor stays saturated} \end{array} \right.$$

$$i_{L(max)} = i_{C(max)} - i_{CC}$$

$$n_{(max)} = \text{Integer} \left[\frac{i_{L(max)}}{i_{k(max)}} \right]$$

For the case that $V_{CC} = 5$ V, $v_D = 0.7$ V, $v_{BES} = 0.7$ V, $v_{CES} = 0.1$ V, and $h_{FE(min)} = 30$,

$$i_B = 1.45 \text{ mA}$$

$$i_{k(max)} = 2.1 \text{ mA}$$

$$i_{C(max)} = 39.3 \text{ mA}$$

$$i_{L(max)} = 38.48 \text{ mA}$$

$$n_{(max)} = 18$$

With an actual fan-out of 18, it is possible that $i_C = i_{C(max)} = 39.3$ mA. In such a situation, the operation of the diode NAND gate is marginal in that there are many possible parameter variations to prevent the transistor from saturating (eg: R_x increasing; V_{CC}, h_{FE}, or R_C decreasing). Such parameter variations can result in LOW output voltages that are greater than the minimum LOW voltage specified. A safety margin can be incorporated by placing a limit lower than that computed on the maximum collector current $i_{C(max)}$ assuring transistor saturation even with large circuit parameter variations. Introducing such a safety margin reduces the maximum fan-out. For example, by requiring that the collector current never exceed 25 mA instead of the computed 39.3 mA, the maximum load current $i_{L(max)}$ that can flow is

$$i_{L(max)} = i_{C(max)} - i_{CC} = 25 - 0.8167 = 24.18 \text{ mA}$$

and the maximum permissible fan-out becomes 11.

Figure 2.18 shows the MC846, a commercial IC DTL NAND gate. The second transistor in the input circuit has the effect of providing an additional voltage drop in the base circuit, thus providing even greater assurance that the output transistor will not turn ON with LOW input voltages. This circuit provides a rather large fan-out capability even with modest transistor gains (eg: if a transistor with $h_{FE(min)} = 30$ is used, the resulting maximum fan-out is $n_{(max)} \cong 40$).

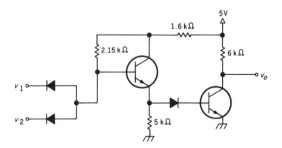

Figure 2.18: *The MC846 DTL NAND gate.*

2.2.3   Transistor-Transistor Logic (TTL)

Transistor-transistor logic (TTL) has been the most important logic family in industrial digital-logic design. Virtually all areas of digital design have felt the enormous impact of TTL. Because of its wide acceptance, demand for TTL has been great, with the resulting mass production making the price extremely low. At the time of this writing, the TTL 7400 IC (the quad two-input NAND containing four TTL NAND gates similar to that shown in figure 2.19d) can be purchased in single quantities by any hobbyist for as little as 12¢. At the same time a single 5 percent, ¼-watt common carbon-composition resistor costs 5¢, the least expensive low-power transistor costs 20¢, a low-power diode costs 10¢, and ironically, the least expensive socket for the TTL 7400 costs 10¢, almost twice as much as the NAND itself. Thus, someone wishing to study the operation of the TTL NAND gate in the laboratory by building it from discrete components will have paid at least $1.40 for the components, compared to 3¢ per NAND gate in the 7400 IC package.

The fundamental digital-logic circuit in the TTL family is the NAND gate. Figure 2.19 shows a progression of TTL gates starting with the simple transistor-resistor AND gate (figure 2.19a) and proceeding to the commercial TTL NAND gate available in the 7400 IC package (figure 2.19f). The

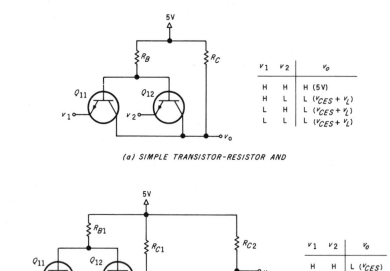

Figure 2.19: *Development of the TTL NAND gate.*

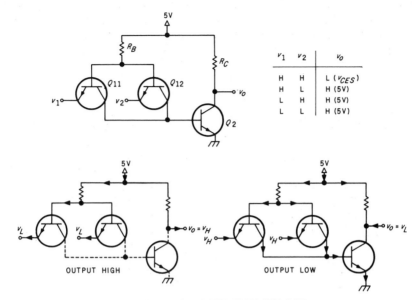

v_1	v_2	v_0
H	H	L (v_{CES})
H	L	H (5V)
L	H	H (5V)
L	L	H (5V)

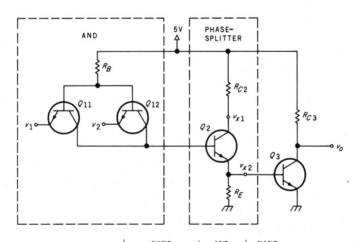

(c) MODIFIED TRANSISTOR-TRANSISTOR NAND

(d) TRANSISTOR-TRANSISTOR NAND WITH PHASE-SPLITTER

		NAND	AND	NAND
v_1	v_2	v_{x1}	v_{x2}	v_0
H	H	L ($v_{BES} + v_{CES}$)	H (v_{BES})	L (v_{CES})
H	L	H (5V)	L (0V)	H (5V)
L	H	H (5V)	L (0V)	H (5V)
L	L	H (5V)	L (0V)	H (5V)

Figure 2.19 cont.

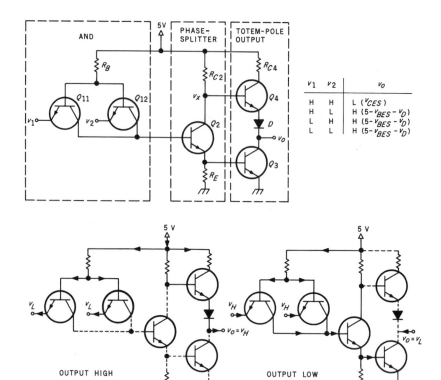

v_1	v_2	v_0
H	H	L (v_{CES})
H	L	H ($5 - v_{BES} - v_D$)
L	H	H ($5 - v_{BES} - v_D$)
L	L	H ($5 - v_{BES} - v_D$)

OUTPUT HIGH

OUTPUT LOW

(e) STANDARD TTL NAND WITH PHASE-SPLITTER TOTEM-POLE OUTPUT

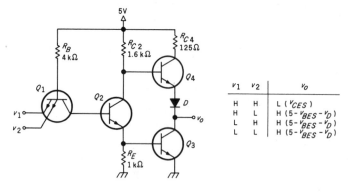

v_1	v_2	v_0
H	H	L (v_{CES})
H	L	H ($5 - v_{BES} - v_D$)
L	H	H ($5 - v_{BES} - v_D$)
L	L	H ($5 - v_{BES} - v_D$)

(f) 7400 TTL IC NAND

operation of the simple transistor-resistor AND gate of figure 2.19a is similar to the operation of the diode-resistor AND gate of figure 2.16a. The transistors replace the diodes and serve the same function as the diodes. The transistors with emitter inputs may seem strange at first, but these transistors are being used as ordinary common-emitter switches. Sufficient base current to turn the transistor ON is obtained by grounding the emitter, thus forward biasing the base-to-emitter diode. A HIGH input reverse biases the base-to-emitter diode, forces the base current to zero, and turns the transistor OFF. The transistor-resistor AND gate, like the DTL gates, is a *current-sinking logic* gate (ie: an input ground provides a current path for both the base and collector currents, turning the transistor ON). To turn the transistor OFF, the flow of base current must be inhibited. This can be done by leaving both input terminals unconnected, thereby providing no path for the flow of base current; a HIGH voltage applied to both input terminals has the same effect.

The main shortcoming of the transistor-resistor AND gate of figure 2.19a stems from the fact that the LOW output voltage is the sum of the LOW input voltage v_L and the collector-to-emitter saturation voltage v_{CES}. A comparable situation was encountered with the diode-resistor AND gate where the LOW output voltage was the sum of the LOW input voltage v_L and the forward-biased diode voltage v_D. Again, the problem is that nonzero LOW input voltages are not attenuated and appear as nonzero LOW output voltages. The effect is cumulative in that if one cascades transistor-resistor AND gates, the LOW level output voltage of one AND gate is higher, by v_{CES} volts, than the LOW output voltage of the gate preceding it. Intolerable in large digital-logic networks where many gates are cascaded, this input sensitivity problem is eliminated by adding the inverter stage to the output, as shown in figure 2.19b. This addition results in the *transistor-transistor* NAND gate. The diode is included in the base circuit of transistor Q_2 to insure that transistor Q_2 is not turned ON by LOW input voltages. Without this diode a relatively low-voltage v_x (eg: approximately 0.5 V), caused by nonzero LOW input voltages and the nonzero collector-to-emitter saturation voltages of transistors Q_{11} or Q_{12}, could generate sufficient base current to turn ON transistor Q_2.

An ingenious modification of the transistor-transistor NAND gate appears in figure 2.19c. The circuit diagrams in figure 2.19c, showing the current paths as solid lines for both the HIGH and LOW output states, are helpful in understanding the circuit's operation. This circuit is easily analyzed once it is noted that transistors Q_{11} and Q_{12} do not act as ordinary transistors in either the HIGH or LOW state. When an input voltage, say v_1, is LOW, the corresponding input transistor, Q_{11}, operates as a simple diode with current flowing only through the base-to-emitter diode. The flow of base-to-emitter current normally turns a transistor ON, but because the reverse-biased collector-to-emitter diode of transistor Q_2 is in the collector circuit of Q_{11}, $i_{C11} = 0$. With one or both input voltages LOW, transistor Q_2 is OFF and $v_o = 5$ V. When both input voltages v_1 and v_2 are HIGH, transistors Q_{11} and Q_{12} operate as ordinary common-emitter switches, with one important twist. The roles of the emitters and collectors are reversed; the collectors of transistors Q_{11} and Q_{12} act as emitters and vice versa. The Q_{11} and Q_{12} base currents flow through R_B, through their respective collectors, and through the base circuit of Q_2; transistor Q_2 is turned ON and v_o is LOW (v_{CES}). Because there is no current-limiting resistor in the conducting paths between the input terminals and the ground provided by the emitter of Q_2, excessively large currents will flow when the input voltages are HIGH. If this circuit were to be used as a fundamental building block, provisions would have to be made to reduce the magnitude of the HIGH voltages so that the transistors would not be burned out.

The advantage of the modified transistor-transistor NAND gate of figure 2.19c over the transistor-transistor NAND gate of figure 2.19b and over the diode-transistor NAND gate (figure 2.16c) is that switching times are significantly faster. There are two important reasons for the improved switching times:

- As explained in section 1.14, the time required for transistor turn-off, t_{OFF}, is longer than the time required for transistor turn-on, t_{ON}. A main component of transistor turn-off time is the storage time t_s occurring when excess charge is removed from the saturated transistor base region; until this excess charge is removed, the transistor cannot respond to input changes. In a typical transistor switch, excess charge is drained from the base region as reverse base current through a large base resistor R_B. In the modified transistor-transistor NAND, however, when an input voltage, v_1, is LOW and transistor Q_2 is being turned OFF, the base circuit of transistor Q_2 has no large resistor in it. Instead, Q_{11} provides a low-resistance path from the base terminal of Q_2 to the LOW source v_1. It is only during this switching period, when Q_2 is being turned OFF, that transistor Q_{11} acts as an ordinary common-emitter transistor switch. Acting as a turned-on common-emitter switch, Q_{11} provides a low-resistance path from its collector to emitter, allowing the base region of transistor Q_2 to be quickly drained. Instead of storage time t_s being associated with a time constant, $R_B C_{BE}$, where C_{BE} is the base-to-emitter parasitic junction capacitor of transistor Q_2, the storage time is now associated with a much smaller time constant, $R_{CE} C_{BE}$, where R_{CE} is the small collector-to-emitter resistance of transistor Q_{11} in the ON state.
- A major component of a transistor's turn-on time, t_{ON}, is the delay time, t_d. A major component of delay time, t_d, is the time required for the holes to propagate from the emitter across the entire base region to the collector; collector current cannot be identified until holes reach the collector. In the modified transistor-transistor NAND gate of figure 2.19c, base current is *always* flowing in the input transistors Q_{11} and Q_{12}. When a NAND gate's input voltage v_1 or v_2 is LOW, base current flows through the base and out of the LOW emitter; when both NAND gate input voltages v_1 and v_2 are HIGH, base current flows through the base and out of the collector. In either case, holes

are ever present in the base region, and transistor turn-on time is reduced.

Capacitively loading the modified NAND gate of figure 2.19c results in slower switching times for the output transistor Q_2. Although the transistor plays an important role during turn-on by providing a low-resistance path to ground, it plays no role during turn-off. Since transistor Q_2 is turned ON during the HIGH-to-LOW output transition, a relatively large capacitive load can be quickly discharged through the low-resistance collector-to-emitter path of Q_2. However, transistor Q_2 is turned OFF during the LOW-to-HIGH output transition, and any capacitive load must be charged through resistor R_C. This results in a relatively slow turn-off time. The time required for a LOW-to-HIGH output transition can be reduced by ingenious designs which take advantage of a transistor's faster turn-on speed. The *phase-splitter totem-pole output circuit* represents such a design.

The NAND gate shown in figure 2.19d is virtually the same circuit as the transistor-transistor NAND gate of figure 2.19c, except that a resistor-transistor *phase-splitter* built around transistor Q_2 has been placed between the input transistor-resistor AND stage and the inverter output stage. The phase-splitter transistor Q_2 gives a NAND output at v_{x1} and an AND output at v_{x2}. The HIGH of the AND output v_{x2} is v_{BES} (typically 0.7 V), which is determined by the base-to-emitter diode of transistor Q_3. The LOW of the NAND output v_{x1} is v_{CES} volts higher than the HIGH output of v_{x2}; a LOW v_{x1} is the sum $v_{BES(Q3)} + v_{CES(Q2)}$ (typically 1 V). The two phase-splitter outputs v_{x1} and v_{x2} can be used to drive a *totem-pole* output as shown in figure 2.19e (note that the term *totem-pole* is not generic, but refers specifically to the device shown). Importantly, transistor Q_3, like transistor Q_2, has a low-resistance path from its base terminal to ground through which to discharge the saturated base region during turn-off, with a resulting small t_{OFF}. Circuit diagrams showing the current-conducting paths as solid lines for both the HIGH and LOW state also appear in figure 2.19e.

The totem-pole output, designed around transistors Q_3 and Q_4 and diode D, is such that Q_3 turns ON during the HIGH-to-LOW transition and Q_4 turns ON during the LOW-to-HIGH transition. In turning ON, transistor Q_3 *actively* discharges the capacitive load through the low resistance provided between its collector and emitter terminals. Transistor Q_4, in turning ON, *actively* charges a capacitive load through its low-resistance collector-to-emitter circuit; resistance R_{C4} is selected as small as possible (typically 125 Ω). Diode D is included in the emitter circuit of transistor Q_4 to insure that Q_4 is OFF when the output v_o is LOW. An output LOW is obtained when Q_3 is ON (ie: $v_o = v_{CES} \cong 0.3$ V) and Q_2 is ON (ie: $v_x = v_{CES(Q2)} + v_{BES(Q3)} \cong 1.0$ V). With $v_o \cong 0.3$ V, $v_x \cong 1.0$ V, and with two diodes (the base-to-emitter diode of Q_4 and diode D) in the path from the collector of Q_2 to the output terminal, the base-to-emitter voltage of Q_4 is less than 0.5 V; this is too low to turn ON Q_4.

In the fabrication of the IC transistor-transistor NAND gate (the TTL 7400), the two input transistors are combined into a single two-emitter transistor (see figure 2.19f). The physical size of the transistors is made deliberately small. This minimizes the parasitic junction capacitors C_{BE} and C_{BC}, reducing switching times even further. Figure 2.20 shows the conducting paths in a 7400 NAND gate during the HIGH and LOW states; typical currents and voltages are also indicated.

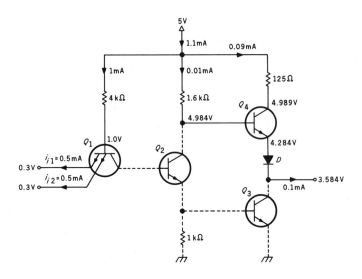

(a) OUTPUT IN THE HIGH STATE

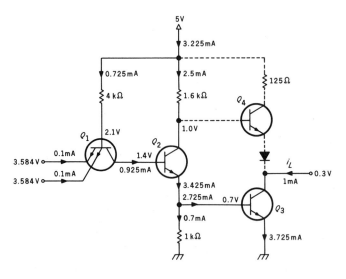

(b) OUTPUT IN THE LOW STATE

Figure 2.20: *Conducting paths for the TTL 7400 NAND gate and typical current and voltage levels.*

Fan-out for the TTL NAND gate is determined when the output v_o is LOW. In the LOW state, transistor Q_3 must sink the input currents of all the TTL NAND gates to which it is connected. The maximum fan-out $n_{(max)}$ is given by

$$n_{(max)} = \text{Integer} \left[\frac{i_{L(max)}}{i_{i(max)}} \right]$$

The current $i_{L(max)}$ is the maximum collector current that output transistor Q_3 can sink and still stay saturated, maintaining $v_o = v_{CES}$. The maximum collector current that can flow while transistor Q_3 is saturated is given by

$$i_{L(max)} = h_{FE(max)} \, i_{B3}$$

The current $i_{i(max)}$ is the maximum emitter current that a single input emitter will need to sink. This maximum occurs when one emitter input is LOW, all other emitter outputs are HIGH, and the entire base current of transistor Q_1 flows out of the single LOW emitter. This maximum emitter current is given by

$$i_{i(max)} = i_{B1} = \frac{5 - v_{CES} - v_{BES}}{R_B}$$

For the case that $v_{BES} = 0.7$ V and $v_{CES} = 0.3$ V, $i_{B3} = 2.725$ mA. If it is conservatively assumed that $h_{FE(min)} = 4$, then

$$i_{L(max)} = 10.9 \text{ mA}$$

$$i_{i(max)} = 1 \text{ mA}$$

and the maximum fan-out is

$$n_{(max)} = \text{Integer} \left[\frac{10.9}{1} \right] = 10$$

Manufacturers of the TTL 7400 NAND IC package conservatively recommend that fan-out not exceed 10.

An often troublesome characteristic of a 7400-series TTL gate is its varying demand for current from the 5 V power supply. For example, figure 2.21 shows that a 7400 TTL NAND gate draws 1.1 mA with the output in the HIGH state versus 3.225 mA with the output in the LOW state. In terms of the entire IC pacakge, which contains four NAND gates, the power-supply current can vary from 4.4 mA to 12.9 mA. Even more significant is the high demand for power-supply current that occurs during the LOW-to-HIGH output transition. This large surge of power-supply current is caused by the rapid charging of capacitive loads through the totem-pole output. During the LOW-to-HIGH transition, any capacitive load is charged through the collector circuit of transistor Q_4, which has just been turned ON. The current flowing through Q_4 and into the capacitive load at the instant Q_4 is turned ON is

$$i_{C4} = \frac{5 - v_{CES(Q4)} - v_D - v_{CES(Q3)}}{R_{C4}}$$

$$= \frac{5 - 0.3 - 0.7 - 0.3}{125} = 29.6 \text{ mA}$$

Initially large, this current decays rapidly as the capacitive load, typically 50 pF to 250 pF, is charged. The result is a large current *spike* of extremely short duration. Because of parasitic inductances within the circuit, the peak value of the current spike is not as large as computed here. Also because of parasitic inductances, the current spike does not decay as rapidly as it otherwise would. Figure 2.20 indicates that this large charging current is supplied by the 5 V power supply. During the HIGH-to-LOW transition, the capacitive load is discharged through transistor Q_3 directly to ground, without affecting the power supply. However, there is a period of overlap in the HIGH-to-LOW transition when transistors Q_3 and Q_4 are conducting simultaneously. This overlap occurs because transistor Q_3 turns ON faster than transistor Q_4 turns OFF, resulting in a current spike during the HIGH-to-LOW transition. Figure 2.21 shows the variations in power-supply current that are possible with the 7400 IC package, which contains four TTL NANDs.

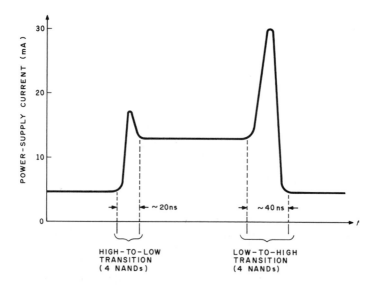

Figure 2.21: *Current-demand variations of the TTL 7400 IC package (quad NAND).*

Because of the internal resistance of the 5 V power supply and the somewhat inflexible limits on the amount of current that can be drawn from DC voltage regulators, the large current spikes supplied to the TTL IC package can produce significant variations in the power-supply voltage. In most digital circuits the operation of the logic gates is synchronized by a master clock. It is common for many gates to switch at the same time, and the effect of each on the power supply is cumulative. Unfortunately, TTL is especially sensitive to variations in power-supply voltage, and unless special care is taken, the power-supply variations caused by large current spikes can affect the operation of all gates connected to the power supply.

A simple method commonly used for filtering out the power-supply variations caused by the switching current spikes is to place a small disk capacitor (0.01 μF to 0.1 μF) between the 5 V and ground terminals of the TTL IC package. One capacitor across the power supply for every three or four TTL IC packages is sufficient.

The TTL 7400 NAND IC comes in a fourteen-pin *dual-in-line package* (DIP) represented in figure 2.22. The DIP is a standard IC package allowing for the application of highly automated processes in the making and assembling of circuit boards. In a DIP the two rows of pins are separated by 0.3 inches (recall that this is the spacing across the gutter of a standard solderless breadboard), and the pins in each row are separated by 0.1 inches (again, this is the spacing between socket holes in a standard solderless breadboard). Epoxy and phenolic boards with prepunched holes having 0.1-inch hole spacings in a rectangular array are commonly available. These *perf-boards* (*perf*orated *boards*) are quite inexpensive and are useful for the permanent wiring of circuits using DIP ICs.

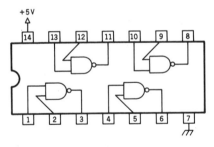

Figure 2.22: *TTL 7400 IC (the quad NAND).*

There are many commerical ICs which have been designed by using a TTL NAND gate, similar to the NAND gate in the 7400, as the fundamental building block. This family of ICs makes up the popular 7400 TTL series which is produced by several manufacturers. Important features of the 7400 series TTL ICs are summarized here:

- A TTL HIGH is any voltage between 2.4 and 3.6 volts; a TTL LOW is any voltage between 0 and 0.8 volts.
- All unconnected TTL inputs naturally go HIGH. In analyzing or designing a TTL circuit, this must be taken into account. In particular,

to assume that an unused input is LOW, that input must be connected to ground.

- The typical fan-out possible with most TTL is 10. However, several TTL gates have fan-outs as low as 5. If in doubt, refer to the specification sheets for that particular IC.
- The 5 volt DC power supply, V_{CC}, can actually be as low as 4.5 V or as high as 5.5 V without affecting the operation of the TTL circuit.
- TTL is fast. Typical switching times from the HIGH-to-LOW state are approximately 7 ns but always less than 15 ns; typical switching times from the LOW-to-HIGH state are approximately 11 ns but always less than 22 ns. The upper limits on actual switching times for a particular device can be obtained from the appropriate specification sheets. Remember that switching times vary as a function of temperature, supply voltage V_{CC}, and capacitive loading. Fortunately, the HIGH-to-LOW switching times decrease with increasing temperature, while the LOW-to-HIGH switching times increase with increasing temperature; these variations tend to cancel each other, resulting in fairly constant average switching time as a function of temperature. Increasing V_{CC} decreases switching time, and the variation in switching time obtained by varying V_{CC} from 4.5 V to 5.5 V can range from 4 to 15 percent. Variations in capacitive loading have significant effects on switching times, which approximately double when the capacitive load is increased from 50 pF to 250 pF. Because the capacitive load is generally associated with the capacitive input of the circuit being driven, increasing fan-out increases switching time.
- A standard 7400-series TTL IC will operate at any ambient temperature between 0 °C and 70 °C.
- Power consumption for a 7400-series TTL IC package is relatively low. For example, the 7400 quad NAND IC package draws an average of 12 mA from the 5 V power supply (ie: an average power consumption of 60 milliwatts).
- A TTL output is capable of sinking up to 16 mA of current in the LOW state.
- The 5 V power supply must be protected from the large current spikes produced by capacitively loaded totem-pole outputs. These transients can be effectively filtered from the power supply by placing small capacitors across the power-supply loads near the TTL IC packages. A commonly used rule of thumb is to place a 0.01 μF to 0.1 μF disk capacitor with short leads between the 5 V and ground terminals and as close to the ICs as possible; one capacitor is required for every three or four TTL ICs.

2.2.4 Loading TTL Devices

Because the totem-pole output cannot supply significant amounts of energy to the loading circuit, TTL is not well suited for driving output loads. The totem-pole output was primarily designed to provide a large fan-out (this requires the output to be able to sink large currents on the order of 12 mA for a NAND gate in a 7400) and to supply the high-current impulses necessary to quickly charge capacitive loads during the LOW-to-HIGH transition. In the HIGH output state, the totem-pole output cannot drive loads requiring large currents (eg: currents greater than 1 mA) over a long time period such as might be required to drive an LED display. Because of transistor Q_4's low current gain ($h_{FE(min)} = 4$) and its low base current (approximately 0.01 mA), relatively small collector currents cause it to become unsaturated. For example, when $i_{C4} = 0.09$ mA, transistor Q_4 is *not* saturated. With transistor Q_4 unsaturated, increases in collector currents cause increases in the collector-to-emitter voltage of transistor Q_4, and the HIGH output voltage drops significantly. An exact analysis of this situation is not straightforward, as a drop in output voltage also results in an increase in the base current of transistor Q_4, and the maximum allowable collector current inceases. In any case a load requiring more than 1 mA should not be driven by a typical TTL totem-pole output if the HIGH output voltage is to be greater than the minimum 2.4 V.

Consider the problem of using a TTL gate to drive a 12 mA LED. Assume the LED drops 1.7 V when 12 mA is flowing through it. Using the TTL output's current-sinking capability, the LED can be used in the simple current-sinking output circuit shown in figure 2.23a. When the output of the NAND gate is HIGH, no current flows through the LED. When the output is LOW, the current through the LED is given by

$$i_L = \frac{5 - v_D - v_{CE}}{220} = \frac{5 - 1.7 - .3}{220} = 13.6 \text{ mA}$$

Thus, the LED lights when the output of the NAND gate is LOW.

If it is necessary for the LED to light when the NAND-gate output is HIGH, then an alternate loading circuit, drawing 1 mA or less from the NAND-gate output, is required. One possibility is the resistor-transistor driver shown in figure 2.23b. With the 3 kΩ resistor in the base circuit, the

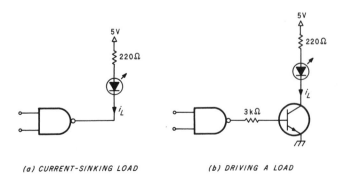

(a) CURRENT-SINKING LOAD   (b) DRIVING A LOAD

Figure 2.23: *Loading a TTL NAND gate.*

base current in the driver circuit is 0.97 mA:

$$i_B = \frac{v_H - v_D}{3000} = \frac{3.6 - 0.7}{3000} = 0.97 \text{ mA}$$

If the transistor in the driver has an h_{FE} of 15, this base current of approximately 1 mA is sufficient to saturate the transistor for any collector current less than 15 mA and to guarantee that $v_{CE} = v_{CES} = 0.3$ V. Therefore,

$$i_L = \frac{5 - v_D - v_{CES}}{220} = \frac{5 - 1.7 - .03}{220} = 13.6 \text{ mA}$$

In this instance, the LED lights when the output of the NAND gate is HIGH.

2.2.5 Complementary Metal-Oxide Semiconductor (CMOS) Logic

Complementary metal-oxide semiconductor (CMOS) logic plays a major role in present-day digital design. Whereas TTL utilizes the bipolar junction transistor as the basic switching element, CMOS logic utilizes the CMOS transistor as the basic switching element. The operation of a CMOS transistor is distinctly different from that of a bipolar junction transistor. Importantly, by using the CMOS transistor as the basic switching element, it is possible to design digital circuits that are smaller, consume less energy, and are less sensitive to variations in the power-supply voltage than digital circuits using bipolar junction transistors. Size and power considerations are especially important in the design of ICs and, as a result, the relative importance of CMOS logic in the development of digital systems continues to increase. The main disadvantages of CMOS logic, when compared to TTL, are its slower switching speeds and its susceptibility to damage by intense electric fields, which can be caused by static electricity. Fundamental to an understanding of the operation of the CMOS transistor is an understanding of the operation of the *metal-oxide semiconductor* (MOS) transistor.

2.2.5.1 The MOS Transistor

The MOS transistor is a four-terminal semiconductor device. There are two types of MOS transistors: the n-channel MOS transistor and the p-channel MOS transistor. Diagrams illustrating the construction of each with their corresponding network symbols are shown in figure 2.24. In many MOS transistor applications, the *source* and *substrate* terminals are connected, and the MOS transistor is used as a three-terminal device. The operation of a MOS transistor is distinctly different from that of a bipolar junction transistor: the bipolar junction transistor is a current-controlled device (ie: a small base current controls a large collector-to-emitter current); the MOS transistor is a voltage-controlled device (ie: a small *gate* voltage controls a large *drain*-to-source current).

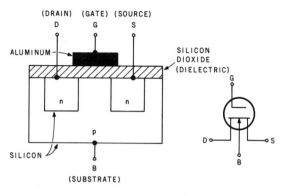

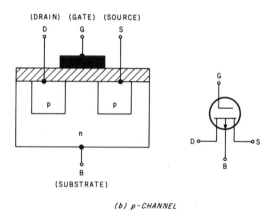

Figure 2.24: *MOS transistors: construction and network symbol.*

Some insight into the operation of the MOS transistor can be obtained from a study of the n-channel MOS transistor circuit shown in figure 2.25a. When the gate voltage v_{GS} is 0, the drain-to-source current i_{DS} is also 0. This is because the current path from the drain to the source, through the transistor, includes two pn-junctions (ie: two back-to-back diodes). Regardless of the polarity of the drain voltage v_{DS}, one of these two diodes is reverse-biased and prevents any current from flowing from the drain to the source. However, the conducting properties of the drain-to-source current path change significantly when the gate voltage v_{GS} is made greater than 0. Because of the insulating properties of the layer of silicon dioxide placed between the gate plate and the substrate, a capacitor is formed; the gate and the substrate act as parallel plates of the capacitor, and the silicon dioxide layer acts as the dielectric. Therefore, except for the current that flows initially to charge the gate-substrate capacitor, no gate current flows into the

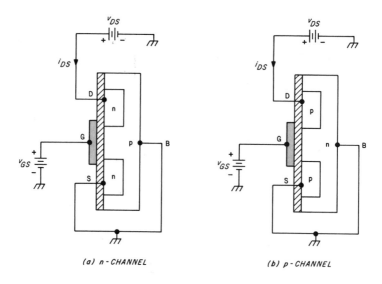

(a) n - CHANNEL   (b) p - CHANNEL

Figure 2.25: *MOS transistor operation.*

gate in response to the application of a positive voltage to the gate. Instead, the gate plate accumulates positive charge, and a thin layer of the substrate, close to the gate plate, accumulates negative charge (see figure 2.26). This layer of negative charge in the substrate is composed of free electrons that are attracted into the substrate from the n-type source material. The quantity of negative charge accumulated and the thickness of the charge layer depend upon the magnitude of the gate voltage. Importantly, with sufficient gate voltage, this thin layer of substrate material accumulates a sufficient number of free electrons so that, in terms of conducting properties, the layer

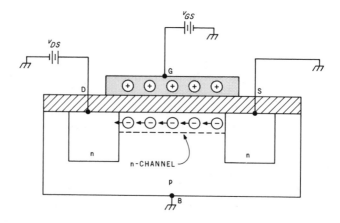

Figure 2.26: *Conduction in a MOS transistor: n-channel conducting layer.*

is equivalent to an n-type semiconductor. Hence, by applying a positive gate voltage v_{GS} to the gate, a thin *channel* of n-type semiconductor is produced within the p-type substrate. This *n-channel* connects the drain and the source regions, which also are n-type semiconductors. With a continuous path of n-type semiconductor between the drain and the source, a low-resistance path of n-type semiconductor exists between the drain and source terminals. The resistance of the path can be controlled by the gate voltage v_{GS}. A set of characteristics typical of an n-channel MOS transistor is shown in figure 2.27a; a similar set of characteristics typical of a p-channel MOS transistor is shown in figure 2.27b. Note that for a given

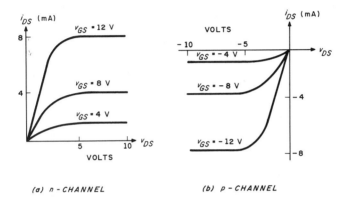

(a) n - CHANNEL   *(b) p - CHANNEL*

Figure 2.27: *MOS transistor characteristics.*

gate voltage v_{GS}, there is a limit to the current i_{DS} that can flow from the source to the drain, regardless of the magnitude of the drain voltage v_{DS}.

In summary, the important features of a MOS transistor are:

- Essentially no current flows from the gate to the source when the gate voltage v_{GS} is zero. The MOS transistor is primarily capacitive between the gate and the source terminals; the resistance between the gate and the source terminals is on the order of $10^{14}\ \Omega$, which, for practical purposes, is an open circuit.

- For low drain-to-source voltages v_{DS}, the relationship between v_{DS} and i_{DS} is linear, and the MOS transistor can be regarded as a voltage-controlled resistor. The current between the drain and the source can flow in either direction. With $v_{GS} = 0$, the drain-to-source resistance is on the order of 10 MΩ; with $v_{GS} > 0$, drain-to-source resistances of 200 Ω to 1000 Ω are typical.

- For high drain-to-source voltages v_{DS}, saturation occurs and variations in v_{DS} do not affect the current i_{DS}. In this case, the MOS transistor can be regarded as a constant-current source.

The advantages of MOS transistors when compared to bipolar junction transistors are:

- smaller size
- lower power consumption
- ease of fabrication in IC form
- high input resistance

Their disadvantages are:

- lower switching speeds
- susceptibility to destruction from intense electric fields

A voltage across the silicon dioxide dielectric of about 70 V will break down the dielectric and generally destroy the MOS transistor. Static electricity, such as that generated by walking across a carpet in winter, is sufficient to destroy a MOS transistor.

An inverter is easily constructed using either an n-channel or a p-channel MOS transistor (see figure 2.28). Although there is a symmetry between the n-channel and p-channel inverters of figure 2.28a and 2.28b, it is generally desirable to avoid the use of negative power supplies. A p-channel inverter using a positive power supply can be constructed by connecting the positive

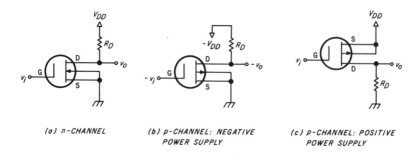

(a) n-CHANNEL   (b) p-CHANNEL: NEGATIVE   (c) p-CHANNEL: POSITIVE
                          POWER SUPPLY   POWER SUPPLY

Figure 2.28: *MOS transistor inverters.*

terminal of the power supply to the source terminal and grounding the drain terminal (figure 2.28c). In this way, a zero gate voltage with respect to the positive source terminal (V_{DD}) is equivalent to a negative gate voltage with respect to a grounded source terminal, and thus the zero gate voltage turns the p-channel MOS transistor ON. On the other hand, a HIGH gate voltage (ie: $v_i = V_{DD}$) with respect to the HIGH source terminal is equivalent to zero volts with respect to a grounded source terminal, resulting in the HIGH gate voltage turning the transistor OFF. Consider the case that

$$V_{DD} = 5 \text{ V}$$

$$R_D = 50 \text{ k}\Omega$$

$$R_{DS} = \begin{cases} R_{DS(OFF)} = 10 \text{ M}\Omega, \text{ when the transistor is OFF} \\ R_{DS(ON)} = 200 \text{ }\Omega, \text{ when the transistor is ON} \end{cases}$$

where R_{DS} is the drain-to-source resistance for both the n-channel and p-channel MOS transistors. In the case of the n-channel inverter:

$$v_{o(OFF)} = \frac{R_{DS(OFF)}}{R_L + R_{DS(OFF)}} V_{DD} = \frac{10M}{50K + 10M} 5 \cong 5 \text{ V}$$

$$v_{o(ON)} = \frac{R_{DS(ON)}}{R_L + R_{DS(ON)}} V_{DD} = \frac{200}{50K + 200} 5 \cong 0 \text{ V}$$

For the p-channel inverter:

$$v_{o(OFF)} = \frac{R_L}{R_L + R_{DS(ON)}} V_{DD} = \frac{50K}{50K + 10M} 5 \cong 0 \text{ V}$$

$$v_{o(ON)} = \frac{R_L}{R_L + R_{DS(OFF)}} V_{DD} = \frac{50K}{50K + 200} 5 \cong 5 \text{ V}$$

For both inverters, the current drawn from the power supply is

$$i_{DS(OFF)} = \frac{V_{DD}}{R_L + R_{DS(OFF)}} = \frac{5}{50K + 10M} \cong 0.0005 \text{ mA}$$

$$i_{DS(ON)} = \frac{V_{DD}}{R_L + R_{DS(ON)}} = \frac{5}{50K + 200} \cong 0.1 \text{ mA}$$

For this set of circuit parameters, the ON current (0.1 mA) is 200 times greater than the OFF current (0.0005 mA). The power-supply requirements are primarily determined from the inverter current demands in the ON state. Notably, the n-channel inverter draws minimum current from the power supply when the output is HIGH, whereas the p-channel inverter draws minimum current when the output is LOW.

2.2.5.2 CMOS Logic

An ingenious inverter design, shown in figure 2.29, in which an n-channel MOS transistor drives the output HIGH and a p-channel MOS transistor drives the output LOW, results in an inverter in which the minimum current is being drawn in both the HIGH and the LOW output states. In this design, the p-channel and n-channel MOS transistors *complement* each other by alternately acting as the *pull-up* resistor. With the input voltage LOW, the p-channel MOS transistor is in the ON state and acts as the pull-up resistor for the n-channel MOS transistor, which is in the OFF state; a HIGH output

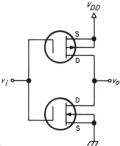

Figure 2.29: *CMOS inverter.*

results (the p-channel MOS transistor *pulls* the output HIGH, or "Up"). With the input voltage HIGH, the n-channel MOS transistor is in the ON state and acts as the pull-up resistor (ie: really a *pull-down* resistor because the output is being pulled to ground) for the p-channel MOS transistor, which is in the OFF state; a LOW output results. Thus, for the case that $R_{DS(OFF)} = 10$ MΩ, $R_{DS(ON)} = 200$ Ω, and $V_{DD} = 5$ V,

$$v_{o(HIGH)} = \frac{R_{DS(OFF)}}{R_{DS(OFF)} + R_{DS(ON)}} V_{DD} = \frac{10M}{10M + 200} 5 \cong 5 \text{ V}$$

$$v_{o(OFF)} = \frac{R_{DS(ON)}}{R_{DS(OFF)} + R_{DS(ON)}} V_{DD} = \frac{200}{10M + 200} 5 \cong 0 \text{ V}$$

$$i_{(ON)} = i_{(OFF)} \frac{V_{DD}}{R_{DS(OFF)} + R_{DS(ON)}} = \frac{5}{10M + 200} \cong 0 \text{ V}$$

The important features of this n-channel, p-channel MOS transistor inverter are:

- Very little power-supply current is required for either the HIGH or LOW state of the inverter.
- Except for the transient periods when the input gate capacitors are being charged or discharged, no input current flows.
- A wide range of power-supply voltages can be used. Generally, any value of V_{DD} between 3 and 15 volts is suitable.
- With no output load on the inverter, $v_{o(LOW)} = 0$ V, and $v_{o(HIGH)} = V_{DD}$.
- There are no large current spikes drawn from the power supply during state transitions. As a result, the power supply is not a source of *glitches*.

The n-channel, p-channel MOS inverter is easily fabricated as an IC on a

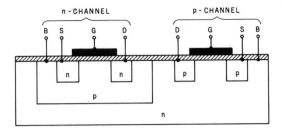

Figure 2.30: *Single-chip construction of a CMOS inverter.*

single chip (figure 2.30) and is called a CMOS (complementary MOS) inverter. The CMOS inverter provides the basis for the CMOS logic family. A CMOS inverter and two CMOS transistor pairs are available in a single IC DIP, the CMOS 4007 (figure 2.31). This package can be used in the construction of simple CMOS logic gates not otherwise available.

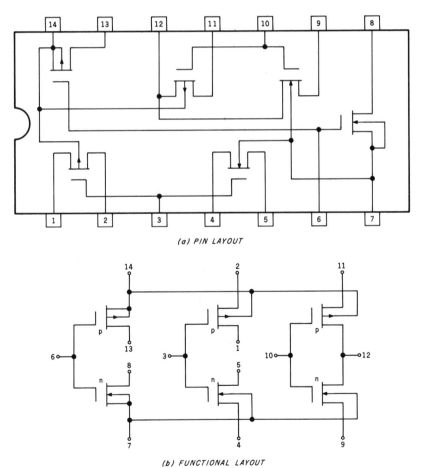

Figure 2.31: *A CMOS 4007 IC (CMOS inverter and two CMOS transistor pairs).*

A large variety of logic functions are commercially available as ICs in the CMOS 4000 series. Figures 2.32a and 2.32b show how the CMOS inverter is utilized in the design of a NOR gate and a NAND gate, respectively. Figures 2.32c and 2.32d show the pin layouts for the 4001 (a DIP quad two-input NOR) and the 4011 (a DIP quad two-input NAND).

Fan-out is rarely an issue in the design of CMOS logic networks. Because no currents flow into CMOS logic gate inputs except in charging or discharging the small gate capacitors, fan-out is virtually unlimited. However, because of the gate capacitors, large fan-outs result in reduced switching speeds; therefore, fan-outs greater than 50 are not advised.

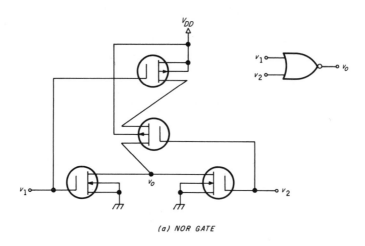

(a) NOR GATE

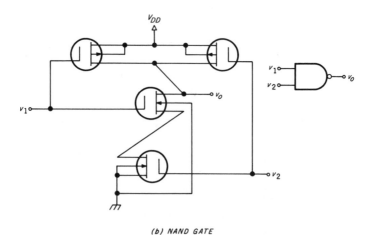

(b) NAND GATE

Figure 2.32: *CMOS logic.*

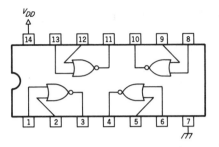

(c) PIN LAYOUT FOR CMOS 4001 IC
(DIP QUAD TWO-INPUT NOR)

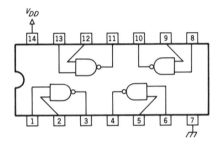

(d) PIN LAYOUT FOR CMOS 4011 IC
(DIP QUAD TWO-INPUT NAND)

Figure 2.32 cont.

Very little input energy is required to change the state of a CMOS logic gate, so it is essential that *all* unused inputs of an IC, including the inputs of unused gates, be connected either to ground or to the supply voltage V_{DD}. Floating inputs can be the cause of excessive current demands on the power supply.

The high density with which CMOS logic circuits can be fabricated onto a single IC chip and the inherently low power consumption of CMOS logic circuits make CMOS logic especially suitable in the construction of large-scale ICs (eg: microprocessors). TTL, on the other hand, because of its high speeds, ruggedness, and enormous past popularity, is used most often in applications requiring small- and medium-scale ICs. Although CMOS logic is rapidly replacing TTL in many applications, the enormous impact that TTL has had on digital-logic design assures that its presence will be felt for many years to come. In design situations constrained by the availability of existing hardware and designs, it is often advantageous to design *hybrid* systems in which both TTL and CMOS logic are used. However, when more than one logic family is used in a single system, special care must be exercised in designing the interfaces between the various logic types to insure that the logic devices function properly. In terms of interfacing CMOS logic and TTL, the problems stem from the following:

- Most CMOS logic devices are incapable of driving standard TTL. In particular, the relatively high capacitive inputs of TTL significantly reduce the switching speeds of the CMOS logic. Also, a standard CMOS logic output cannot reliably sink the approximate 1 mA of current from a LOW TTL input and still maintain a LOW and less than 0.5 V, as specified for a TTL input.
- TTL requires a 5 V power supply, whereas CMOS logic can be designed to operate with power-supply voltages ranging from 3 to 15 volts. Even when both the TTL and CMOS logic use a 5 V supply, a HIGH TTL output is approximately 3.6 V and cannot be used to drive a CMOS input requiring a HIGH of 5 V. Therefore, when interfacing TTL and CMOS logic, it is generally necessary to introduce interface circuitry to compensate for the different voltage levels defining a HIGH.

Perhaps the simplest scheme for driving TTL with CMOS logic is through the use of the special CMOS buffers. For example, the 4049 and 4050 are hex inverting and noninverting buffers, respectively; the 4502 and 4503 are *tristate* (see section 5.3) hex inverting and noninverting buffers, respectively. Each of these buffers is designed to drive *two* regular TTL inputs. Figure 2.33a shows how these buffers can be used as interfaces in driving TTL with CMOS logic.

An especially simple scheme can be used in driving CMOS logic with TTL when the CMOS logic power-supply voltage is 5 V. In this case, a direct connection can be made from the TTL output to the CMOS input. However, a pull-up resistor of approximately 1 kΩ is used to bring the TTL HIGH output up to 5 V from its normal 3.6 V (see figure 2.33b).

When the CMOS power-supply voltage V_{DD} is other than 5 V, an interface must be included to translate the TTL HIGH voltage (approximately 3.6 V) to the CMOS HIGH voltage V_{DD} (3 to 15 volts). A simple resistor-transistor inverter can provide this voltage translation (figure 2.33c).

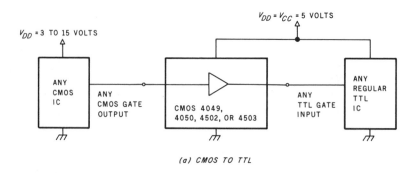

(a) CMOS TO TTL

Figure 2.33: *CMOS-TTL interfacing.*

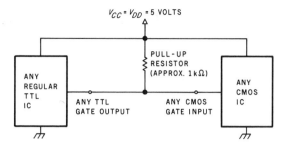

(b) TTL TO CMOS WHEN $V_{CC} = V_{DD} = 5$ VOLTS

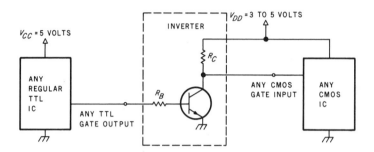

(c) TTL TO CMOS WHEN $V_{CC} = 5$ VOLTS $= V_{DD}$

Figure 2.33 cont.

PROBLEMS

P2.1. Build and test the diode-resistor AND gate and the diode-resistor NAND gate of figures P2.1a and P2.1b, respectively. Use 2N3393 transistors and 1N4148 diodes. Record the results in the appropriate tables. Note that each logic gate is tested by using a LOW corresponding to 0 V and 0.5 V. Use the voltage divider of figure P2.1c to get an approximate 0.5 voltage source. Compare the two logic gates in terms of their potential for use as a universal building block in the design of large digital networks.

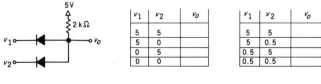

v_1	v_2	v_o
5	5	
5	0	
0	5	
0	0	

v_1	v_2	v_o
5	5	
5	0.5	
0.5	5	
0.5	0.5	

(a) AND GATE

Figure P2.1: *Diode-resistor logic gates.*

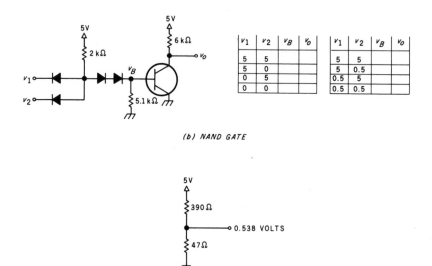

v_1	v_2	v_B	v_o		v_1	v_2	v_B	v_o
5	5				5	5		
5	0				5	0.5		
0	5				0.5	5		
0	0				0.5	0.5		

(b) NAND GATE

(c) 0.5 VOLT SOURCE

Figure P2.1 cont.

P2.2. Build and test the transistor-transistor logic (TTL) gates of figures P2.2a, P2.2b and P2.2c. Use 2N3393 transistors and 1N4148 diodes. Record the results in the appropriate tables. Note that in these tables, a Z is entered wherever an input is to be left unconnected. In such cases, do not connect that input to either 5 V or ground. Connecting v_1 or v_2 to 5 V in the circuit of figure 2.2c can cause transistors to be burned out. Why?

Compare the above three logic gates in terms of their potential for use as a universal building block in the design of large digital networks.

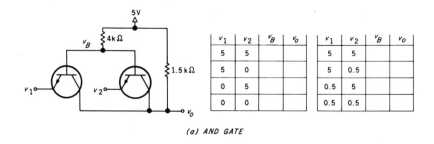

v_1	v_2	v_B	v_o		v_1	v_2	v_B	v_o
5	5				5	5		
5	0				5	0.5		
0	5				0.5	5		
0	0				0.5	0.5		

(a) AND GATE

Figure P2.2: *TTL gates.*

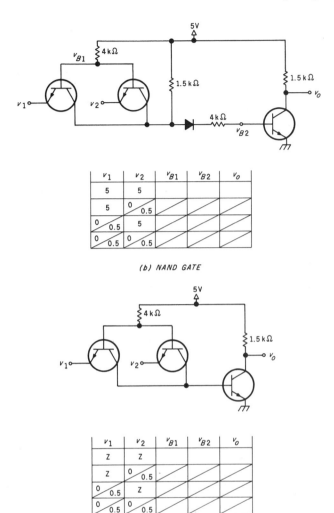

v_1	v_2	v_{B1}	v_{B2}	v_o
5	5			
5	0 / 0.5			
0 / 0.5	5			
0 / 0.5	0 / 0.5			

(b) NAND GATE

v_1	v_2	v_{B1}	v_{B2}	v_o
Z	Z			
Z	0 / 0.5			
0 / 0.5	Z			
0 / 0.5	0 / 0.5			

(c) SIMPLIFIED NAND GATE

Figure P2.2 cont.

P2.3.   (a) Become familiar with the TTL 7400 IC quad NAND by testing one in the laboratory for proper logic and proper voltage levels.
(b) Use interconnections of the NANDs on the TTL 7400 IC you have just tested to construct the following:

- an inverter
- an AND
- an OR
- a NOR

P2.4.   Use a CMOS 4007 IC (see figure 2.31) to construct first a NOR gate and then a NAND gate. Test the operation of this circuit using various power-supply voltages V_{DD}.

P2.5. An exclusive-OR (XOR) is a two-input, one-output digital system such that the output is HIGH if either input, but not both, is HIGH. The truth table for the XOR is given in figure P2.5. Construct an XOR using *one* 7400 (ie: use no more than four NANDS). It can be done!

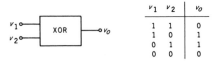

v_1	v_2	v_o
1	1	0
1	0	1
0	1	1
0	0	0

Figure P2.5: *Definition of XOR (exclusive-OR).*

P2.6. Repeat problem 2.3 using the CMOS 4011 quad NAND. Compare the results.

Chapter 3

Logic Design With Integrated Circuits: Combinational Logic

Logic design is a continuously evolving art which is influenced primarily by the state-of-the-art in the manufacture of integrated circuits (ICs). Before the introduction of ICs, logic design was essentially equivalent to circuit design; the designer of a digital-logic system was responsible for the selection of every circuit component. Any circuit-design trick, no matter how subtle or specialized, resulting in the saving of circuit components, especially transistors, was considered to be extremely important in the overall system design. The power, space, and cooling requirements of a digital-logic system, as well as its cost, were roughly proportional to the number of transistors used in the system. Minimization of the number of transistors in a design became a worthwhile objective. However, with the introduction of ICs, circuit design *per se* became less of a factor in logic design. Simple logic gates, such as the resistor-transistor NOR gate, based upon standard circuit designs, became commonly available in IC packages. The early IC packages contained only one or two gates per package. Now, ICs containing fewer than a dozen gates are referred to as small-scale integration (SSI) circuits. SSI logic design involves determining the appropriate interconnection of the available IC logic gates to achieve a desired logic function. Initially, only implementations of simple logic functions were available in SSI packages. A typical approach to a logic design was based upon deriving a switching-algebra expression of the specified logic function in terms of the few logic functions which were then available as IC packages. For example, a typical design objective might have been to implement a specified logic function using only NOR gates. The best logic designer in this setting was the one who could implement the specified logic function with the fewest number of logic gates and, thus, the fewest number of IC packages.

The approach to logic design changed drastically with the introduction of medium-scale integration (MSI); ICs containing between a dozen and one hundred logic gates are referred to as MSI ICs. An assortment of inexpensive MSI IC packages are available; included are implementations of a wide variety of logic functions from the very simple (eg: the inverter, the NOR, or the NAND) to the quite complex (eg: the 4-bit adder). With inexpensive MSI circuits available, good logic design involves using the fewest number of MSI packages necessary to implement the given logic function. Little attention is given to the number of logic gates used. It is not uncommon to utilize only a fraction of the gates contained in an MSI package and, thus, waste a major portion of the circuitry available in the IC. A logic designer must be familiar with the commercially available MSI packages to be able to utilize them advantageously in his particular design. Because new MSI packages are continuously being marketed and because other existing MSI packages are continuously becoming obsolete, a logic designer must stay abreast of the existing technology.

The introduction of large-scale integration (LSI) ICs, which contain over one hundred gates on a single chip, led to a totally new concept in logic design. Perhaps the most remarkable event in the development of LSI technology was the introduction of a complete programmable central processing unit (CPU) for a digital computer all on a single chip, a *microprocessor*. Ironically, LSI has created disturbing identity problems for logic designers and system programmers. It has obscured what was a rather well-defined dividing line between *hardware* problems, which were the specialty of logic designers, and *software* problems, which were the specialty of system programmers. For example, the inexpensive microprocessor, which can be used to implement virtually any logic function, makes it feasible to dedicate an entire digital computer to the implementation of a single logic function. The desired logic function is obtained by storing an appropriate program, which controls the operation of the microprocessor, in one or more LSI memory ICs. The interconnected package of the microprocessor IC, the memory ICs, and the appropriate interfaces is called a *microcomputer*. By using microprocessors, the hardware problem is, if not simple, at the very least, monotonous: one LSI IC can be used as the basis for practically all logic designs. In terms of the changing role of the logic designer, software development is now a large part of many hardware development projects.

Whereas large-scale integration has had a great impact on logic design, the effect on system programming has been minor. It seems reasonable to predict that the biggest changes are yet to come. With the cost of software development increasing rapidly, particularly for large projects, and with the revolutionary LSI technology driving down hardware costs even more rapidly, the point is being reached where the system programmer must seriously consider the possibility of designing a new computer or drastically modifying an existing one for use in a single software development project. In such a setting, the system programmer will have to be intimately aware of computer design principles and existing hardware possibilities.

The crossover point beyond which a logic design using a microprocessor is more economical than a logic design using MSI ICs depends primarily upon the complexity of the logic function being implemented. While logic-function complexity is generally the main factor influencing the cost of an MSI implementation, the cost of a microprocessor implementation is relatively insensitive to the complexity of the logic function. As the cost of LSI technology continues to drop, the crossover point at which the cost of an MSI implementation is equal to the cost of a microprocessor implementation continues to shift in favor of the microprocessor implementation.

Although the art of logic design has evolved from pure circuit design using only discrete electrical components to designs using SSI ICs, then to designs using MSI ICs, and finally to designs using LSI technology, the earlier logic-design methods have *not* become obsolete. In using LSI components for a logic design, it is not uncommon for a designer to use an assortment of both MSI and SSI components to interface the various LSI components into a single working system. Similarly, the judicious use of discrete components such as resistors, capacitors, and transistors in a logic design often results in the most efficient overall design possible. A logic designer must be familiar with the fundamentals of logic design from the electric-circuit level to the LSI microprocessor level. This chapter deals with the use of SSI, MSI, and LSI technology in the design of combinational logic.

3.1 Combinational Logic

A *combinational-logic* system is a digital-logic input/output (I/O) system in which the outputs are unambiguously defined for every *combination* of input values. Therefore, all well-formed expressions of switching algebra define a switching-algebra function and, thus, a combinational-logic system. For example, the expression $\overline{X + (Y \cdot Z)} \cdot X$ defines the switching-algebra function

$$F = \overline{X + (Y \cdot Z)} \cdot X$$

A combinational-logic system realizing this switching-algebra function is shown in figure 3.1. This combinational-logic system has three inputs and one output. The value of the output variable F is unambiguously defined for every possible combination of input variables X, Y, and Z; a truth table can be constructed which completely defines the relationship between the input variables X, Y, and Z and the output variable F. Such a multi-input, single-output system can be defined for every well-formed expression of switching algebra.

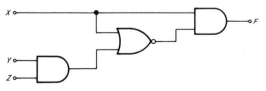

Figure 3.1: *Realization of* $F = \overline{X + (Y \cdot Z)} \cdot X$.

Not all interconnections of combinational-logic systems result in a combinational-logic system. For example, consider the two combinational-logic systems modeled by NANDs:

$$U_1 = \overline{X \cdot V_1}$$

$$V_2 = \overline{Y \cdot V_1}$$

These two NAND systems appear in figure 3.2a.

Now consider interconnecting these combinational-logic systems so that

$$U_1 = U_2 = U$$

$$V_1 = V_2 = V$$

Such an interconnection is shown in figure 3.2b. This system, which is an interconnection of two combinational-logic systems, is not itself a combinational-logic system: the input variables X and Y do not uniquely define the outputs. Specifically, the combination of input values $X = 1$ and $Y = 1$ does not uniquely define the outputs U and V. For this particular combination of inputs, the outputs can be either $U = 1$ and $V = 0$, or $U = 0$ and $V = 1$. All other combinations of inputs do give a unique output. The *pseudo* truth table of figure 3.2c summarizes the I/O relationships of this system. Logic systems such as this one, having two output states for one input combination, form the basis for memory cells (section 4.2).

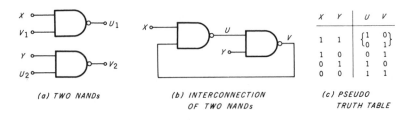

X	Y	U	V
1	1	$\{\begin{smallmatrix}1\\0\end{smallmatrix}$	$\begin{smallmatrix}0\\1\end{smallmatrix}\}$
1	0	0	1
0	1	1	0
0	0	1	1

(a) TWO NANDs   *(b) INTERCONNECTION OF TWO NANDs*   *(c) PSEUDO TRUTH TABLE*

Figure 3.2: *A noncombinational-logic system showing two stable output states for one input combination.*

Another example of an interconnection of combinational-logic systems that is not itself a combinational-logic system is shown in figure 3.3. In this system, a NAND and two NOTs are interconnected. This system is unusual in that, for the input value $X = 1$, there is no set of output values that satisfy the system equations. If this system were constructed in the laboratory from actual logic gates, a rapid oscillatory behavior of the outputs would result. The logic gates of this system would be continuously switching from HIGH to LOW and from LOW to HIGH in an endless search for the nonexistent set of values U, V, and W which satisfy the system equations. The frequency of the oscillations would be determined by the switching times of the gates and their capacitive loads. Although this interconnection is not useful as a system of combinational logic, it could be used as an *oscillator* (ie: a *clock*). The frequency of such an oscillator could be reduced by using appropriately placed loading capacitors to increase the switching time of one or more of the logic gates (see section 4.2). For the case that the input $X = 0$, this system is well behaved in that it has a unique set of outputs.

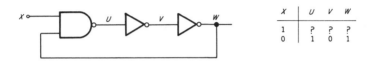

X	U	V	W
1	?	?	?
0	1	0	1

Figure 3.3: *A noncombinational-logic system with no stable output state for one input value.*

An important property of logic systems is that any interconnection of combinational-logic systems that is not itself a combinational-logic system *always* contains at least one loop. A *loop* is defined as any closed path through a system (ie: starting at any point on a closed path, one can proceed through a series of gates, from input to output, and return to the same starting point). In the two examples of noncombinational-logic systems just given (figures 3.2 and 3.3), the loops are obvious. *Loop-free interconnections of combinational-logic systems are always combinational-logic systems.* The existence of a loop does not necessarily mean that the system is not a combinational-logic system (see figure 3.4). Nevertheless, except when constructing memory cells or clocks, it is advisable to avoid loops in logic design. Memory cells and clocks, extremely important in the design of digital computers, are discussed in detail in the study of *sequential logic* (Chapter 4).

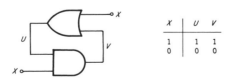

X	U	V
1	1	1
0	0	0

Figure 3.4: *A combinational-logic system containing a loop.*

3.2   Combinational-Logic Design Using ICs

Switching algebra provides the basis for combinational-logic design. The electronic implementation of gates corresponding to the primitive operators of switching algebra (ie: the AND, OR, and NOT) is simple. When primitive-logic gates (ie: ANDs, ORs, and NOTs) are used in the most obvious manner (ie: one primitive-logic gate is used for each primitive operator in the logic function to be implemented), there is a one-to-one correspondence between the logic function to be implemented and the resulting combinational-logic design. Therefore, at least one combinational-logic design can be realized from a logic function in a straightforward manner. Alternately, a truth table provides a complete I/O description of a combinational-logic system, and a corresponding logic function can be derived from a truth table by using either the minterm or maxterm approach. At least one combinational-logic design can also be realized from a truth table in a straightforward manner.

Although a combinational-logic design can always be realized from either a logic function or a truth table in a straightforward, algorithmic fashion, obtaining an efficient, economical design is not at all simple. Good logic design is an art in which experience and knowledge of the existing IC hardware play a major role. In the next sections, examples of logic design are explored, and some of the considerations that enter into combinational-logic designs are illustrated. Special emphasis is placed upon the realization of efficient combinational-logic designs by using available ICs. The particular combinational-logic functions considered in the examples are fundamental to the design of digital computers.

3.2.1   The Half-Adder

The *half-adder* is defined as a two-input, two-output combinational-logic system in which the two outputs are the binary sum of the two inputs. Output S is referred to as the *sum*, and output C is referred to as the *carry*. A block diagram of the half-adder and its defining truth table are shown in figure 3.5. The logic functions for S and C, obtained by using the minterms, are

$$\left. \begin{array}{l} S = V_1 \cdot \overline{V_2} + \overline{V_1} \cdot V_2 \\ C = V_1 \cdot V_2 \end{array} \right\} \tag{3.1}$$

It is interesting to compare several logic designs of the half-adder in which the hardware constraints differ.

First, consider the design of the half-adder using only NAND gates (eg: using the TTL 7400 quad NAND or the CMOS 4011 quad NAND; figures 2.22 and 2.32d, respectively). The obvious and least efficient approach is to use NAND gates to construct primitive-logic gates corresponding to the primitive operators of switching algebra (ie: the AND gate, the OR gate, and the NOT gate — see problem 2.3), and then use these primitive gates to implement the logic functions given in equations (3.1). A design using such an approach results in the use of three AND gates, two NOT gates, and one OR gate. Because it takes two NAND gates to construct one AND gate, one NAND gate per NOT gate, and three NAND gates per OR gate, it takes eleven NAND gates to implement the half-adder in this manner. Both the TTL 7400 and the CMOS 4011 contain four NANDs per IC. Thus, three IC packages are required for this implementation of the half-adder.

V_1	V_2	C	S
1	1	1	0
1	0	0	1
0	1	0	1
0	0	0	0

Figure 3.5: *Definition of the half-adder.*

An alternate approach, based upon the application of De Morgan's theorem, leads to a simpler implementation. In accordance with De Morgan's theorem, the output of a NAND is the OR of the inverse of its two inputs, $\overline{X \cdot Y} = \overline{X} + \overline{Y}$ (see figure 3.6a). Specifically, note that

$$\overline{(V_1 \cdot \overline{V_2}) \cdot (\overline{V_1} \cdot V_2)} = V_1 \cdot \overline{V_2} + \overline{V_1} \cdot V_2 = S$$

Thus, a NAND with inputs $V_1 \cdot \overline{V_2}$ and $\overline{V_1} \cdot V_2$ provides the desired S as its output. Similarly, $V_1 \cdot \overline{V_2}$ and $\overline{V} \cdot V_2$ can be obtained as the output of NANDs. Figure 3.7 shows an implementation of the half-adder based upon these applications of De Morgan's theorem. Only seven NANDs (ie: only two 7400 IC packages or only two 4011 IC packages) are used in this implementation. Figure 3.8 shows a more ingenious design of the half-adder in which only five NANDs are used.

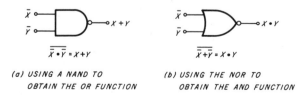

$$\overline{X \cdot \overline{Y}} = X + Y$$

(a) USING A NAND TO OBTAIN THE OR FUNCTION

$$\overline{\overline{X} + \overline{Y}} = X \cdot Y$$

(b) USING THE NOR TO OBTAIN THE AND FUNCTION

Figure 3.6: *Application of De Morgan's theorem in logic design.*

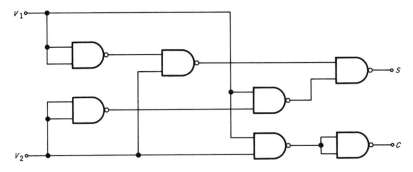

Figure 3.7: *Implementation of a half-adder using seven NAND gates.*

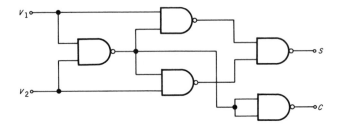

Figure 3.8: *Clever implementation of a half-adder using five NAND gates.*

Now consider the design of the half-adder using only NOR gates. Either the TTL 7402 (a quad NOR; see figure 3.9) or the CMOS 4001 (also a quad NOR; see figure 2.32c) can be the basis of such an implementation. It is natural to use the NOR gate to output S once the signals representing the terms $V_1 \cdot \overline{V_2}$ and $\overline{V_1} \cdot V_2$ are available. However, implementing the AND function for each of the terms $V_1 \cdot \overline{V_2}$ and $\overline{V_1} \cdot V_2$ by using AND gates made from NOR gates is unattractive because it takes three NOR gates to make one AND gate. Again, application of De Morgan's theorem is useful: the output of a NOR gate is the AND of the inverse of its two inputs (ie: $\overline{X + Y} = \overline{X} \cdot \overline{Y}$; see figure 3.6b). The implementation of AND functions for terms $V_1 \cdot \overline{V_2}$ and $\overline{V_1} \cdot V_2$ can be obtained rather efficiently by using NOR gates. Figure 3.10 shows a half-adder design using seven NOR gates (ie: two 7402 IC packages or two 4001 IC packages); figure 3.11 shows a more ingenious design using five NOR gates.

Figure 3.9: *Pin connections for the TTL 7402 quad NOR.*

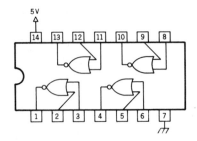

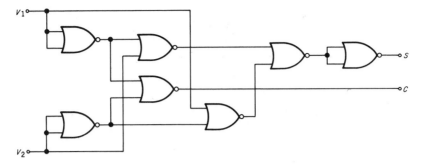

Figure 3.10: *Implementation of a half-adder using seven NOR gates.*

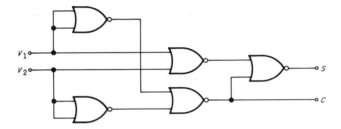

Figure 3.11: *Clever implementation of a half-adder using five NOR gates.*

An *exclusive-OR* (XOR) gate is a two-input, one-output gate such that the output is HIGH only if exactly one input is HIGH. Figure 3.12 shows the standard logic symbol for the XOR gate and gives its truth table. The logic function modeling the XOR can be obtained from the truth table using the minterms method:

$$V_o = V_1 \cdot \overline{V_2} + \overline{V_1} \cdot V_2$$

Note that this is the logic function required for the implementation of the S output of the half-adder. The XOR gate can be quite useful in the design of a half-adder. A design of a half-adder using an XOR gate and two NAND gates is shown in figure 3.13. Quad XORs are available in TTL (the 7486) and CMOS (the 4030); the pin connections for both the 7486 and the 4030 are identical and are shown in figure 3.14.

V_1	V_2	V_o
1	1	0
1	0	1
0	1	1
1	0	0

Figure 3.12: *Definition of the exclusive-OR (XOR).*

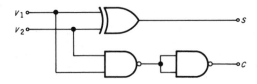

Figure 3.13: *Implementation of a half-adder using an XOR gate and two NAND gates.*

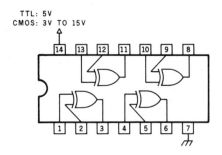

Figure 3.14: *Pin connections for the TTL 7486 and CMOS 4030 quad XORs.*

3.2.2 The Full-Adder

The *full-adder* is defined as a three-input, two-output combinational-logic system in which the two outputs are the binary sum of the three inputs. Like the half-adder, one output S is called the sum, and the other output C is called the carry. A block diagram of a full-adder and its truth table are shown in figure 3.15. The full-adder is used as the fundamental element in the construction of general-purpose binary adders in which two multi-digit binary numbers are added. For example, consider the addition of the two four-digit numbers $A = A_3A_2A_1A_0$ and $B = B_3B_2B_1B_0$, where A_i and B_i represent the ith digit of the numbers A and B, respectively (eg: if $A = 1010$ and $B = 0101$, then $A_0 = 0$, $A_1 = 1$, $A_2 = 0$, $A_3 = 1$, $B_0 = 1$, $B_1 = 0$, $B_2 = 1$, and $B_3 = 0$). The process of addition proceeds as follows: A_0 and B_0 are added obtaining S_0, the zeroth digit of the sum, and C_1, the carry digit; now C_1, A_1, and B_1 are added obtaining S_1, the first digit of the sum, and C_2, the carry digit, and so forth. This process is summarized below:

$$
\begin{array}{r}
A_3 \quad A_2 \quad A_1 \quad A_0 \\
+ \quad \quad B_3 \quad B_2 \quad B_1 \quad B_0 \\
\hline
\end{array}
$$

Carry	C_4	C_3	C_2	C_1	
Sum	S_4	S_3	S_2	S_1	S_0

The general addition step in this process involves the addition of three one-digit binary numbers, A_i, B_i, and C_i. A full-adder can be used as the basic element in the implementation of a multi-digit adder. Figure 3.16 shows how four full-adders are used to implement a 4-*bit* adder (a *bit* is equivalent to *binary digit*, from which the word *bit* was originally contracted). Several approaches to the implementation of a full-adder are now considered.

A primitive approach to the design of a full-adder involves deriving the sum and carry logic functions from the defining truth table given in figure 3.15. Using the minterm method results in

$$S = V_0 \cdot V_1 \cdot V_2 + V_0 \cdot \overline{V_1} \cdot \overline{V_2} + \overline{V_0} \cdot V_1 \cdot \overline{V_2} + \overline{V_0} \cdot \overline{V_1} \cdot V_2$$

$$C = V_0 \cdot V_1 \cdot V_2 + V_0 \cdot V_1 \cdot \overline{V_2} + V_0 \cdot \overline{V_1} \cdot V_2 + \overline{V_0} \cdot V_1 \cdot V_2$$

Identities and theorems of switching algebra are applied heuristically to simplify the expressions for S and C:

$$S = V_0 \cdot (\overline{V_1 \cdot \overline{V_2} + \overline{V_1} \cdot V_2}) + \overline{V_0} \cdot (V_1 \cdot \overline{V_2} + \overline{V_1} \cdot V_2)$$

$$C = V_1 \cdot V_2 + V_0 \cdot (V_1 \cdot \overline{V_2} + \overline{V_1} \cdot V_2)$$

To emphasize the simplicity of the above expressions in terms of the exclusive-OR (XOR) function, this function is denoted by the symbol $\oplus$:
$$X \cdot \overline{Y} + \overline{X} \cdot Y = X \oplus Y. \text{ Thus,}$$

$$S = V_0 \oplus (V_1 \oplus V_2)$$

$$C = V_1 \cdot V_2 + V_0 \cdot (V_1 \oplus V_2) = \overline{(\overline{V_1 \cdot V_2}) \cdot \overline{V_0 \cdot (V_1 \oplus V_2)}}$$

The above expressions result in the rather efficient implementation of the full-adder using XORs and NANDs shown in figure 3.17.

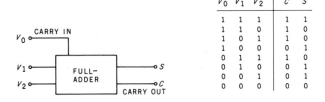

V_0	V_1	V_2	C	S
1	1	1	1	1
1	1	0	1	0
1	0	1	1	0
1	0	0	0	1
0	1	1	1	0
0	1	0	0	1
0	0	1	0	1
0	0	0	0	0

Figure 3.15: *Definition of the full-adder.*

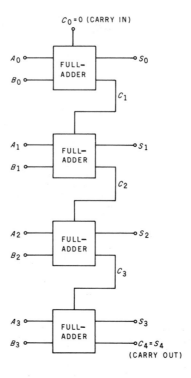

Figure 3.16: *Implementation of a four-bit adder from four full-adders.*

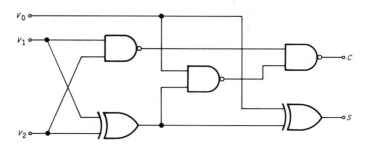

Figure 3.17: *Implementation of a full-adder from two XOR gates and three NAND gates.*

Although the above approach to designing a full-adder eventually leads to a relatively simple implementation, the process is somewhat tortuous and depends upon the designer's dexterity in manipulating expressions in switching algebra. The major shortcoming of this primitive approach to logic design, in which the truth table provides the defining I/O relationships, lies in the fact that common, elementary-school knowledge about the process of addition, which could prove useful in the design of an adder, is ignored. Instead, the design proceeds as though the function defined by the truth table is a total abstraction. Attempts to discover simplified structures are limited to applying only switching-algebra identities and theorems. In situations where the logic function represents a well-known process such as addition, a functional approach to combinational-logic design may prove more effective. For example, the process realized by the full-adder can be broken down as follows:

Step 1: Add the two 1-bit numbers V_1 and V_2 to obtain the intermediate sum S_x and carry C_x:

$$
\left.
\begin{array}{r}
V_1 \\
+ \quad V_2 \\
\hline
C_x S_x
\end{array}
\right\}
\quad \text{Half-adder}
$$

Step 2: Add the intermediate sum S_x to the third 1-bit number V_0 to obtain the final sum S and the second intermediate carry C_y:

$$
\left.
\begin{array}{r}
S_x \\
+ \quad V_0 \\
\hline
C_y S
\end{array}
\right\}
\quad \text{Half-adder}
$$

Step 3: Add the two intermediate carries C_x and C_y to obtain the final carry C:

$$
\left.
\begin{array}{r}
C_x \\
+ \quad C_y \\
\hline
C
\end{array}
\right\}
\quad \text{Half-adder or OR}
$$

Because the largest binary number that can be obtained from the addition of three 1-bit numbers is the two-digit binary number 11, an OR can be used instead of a third half-adder; the sum of the two intermediate carries C_x and C_y is always a 1-bit number (ie: C_x and C_y cannot both be 1s), and the simple OR is sufficient to provide the sum C. Figure 3.18 shows the implementation of a full-adder using two half-adders and an OR.

This functional approach to logic design becomes increasingly powerful as one develops a collection of designs and, more importantly, as one becomes familiar with the logic functions available in commercial IC packages. For example, after having gone through detailed designs of half-adders and full-adders, as was done here, it may be disappointing to learn that complete 4-bit full-adders exist in single sixteen-pin IC packages: the TTL 7483 and the CMOS 4008. Figure 3.19 shows the pin connections for these packages. Note that one pin of each of these packages (pin 13 of the TTL 7483; pin 14 of the CMOS 4008) is a *carry-in* pin allowing an external carry-in C_0 to be added to the two lower-order bits A_0 and B_0. Thus, two 7483s or two 4008s can be used to construct an 8-bit full-adder. In the construction of a TTL 8-bit full-adder, one 7483 is used for the four lower-order bits and the other 7483 is used for the four higher-order bits. The *carry-out* C_4 of the 7483, which is used to add the lower-order bits, is the *carry-in* C_0 of the 7483, which is used to add the higher-order bits.

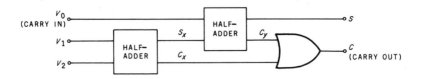

Figure 3.18: *Implementation of a full-adder using two half-adders and an OR gate.*

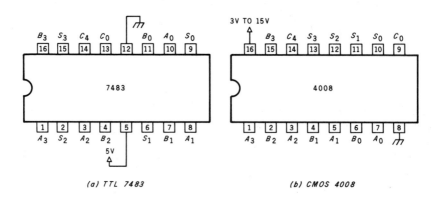

Figure 3.19: *Pin connections for the TTL and CMOS 4-bit adders.*

3.2.3   The Comparator (the Exclusive-NOR: XNOR)

The negation of the exclusive-OR (ie: the *exclusive-NOR*, or simply, the *XNOR*) is an important logic gate in that it can be used as a 1-bit *comparator*; the output of the XNOR is HIGH only when the two inputs are equal (see figure 3.20). This property makes the XNOR especially useful in constructing multi-digit comparators. For example, consider designing a *2-bit comparator* to compare the two 2-bit numbers $A = A_1A_0$ and $B = B_1B_0$. The comparator is to have three outputs: the first output G is HIGH only if $A > B$, the second output E is HIGH only if $A = B$, and the third output L is HIGH only if $A < B$.

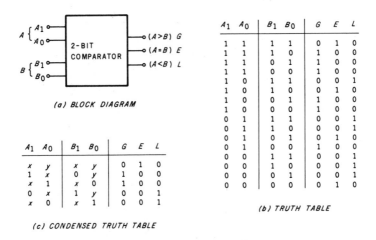

V_1	V_2	V_0
1	1	1
1	0	0
0	1	0
0	0	1

Figure 3.20: *Definition of the exclusive-NOR (XNOR), the 1-bit comparator.*

$$V = \overline{V_1 \oplus V_2}$$

A block diagram for this 2-bit comparator is shown in figure 3.21a; the corresponding truth table is shown in figure 3.21b. Perhaps more useful than the standard truth table, in terms of design, is the condensed version of the truth table given in figure 3.21c. This condensed truth table emphasizes the function of the comparator and lends insight into its design. The first

(a) BLOCK DIAGRAM

A_1	A_0	B_1	B_0	G	E	L
1	1	1	1	0	1	0
1	1	1	0	1	0	0
1	1	0	1	1	0	0
1	1	0	0	1	0	0
1	0	1	1	0	0	1
1	0	1	0	0	1	0
1	0	0	1	1	0	0
1	0	0	0	1	0	0
0	1	1	1	0	0	1
0	1	1	0	0	0	1
0	1	0	1	0	1	0
0	1	0	0	1	0	0
0	0	1	1	0	0	1
0	0	1	0	0	0	1
0	0	0	1	0	0	1
0	0	0	0	0	1	0

(b) TRUTH TABLE

A_1	A_0	B_1	B_0	G	E	L
x	y	x	y	0	1	0
1	x	0	y	1	0	0
x	1	x	0	1	0	0
0	x	1	y	0	0	1
x	0	x	1	0	0	1

(c) CONDENSED TRUTH TABLE

Figure 3.21: *Definition of the 2-bit comparator.*

row of the condensed truth table, which is equivalent to four rows of the actual truth table, summarizes all the conditions for equality: ie: for any values of x and y, $A_1 = B_1$, $A_0 = B_0$ and thus, $A = B$ and $E = 1$. In terms of switching algebra,

$$E = \overline{(A_1 \oplus B_1)} \cdot \overline{(A_0 \oplus B_0)} = E_1 \cdot E_0$$

where $E_0 = \overline{A_0 \oplus B_0}$ and $E_1 = \overline{A_1 \oplus B_1}$. Figure 3.22a shows the design of a combinational-logic system having an output E.

The second row of the condensed truth table gives a sufficient condition for inequality: for any values of x and y, $A_1 = 1$ and $B_1 = 0$; thus, $A > B$, regardless of the values of A_0 and B_0. Equivalently, in terms of switching algebra,

$$G_1 = A_1 \cdot \overline{B_1}$$

where $G_1 = 1$ is sufficient to establish $A > B$. Figure 3.22b shows a combinational-logic system providing G_1 as an output. There is, however, another condition sufficient to establish $A > B$. This condition is given by the third row of the condensed truth table: for any value of x, $A_0 = 1$, $B_0 = 0$, and $A_1 = B_1$; thus, $A > B$. Equivalently, in terms of switching algebra,

$$G_0 = E_1 \cdot A_0 \cdot \overline{B_0}$$

where $G_0 = 1$ is sufficient to establish $A > B$. Figure 3.22c shows a combinational-logic system providing G_0 as an output.

Similarly, rows 3 and 5 of the condensed truth table give

$$L_1 = \overline{A_1} \cdot B_1$$

$$L_0 = E_1 \cdot \overline{A_0} \cdot B_0$$

where $L_1 = 1$ and $L_0 = 1$ are both sufficient conditions for establishing $A < B$. The combinational-logic systems providing L_1 and L_0 as outputs are shown in figures 3.22d and 3.22e, respectively. Necessary and sufficient conditions to establish $A > B$ are obtained from G_1 and G_0:

$$G = G_0 + G_1$$

Similarly, necessary and sufficient conditions to establish $A < B$ are obtained from L_1 and L_0:

$$L = L_0 + L_1$$

Simple OR gates can be used to generate G and L from G_1 and G_2 and from L_1 and L_2, respectively (figure 3.22f). It is now a relatively simple matter to combine all the logic designs of figures 3.22a through 3.22f into a single design for the entire 2-bit comparator (figure 3.22g).

Four-bit comparators are available in single IC packages: the TTL 7485 and the CMOS 4063 (see figure 3.23). In addition to the eight pins for inputting the two 4-bit numbers being compared and the three output pins for G, E, and L, these comparators have three additional pins: the three *cascade input* pins, also labeled G, E, and L, are used to construct an 8-bit comparator from two 4-bit IC packages. To obtain an 8-bit comparator, one 7485 is used for the 4 low-order bits of each number, and the G, E, and L outputs of this comparator provide the 3 cascade inputs for the second 7485, which is used for the 4 high-order bits of each number. The outputs of the high-order 7485 are the outputs of the 8-bit comparator.

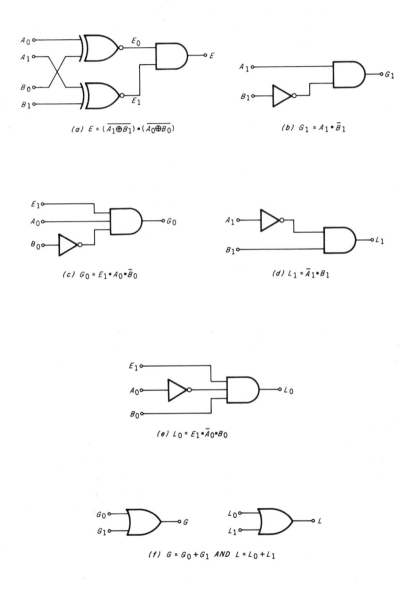

(a) $E = (\overline{A_1 \oplus B_1}) \cdot (\overline{A_0 \oplus B_0})$

(b) $G_1 = A_1 \cdot \overline{B}_1$

(c) $G_0 = E_1 \cdot A_0 \cdot \overline{B}_0$

(d) $L_1 = \overline{A}_1 \cdot B_1$

(e) $L_0 = E_1 \cdot \overline{A}_0 \cdot B_0$

(f) $G = G_0 + G_1$ AND $L = L_0 + L_1$

Figure 3.22: *Step-by-step implementation of the 2-bit comparator.*

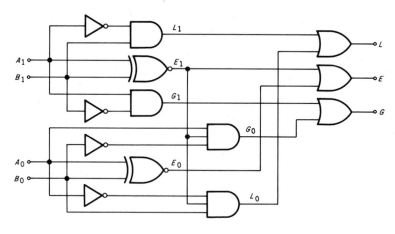

(g) THE 2-BIT COMPARATOR

Figure 3.22 cont.

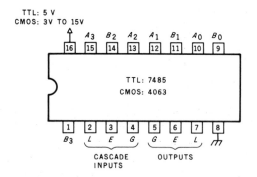

Figure 3.23: *Pin connections for the TTL 7485 and CMOS 4063 4-bit comparators.*

3.2.4   The Seven-Segment Display

Seven-segment displays are frequently used to display the output of a digital system. The seven-segment LED display is especially popular because of its low power requirements, high reliability, and low cost. Figure 3.24a shows the face of a typical seven-segment LED display. Each of the seven segments is an LED which can be lighted up by passing a specified current through it. Thus, various patterns can be created. Figure 3.24b shows the patterns that are typically used to display the decimal digits 0 through 9.

(a) THE SEVEN SEGMENTS   *(b) PATTERNS FOR THE DECIMAL DIGITS*

Figure 3.24: *Seven-segment LED display.*

Seven-segment LEDs are available in two general categories: the *common anode* and the *common cathode*. In a common-anode seven-segment LED display, the anodes of all seven LEDs are connected together, whereas in a common-cathode LED, all seven cathodes are connected together (see figure 3.25). For applications with TTL, the common-anode display is usually more convenient; because the totem-pole output of a typical TTL gate can sink at least 12 mA of current, the appropriate TTL must be designed to provide a LOW for the segment to be illuminated.

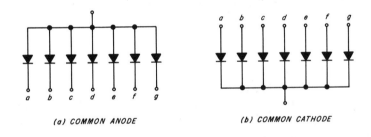

(a) COMMON ANODE   *(b) COMMON CATHODE*

Figure 3.25: *Common-anode and common-cathode connections for a seven-segment LED display.*

In digital systems it is often necessary to display the decimal number corresponding to a binary number. Consider a typical situation in which the outputs of four TTL gates A_3, A_2, A_1, and A_0 represent a *binary-coded decimal* (BCD) digit. Figure 3.26a illustrates a system that might be used to provide a visual display of the decimal digit corresponding to the BCD number $A_3 A_2 A_1 A_0$. The TTL combinational-logic network is defined by the truth table of figure 3.26b, which gives the relationship between the BCD number $A_3 A_2 A_1 A_0$ and the appropriate decimal patterns of a seven-segment display. This truth table reflects the intent to use the TTL combinational-logic interface with a common-anode seven-segment LED display: a LOW is provided at the output corresponding to a segment that is to be lighted up.

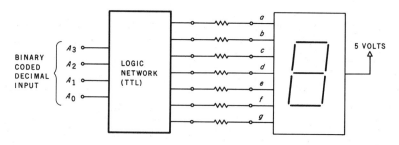

(a) TTL COMBINATIONAL-LOGIC NETWORK
INTERFACE FOR COMMON-ANODE LED

DECIMAL DIGIT DISPLAYED	BCD INPUT				a	b	c	d	e	f	g
	A_3	A_2	A_1	A_0							
0	0	0	0	0	0	0	0	0	0	0	1
1	0	0	0	1	1	0	0	1	1	1	1
2	0	0	1	0	0	0	1	0	0	1	0
3	0	0	1	1	0	0	0	0	1	1	0
4	0	1	0	0	1	0	0	1	1	0	0
5	0	1	0	1	0	1	0	0	1	0	0
6	0	1	1	0	1	1	0	0	0	0	0
7	0	1	1	1	0	0	0	1	1	1	1
8	1	0	0	0	0	0	0	0	0	0	0
9	1	0	0	1	0	0	0	1	1	0	0

(b) BCD TO SEVEN-SEGMENT TRUTH TABLE

Figure 3.26: *BCD to seven-segment decoding.*

   To illustrate what is involved in designing a TTL combinational-logic network to decode a BCD number into its seven-segment code, consider the logic for generating the *e-segment* signal (lighting LED *e*). Obtaining the maxterms for *e* from the truth table of figure 3.26b results in the product-of-sums expression for *e* in terms of the BCD variables:

$$e = (A_3 + A_2 + A_1 + A_0) \cdot (A_3 + A_2 + \overline{A_1} + A_0)$$
$$\cdot (A_3 + \overline{A_2} + \overline{A_1} + A_0) \cdot (\overline{A_3} + A_2 + A_1 + A_0)$$

This can be simplified by using identities and fundamental theorems of switching algebra:

$$e = A_0 + (A_3 + \overline{A_1}) \cdot A_2 + A_1 \cdot A_3$$

An implementation of the combinational-logic system realizing the above switching-algebra formula is shown in figure 3.27. The combinational logic for the other segments of the seven-segment LED display can be similarly designed.

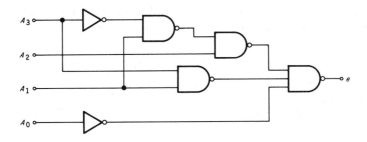

Figure 3.27: *Logic for lighting the e-segment of a seven-segment LED display.*

The need for BCD to seven-segment decoding is sufficiently common to justify the manufacture of a single TTL IC that performs this function. The sixteen-pin TTL 7447 BCD to seven-segment decoder/driver (see figure 3.28) is such an IC. The 7447 can drive seven-segment common-anode LED displays requiring up to 40 mA per segment. Figure 3.29 shows how a 10 mA per segment, common-anode, seven-segment LED display can be interfaced to a 7447. The 330 Ω resistor in series with each LED limits the current to somewhat less than 10 mA:

$$i_D \frac{5 - v_D - v_{CES}}{330} = \frac{5 - 1.7 - 0.3}{330} = 9.1 \text{ mA}$$

where v_D is the voltage drop across the conducting LED, and v_{CES} is the voltage across the lower totem-pole output transistor when saturated.

Figure 3.28: *The 7447: A BCD to seven-segment decoder/driver.*

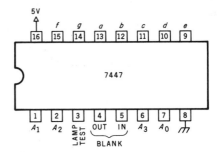

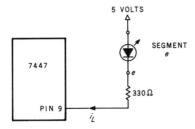

Figure 3.29: *Loading the 7447 with an LED.*

3.2.5 Digital Multiplexers and Demultiplexers

A *multiplexer* (or *data selector*) is a combinational-logic system having multiple inputs (eg: n inputs) and only one output such that, upon command, the output will follow any one input selected. A *demultiplexer* (or *data distributor*) is a combinational-logic system having only one input and multiple outputs (eg: n outputs) such that, upon command, any one output selected will follow the input. As figure 3.30 shows, multiplexers and demultiplexers are easily realized with simple multi-contact switches. For the multiplexer, the switch position determines which of the n inputs is connected to the one output, whereas for the demultiplexer, the switch position determines which of the n outputs is connected to the one input. In high-speed digital systems, multiplexers and demultiplexers are reliable high-speed electronic devices and not mechanical switches.

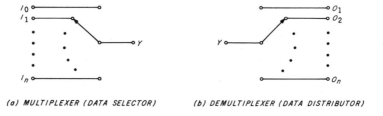

(a) MULTIPLEXER (DATA SELECTOR)   (b) DEMULTIPLEXER (DATA DISTRIBUTOR)

Figure 3.30: *Switches as multiplexers and demultiplexers.*

Consider the design of a two-input multiplexer such as is represented in figure 3.31a. A realization of such a multiplexer, using a single-pole, double-throw switch, is shown in figure 3.31b. If switching variable A is defined to represent the position of switch A (eg: $A = 0$ implies that the switch is in position 0, and $A = 1$ implies that the switch is in position 1), the relationship between the multiplexer output Y and the inputs I_0 and I_1 is given by

$$Y = I_0 \cdot \overline{A} + I_1 \cdot A$$

A may be thought of as an *address* defining the location of the switch arm.

For synchronization purposes, it is often necessary to *strobe* a multiplexer (ie: to disable the multiplexer upon command by forcing its output to be LOW regardless of the state of the data inputs and the address). Most multiplexer ICs allow for a strobe input signal, S. A typical two-input, strobed multiplexer is modeled by

$$Y = (I_0 \cdot \overline{A} + I_1 \cdot A) \cdot \overline{S}$$

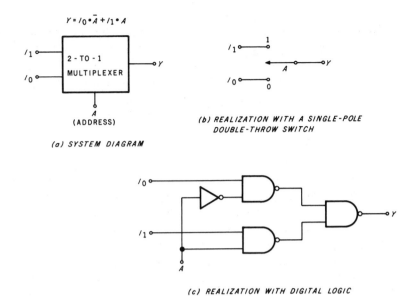

$$Y = I_0 \cdot \bar{A} + I_1 \cdot A$$

(a) SYSTEM DIAGRAM

(b) REALIZATION WITH A SINGLE-POLE DOUBLE-THROW SWITCH

(c) REALIZATION WITH DIGITAL LOGIC

Figure 3.31: *A two-input multiplexer.*

Therefore, if $S = 1$, then $Y = 0$ regardless of I_0, I_1, and A. A strobed multiplexer is easily obtained by ANDing the output of a multiplexer and its strobe signal (see figure 3.32a). The strobe input is also called an *enable* input. Figure 3.32b shows the pin connections for the 74157, a quad, two-input, strobed TTL multiplexer.

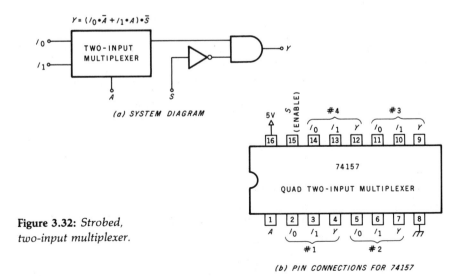

$$Y = (I_0 \cdot \bar{A} + I_1 \cdot A) \cdot \bar{S}$$

(a) SYSTEM DIAGRAM

Figure 3.32: *Strobed, two-input multiplexer.*

(b) PIN CONNECTIONS FOR 74157

Figure 3.33a defines a four-input multiplexer. Note that a 2-bit address is required to address all four inputs. Figure 3.33b shows the pin positions for the 74153, which is a dual, four-input, strobed TTL multiplexer. Similarly, figure 3.34a defines an eight-input multiplexer, and figure 3.34b shows the pin positions for the corresponding TTL IC, the sixteen-pin 74151. Also available is the twenty-four pin 74154, a sixteen-input, strobed, TTL multiplexer.

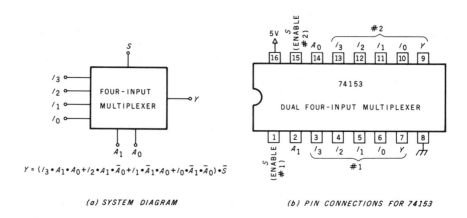

(a) SYSTEM DIAGRAM

(b) PIN CONNECTIONS FOR 74153

Figure 3.33: *A four-input multiplexer.*

As an application of a multiplexer in logic design, consider designing a system of combinational logic to drive the e segment of a seven-segment LED display in response to a BCD input. From the truth table in figure 3.26b we see that (note that to conserve space the AND symbols have been omitted here and in the following equations, ie: A_0A_1, means $A_0 \cdot A_1$)

$$e = \overline{A_3}\,\overline{A_2}\,\overline{A_1}\,A_0 + \overline{A_3}\,\overline{A_2}\,A_1\,A_0 + \overline{A_3}\,A_2\,\overline{A_1}\,\overline{A_0}$$
$$+\; \overline{A_3}\,A_2\,\overline{A_1}\,A_0 + \overline{A_3}\,A_2\,A_1\,A_0 + A_3\,\overline{A_2}\,\overline{A_1}\,A_0$$

This can be rewritten as follows:

$$e = (\overline{A_3})A_2\,A_1\,A_0 + (0)A_2\,A_1\,\overline{A_0} + (\overline{A_3})A_2\,\overline{A_1}\,A_0$$
$$+\; (\overline{A_3})A_2\,\overline{A_1}\,\overline{A_0} + (\overline{A_3})\overline{A_2}\,A_1\,A_0 + (0)\overline{A_2}\,A_1\,\overline{A_0}$$
$$+\; (A_3 + \overline{A_3})\overline{A_2}\,\overline{A_1}\,A_0 + (0)\overline{A_2}\,\overline{A_1}\,\overline{A_0}$$

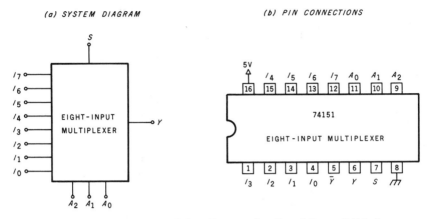

$$Y = (I_7 A_2 A_1 A_0 + I_6 A_2 A_1 \overline{A}_0 + I_5 A_2 \overline{A}_1 A_0 + I_4 A_2 \overline{A}_1 \overline{A}_0 + I_3 \overline{A}_2 A_1 A_0 + I_2 \overline{A}_2 A_1 \overline{A}_0 + I_1 \overline{A}_2 \overline{A}_1 A_0 + I_0 \overline{A}_2 \overline{A}_1 \overline{A}_0) S$$

Figure 3.34: *An eight-input multiplexer.*

Recall the equation for an eight-input multiplexer:

$$Y = (I_7)A_2 A_1 A_0 + (I_6)A_2 A_1 \overline{A}_0 + (I_5)A_2 \overline{A}_1 A_0$$
$$+ (I_4)A_2 \overline{A}_1 \overline{A}_0 + (I_3)\overline{A}_2 A_1 A_0 + (I_2)\overline{A}_2 A_1 \overline{A}_0$$
$$+ (I_1)\overline{A}_2 \overline{A}_1 A_0 + (I_0)\overline{A}_2 \overline{A}_1 \overline{A}_0$$

Comparing the last two equations shows that an eight-input multiplexer can be used to realize the necessary logic function if the following equivalences are defined:

$$Y = e$$
$$I_7 = \overline{A}_3$$
$$I_6 = 0$$
$$I_5 = \overline{A}_3$$
$$I_4 = \overline{A}_3$$
$$I_3 = \overline{A}_3$$
$$I_2 = 0$$
$$I_1 = A_3 + \overline{A}_3 = 1$$
$$I_0 = 0$$

Figure 3.35a shows such an implementation.

The logic for driving the d segment of a *common-cathode* LED display requires the realization of $\overline{d}$, which is given by

$$\overline{d} = \overline{A_0}A_1\overline{A_2}\overline{A_3} + \overline{A_0}A_1\overline{A_2}A_3 + A_0A_1\overline{A_2}A_3$$
$$+ A_0\overline{A_1}A_2\overline{A_3} + \overline{A_0}A_1A_2\overline{A_3} + \overline{A_0}\overline{A_1}\overline{A_2}A_3$$

Equivalently,

$$\overline{d} = (0)A_1A_2A_3 + (\overline{A_0})A_1A_2\overline{A_3} + (0)A_1\overline{A_2}A_3$$
$$+ (A_0 + \overline{A_0})A_1\overline{A_2}\overline{A_3} + (0)\overline{A_1}A_2A_3$$
$$+ (A_0)\overline{A_1}A_2\overline{A_3} + (\overline{A_0})\overline{A_1}\overline{A_2}A_3 + (\overline{A_0})\overline{A_1}A_2\overline{A_3}$$

Figure 3.35b shows an eight-input multiplexer realization of this logic function. Note that in this case the comparison to the multiplexer equation is somewhat trickier because the multiplexer inputs I_0 thru I_7 are generated from the A_0 factor rather than A_3. Thus, the multiplexer address inputs A_2, A_1, and A_0 are determined from the BCD digits A_1, A_2, and A_3, respectively. Also note that both A_0 and $\overline{A_0}$ are factors of $A_1\overline{A_2}\overline{A_3}$; hence, a logic 1 is provided to input I_4.

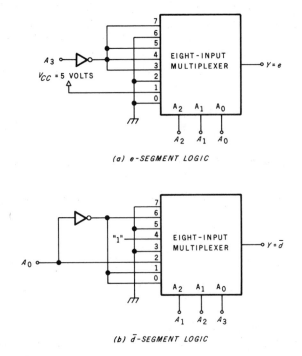

(a) e-SEGMENT LOGIC

(b) $\overline{d}$-SEGMENT LOGIC

Figure 3.35: *Multiplexers in logic design.*

Whereas a multiplexer selects one of several inputs for its one output, a demultiplexer selects one of several outputs for its one input. A system diagram for a four-output demultiplexer is shown in figure 3.36a; the truth table defining the demultiplexer appears in figure 3.36b. The demultiplexer equations are

$$O_3 = A_1 A_0 Y \bar{S}$$

$$O_2 = A_1 \bar{A_0} Y \bar{S}$$

$$O_1 = \bar{A_1} A_0 Y \bar{S}$$

$$O_0 = \bar{A_1} \bar{A_0} Y \bar{S}$$

Figure 3.36c shows the pin connections for the 74155, a dual, four-output, strobed TTL demultiplexer. The two four-output demultiplexers contained in the 74155 IC are not identical: the #1 demultiplexer is such that the selected output goes LOW when the data input is *HIGH*, whereas the #2 demultiplexer is such that the selected output goes LOW when the data input is *LOW*; thus, for both demultiplexers, the "active" output is LOW.

The 74155 can be used as an eight-output demultiplexer simply by connecting the two data inputs together (ie: pins 1 and 15) and using them as the high-order bit of the 3-bit address, and by connecting the two strobes together (ie: pins 2 and 14) and using them as the data input. Note that when the 74155 is used as an eight-output demultiplexer, there is no strobe

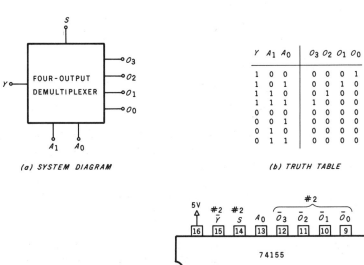

(a) SYSTEM DIAGRAM

Y	A_1	A_0	O_3	O_2	O_1	O_0
1	0	0	0	0	0	1
1	0	1	0	0	1	0
1	1	0	0	1	0	0
1	1	1	1	0	0	0
0	0	0	0	0	0	0
0	0	1	0	0	0	0
0	1	0	0	0	0	0
0	1	1	0	0	0	0

(b) TRUTH TABLE

Figure 3.36: *A four-output demultiplexer.*

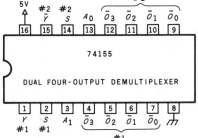

(c) PIN CONNECTIONS FOR THE 74155

input available. A sixteen-output TTL demultiplexer is available as the twenty-four-pin 74154.

Perhaps the most obvious application of a demultiplexer is in the construction of a data-multiplexing system, in which data from many sources are transmitted over one data line in a time-sharing process. Figure 3.37 shows such a data-multiplexing system, in which 4 bits of data I_0, I_1, I_2, and I_3 can be transmitted to four output locations $\overline{O}_0$, $\overline{O}_1$, $\overline{O}_2$, and $\overline{O}_3$ over a single data line by using the same synchronized addressing sequence on both the multiplexer and the demultiplexer. This alternately connects I_0 to O_0, I_1 to O_1, I_2 to O_2, and I_3 to O_3. The 4 bits of the input data word $I_3I_2I_1I_0$ can be transmitted over the 1-bit data line in the time that it takes to cycle through the four addresses 00, 01, 02, and 03. The 4-bit data word does not appear at the demultiplexer output at any one time. However, with proper provisions for storing data at the output, each bit can be stored until all 4 bits have been transmitted and the entire word has been reconstructed.

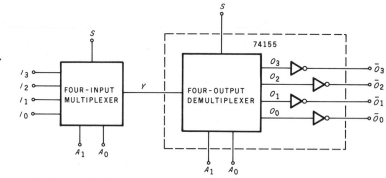

Figure 3.37: *A data-multiplexing system.*

Another important application of demultiplexers is in the construction of memory devices. Consider the construction of *read-only memory* (ROM). Figure 3.38 shows a system diagram of a 16-*byte* ROM. (A byte is 8 bits.

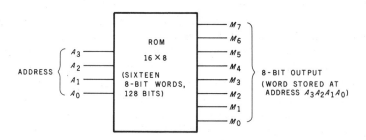

Figure 3.38: *Read-only memory (ROM) system diagram.*

Therefore, a 16-byte ROM stores sixteen 8-bit words, or 128 bits.) This ROM has four inputs, the 4-bit address that is capable of addressing any one of sixteen words, and eight outputs, the 8-bit word being addressed. A ROM is a combinational-logic system in that knowledge of all its inputs at any given time is sufficient to determine all its outputs.

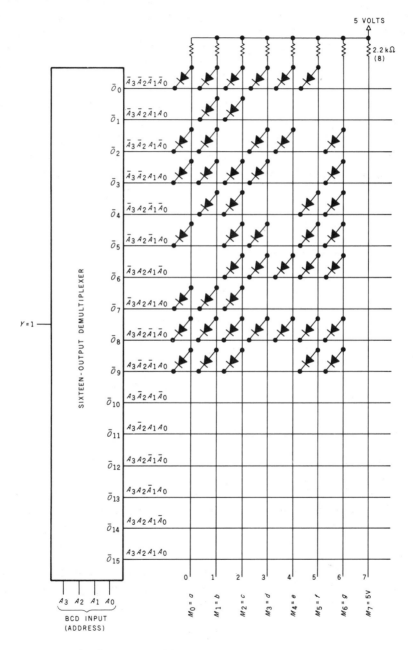

Figure 3.39: *Read-only memory (ROM) construction.*

Figure 3.39 details a typical ROM construction using a demultiplexer. A 16-byte ROM requires a sixteen-output demultiplexer. Each of the sixteen mutliplexer output lines $\overline{O_i}$, i = 0, 1,...,15, crosses the eight ROM output lines M_j, j = 0, 1,...,7. Depending upon what is stored in ROM, a diode may be connected between a demultiplexer output line and the ROM output line. With a diode present at the intersection of $\overline{O_i}$ and M_j, output M_j goes LOW whenever i is addressed; without a diode present at this intersection, M_j is HIGH whenever i is addressed. Thus, for example, if one wishes to store the 8-bit word 11100110 at address 9 (ie: at address $A_3A_2A_1A_0$ = 1001), then diodes would be placed at intersections (9,0), (9,1), (9,2), (9,5), and (9,6) as shown in figure 3.39. This particular ROM has been *loaded* (ie: the diode connections have been made), so that the ROM can be used as a BCD to seven-segment display decoder. In such an application, a portion of the 16-byte ROM is not used. Only seven outputs are required, and thus, output M_7 is not used. Also, only ten output words are required (one for each decimal digit); no use is made of the last 6 bytes of memory.

PROBLEMS

P3.1. (a) Construct a half-adder using only NANDs.
(b) Construct a half-adder using only NORs.
(c) Use the two half-adders constructed in parts (a) and (b) to construct a full-adder.

P3.2. Study a seven-segment decoder/driver (TTL 7447) and a seven-segment LED display (MAN-52 or MAN-72); see figure P3.2. Use the 8-bit switch to input to the 7447. Note that a HIGH to a 7447 input is obtained by *opening* the appropriate switch. The MAN-52 and MAN-72 are common-anode LED displays. The 7447 provides a sink for each of the seven LEDs. Use 330 Ω resistors to limit the current through the LEDs. Make a table showing the LED display pattern for each of the sixteen input combinations.

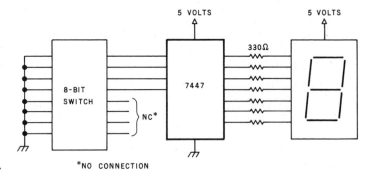

Figure P3.2.   *NO CONNECTION

P3.3.   Study a 4-bit full-adder (the TTL 7483); see figure P3.3. Use the 8-bit switch to input both 4-bit numbers. Display the sum using a seven-segment LED display; a single transistor-driven LED is used for the carry-out. Thus, the seven-segment display is used to display a *hexadecimal* digit (ie: a digit in base 16). The table which was made for problem P3.1 can be used to interpret the display.

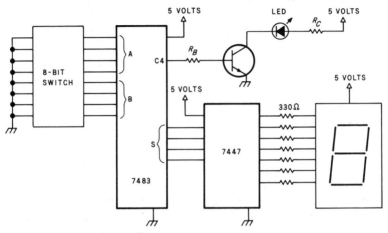

Figure P3.3.

P3.4.   Study a 4-to-1 multiplexer (the TTL 74153); see figure P3.4. Use the 8-bit switch to input both the 4-bit input and the 2-bit address. Use a transistor-driven LED to observe the multiplexer output. Try all four addresses (ie: 00,01,10, and 11) for various input combinations.

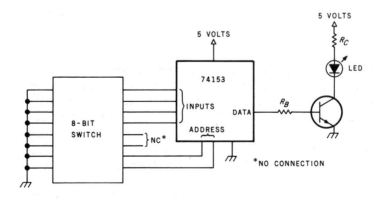

Figure P3.4.

P3.5.   Use the 4-to-1 multiplexer circuit which was constructed for problem P3.4 in the study of a 1-to-4 demultiplexer (ie: a data distributor, the TTL 74155); see figure P3.5. Use four LEDs to display the four demultiplexer outputs. Note that the LEDs light up when the corresponding output is LOW. You should be able to address any one of the four LEDs, so that it can be turned ON or OFF by a corresponding input switch.

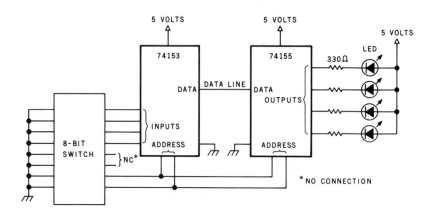

Figure P3.5.

Chapter 4

Logic Design With Integrated Circuits: Sequential Logic

Any well-formed formula of switching algebra can be realized by a combinational-logic system. For example, consider the relationship between switching variables Y and $U_1, U_2, ..., U_m$ defined by the equation

$$Y = F(U_1, U_2, ..., U_m)$$

where F defines a well-formed formula of switching algebra which can be realized by a combinational-logic system having m inputs $U_1, U_2, ..., U_m$, and one output Y (see figure 4.1).

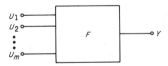

Figure 4.1: *System of combinational logic implementing a logic function defined by* $Y = F(U_1 U_2, ..., U_m)$.

A combinational-logic system is a *static* system in the sense that time plays absolutely no role in the relationship between the inputs and the outputs, ie: the output values at any given time can always be determined from only the input values at that time; neither the time at which the inputs are applied nor the history of the system, in terms of past values of system variables, is a factor in determining outputs. Thus, combinational-logic systems have no *memory* in the sense that the outputs of a combinational-logic system are always uniquely defined in terms of the system's present inputs, and memory for storing past values of system variables is not required.* However, there are important digital *dynamic* systems in which events of the past influence the present to the extent that the output values at any given time cannot be determined from only the input values at that time.

As an example of a digital dynamic system, consider the *binary clock* shown in figure 4.2. This binary clock is a single-input, single-output digital system, whose output X is a periodic pulse sequence (with pulse width $T/2$ and period T) which begins any time t_0 the clock input U goes HIGH. Clearly, knowing the value of the input U at any given time is not sufficient information from which to determine the output X. Therefore, there is no combinational-logic system that can realize the binary clock.

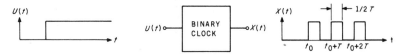

Figure 4.2: *A binary clock.*

The *binary counter* is another important dynamic digital system in which time plays an essential role. The binary counter is a single-input, multi-output system in which the combination of output values at any time is a binary-coded representation of the count of input pulses received up until that time. The highest count possible for a binary counter with n outputs is $2^n - 1$. Figure 4.3 shows a three-output binary counter which counts from 0 to 7 and then starts at 0 again (ie: a divide-by-8 counter or a 3-bit counter). Again, knowing the value of the input U at any given time is not sufficient information from which to determine the value of the outputs X_0, X_1, and X_2 at that time. Therefore, a counter cannot be realized by any combinational-logic system.

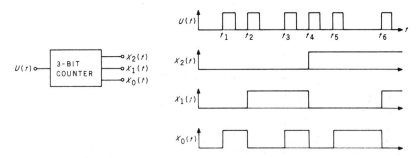

Figure 4.3: *A 3-bit binary counter (ie: a divide-by-8 counter).*

---

*Interestingly, in this sense, ROM memory (figure 3.37) is not really memory. The ROM output is determined only by its structure (ie: the location of the diodes) and its present inputs. What ROM remembers is where the diodes are placed. Clearly, all combinational-logic systems have memory in the sense that they remember how they are structured.

4.1   Sequential Logic

Both the binary clock and the binary counter are examples of digital systems in which the input/output (I/O) relationships that apply at any given time depend upon sequences of past events. In neither of these two systems can one determine the value of the outputs at any given time from a knowledge of only the input value at that time. A system in which events of the past influence the present (and therefore the future) is called a *dynamic system*. A *digital* dynamic system is called a *sequential-logic* system in that sequences of past events influence the sequence of future events.

For the binary clock, because the input U is used to turn the clock ON, the output X is LOW if the input U is LOW. However, the output X is also LOW for one-half of each cycle when U is HIGH and the clock is running. Thus, the binary-clock output can be LOW with the input either LOW or HIGH. Clearly, at any given time, the binary clock output depends not only upon the input value at that time, but also upon past values of the output.

For the binary counter, the outputs at any given time are determined not only by the input value at that time, but also by the entire input sequence received until that time. However, because the set of outputs represents the input count up to that time, the outputs provide a summary of the entire input sequence sufficient to determine the effect of the next pulse on the outputs. Therefore, to determine the effect of the next input pulse, it is not necessary to know the entire input history (ie: the time at which every past input pulse occurred). Rather, it is sufficient to know the present count, as reflected by the present state of the outputs. Clearly, for the binary counter, any combination of output values is possible with the input either HIGH or LOW.

Switching algebra, which is so well suited for the modeling of combinational-logic systems, is also a powerful tool in the modeling of sequential-logic systems. But, because the outputs of sequential-logic systems depend upon the values of system variables at times other than the present, a time index must be associated with each switching variable. Both the binary clock and the binary counter are easily modeled in terms of switching algebra. For the binary clock, t_0 is defined as the last instant of time that the input U switched from LOW to HIGH (ie: the time when the last *rising edge* of input U occurred). Thus,

$$X(t) = \overline{X}(t - T/2) \cdot U(t) \qquad t > t_0$$

For the binary counter, the sequence $t_1, t_2, \ldots$ is defined such that t_k (where k is a positive integer) is the instant of time at which the k-th input pulse is initiated (ie: the time when the rising edge of the k-th input pulse occurs); it is not necessary for the time intervals between successive input pulses to be equal (ie: in general, $(t_k - t_{k-1}) \neq (t_{k+1} - t_k)$). Thus,

$$X_0(t_k + \delta_k) = X_0(t_k) \oplus U(t_k) = \overline{X}_0(t_k) \text{ since } U(t_k) = 1 \text{ by definition of } t_k$$

$$X_1(t_k + \delta_k) = X_1(t_k) \oplus X_0(t_k)$$

$$X_2(t_k + \delta_k) = X_2(t_k) \oplus (X_1(t_k) \cdot X_0(t_k))$$

where t_k = time when the k-th input pulse is initiated, $t_{k+1} > t_k$, and $0 < \delta_k < t_{k+1} - t_k$. Thus, the time $t_k + \delta_k$ refers to an instant of time after the k-th input pulse has occurred, but before the $(k + 1)$-th input pulse occurs.

In sum, a sequential-logic system is a system in which the outputs are not only a function of the values of the present inputs, but also of the past values of system variables. This dependency of the present values of system variables upon past values of system variables implies that sequential-logic systems contain *memory cells*, in which appropriate values of switching variables can be stored for use in determining future outputs.

4.1.1   Memory

The *digital T-Delay* is a fundamental memory cell that is useful in the implementation of sequential-logic systems (see figure 4.4). The most general

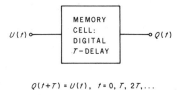

Figure 4.4: *Fundamental memory cell: the digital T-Delay.*

T-Delay device is a single-input, single-output system such that, at any given time, the value of the output is simply the value that the input was T seconds ago: ie, the output is the input *delayed*, or *stored*, for T seconds, so that

$$Q(t + T) = U(t)$$

However, an important simplification is made in defining the *digital T*-Delay. Namely, time is defined only for *discrete* instants $t_0, t_1, t_2, \ldots$. For example, the discrete instants could be $0, T, 2T, \ldots$, where each discrete instant corresponds to the tick of a periodic clock with period T (eg: the binary clock of figure 4.2; the ticks could be defined as the rising edges of the output pulses). For all that follows, a periodic time discretization is assumed. Thus, the digital *T*-Delay operates in *synchronism* with a clock; it responds to one and only one input value every T seconds and transmits one and only one output value every T seconds. Importantly, at any given time, the digital T-Delay is never storing more than 1 bit of data. Most digital systems are synchronous systems, in which all the system logic gates switch only at periodic intervals, in synchronism with a system clock. Clearly, the digital T-Delay is a sequential-logic system in that its output at any given time cannot be determined from its input at that time.

The *strobed-memory cell*, shown in figure 4.5a, is somewhat different from the digital T-Delay in that it has two inputs. In addition to the input U, which carries the value to be stored in the memory cell, there is a second input called the *strobed input S*. The strobe input serves to enable or disable the memory cell depending upon whether or not the stored value Q is to be changed to correspond to the present input value U. Again, time is discrete; the strobed-memory cell, like the T-Delay, is driven by a periodic clock, and the strobed signal S is allowed to change only at discrete times 0, T, $2T,...$. The operation of the strobed-memory cell is such that setting the strobe input S HIGH, at time t, causes the output to follow the input U, ie: if $S(t) = 1$, then the next value of the output, $Q(t + T)$, will be set to the present value of the input $U(t)$. On the other hand, setting the strobe S LOW prevents the output from changing, regardless of the input U; ie: if $S(t) = 0$, then the next value of the output, $Q(t + T)$, is the same as the present value, $Q(t)$. In terms of switching algebra,

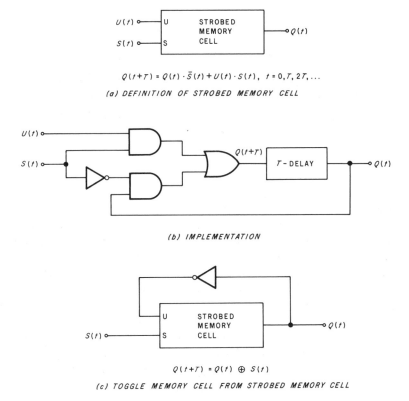

$$Q(t+T) = Q(t) \cdot \bar{S}(t) + U(t) \cdot S(t), \quad t = 0, T, 2T, ...$$

(a) DEFINITION OF STROBED MEMORY CELL

(b) IMPLEMENTATION

$$Q(t+T) = Q(t) \oplus S(t)$$

(c) TOGGLE MEMORY CELL FROM STROBED MEMORY CELL

Figure 4.5: *Strobed memory cell.*

$$Q(t + T) = Q(t) \cdot \overline{S}(t) + U(t) \cdot S(t) \qquad t = 0, T, 2T, \ldots$$

Because the value of the output at time $t + T$ depends upon the past output, $Q(t)$, and the past inputs, $U(t)$ and $S(t)$, the strobed-memory cell is also a sequential-logic device. The strobed-memory cell can be easily constructed by interconnecting a digital T-Delay and four simple combinational-logic gates, as shown in figure 4.5b.

The *toggle* is a useful memory cell which can be constructed from a strobed-memory cell simply by connecting the output Q to the input U, as shown in figure 4.5c. In this case, $Q(t) = U(t)$, and

$$Q(t + T) = Q(t) \oplus S(t)$$

Thus, in a toggle, the next value of Q is the exclusive OR of the present values of Q and S. Equivalently, and more descriptively, Q will change from its present value whenever the present value of S is HIGH, ie: a HIGH S *toggles* the output.

A binary counter can be constructed by using either strobed-memory cells or toggle-memory cells (see figure 4.6). The equations for this synchronous binary counter are

$$\left.\begin{array}{l} X_0(t + T) = X_0(t) \oplus U(t) \\ X_1(t + T) = X_1(t) \oplus X_0(t) \\ X_2(t + T) = X_2(t) \oplus (X_1(t) = X_0(t)) \end{array}\right\} \quad t = 0, T, 2T, \ldots$$

Because this binary counter is constructed with synchronous clock-driven memory cells, it is necessary that an input pulse be HIGH during the rising edge of a clock pulse, if that input pulse is to be counted. Also, so that a wide pulse will not be counted more than once, the width of each input pulse must be less than T seconds long. If wide input pulses are expected, an *edge-trigger* circuit can be used to narrow the pulses (see figure 4.17); an edge-trigger circuit outputs one narrow pulse for every input pulse, regardless of the width of the input pulse.

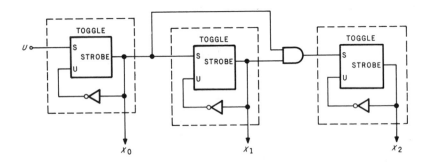

Figure 4.6: *Implementation of a binary counter.*

4.1.2   State

In sum, a sequential-logic system is a digital system in which at least one system variable depends upon past values of system variables. For a general sequential-logic system with inputs $U_1, U_2, ..., U_m$ and outputs $Y_1, Y_2, ..., Y_p$, the *state-transition equations* are

$$Q_1(t + T) = F_1(U_1(t), U_2(t), ..., U_m(t), Q_1(t), Q_2(t), ..., Q_n(t))$$

$$Q_2(t + T) = F_2(U_1(t), U_2(t), ..., U_m(t), Q_1(t), Q_2(t), ..., Q_n(t))$$

$$\vdots$$

$$Q_n(t + T) = F_n(U_1(t), U_2(t), ..., U_m(t), Q_1(t), Q_2(t), ..., Q_n(t))$$

$$Y_1(t) = G_1(U_1(t), U_2(t), ..., U_m(t), Q_1(t), Q_2(t), ..., Q_n(t))$$

$$Y_2(t) = G_2(U_1(t), U_2(t), ..., U_m(t), Q_1(t), Q_2(t), ..., Q_n(t))$$

$$\vdots$$

$$Y_p(t) = G_p(U_1(t), U_2(t), ..., U_m(t), Q_1(t), Q_2(t), ..., Q_n(t))$$

where $Q_1, Q_2, ..., Q_n$ are the system variables whose values must be stored to determine the future outputs; $F_1, F_2, ..., F_n$ and $G_1, G_2, ..., G_p$ are switching-algebra functions defined either by well-formed switching-algebra formulas or by truth tables (thus, each function defines a combinational-logic system). Figure 4.7 shows a block diagram representation of such a system.

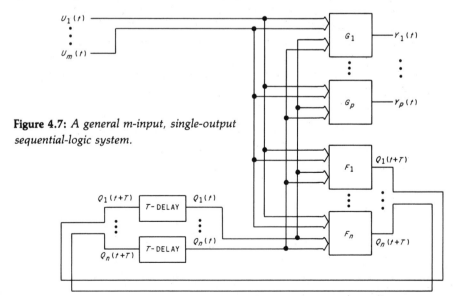

Figure 4.7: *A general m-input, single-output sequential-logic system.*

The set of n stored variables $Q_1, Q_2, ..., Q_n$ is called the *state* of the system; a variable Q_i, $i = 1, 2, ..., n$, that is a component of the state is called a *state variable*. In a sequential-logic system, there is one memory cell associated with each state variable. Therefore, the system's state is associated with the system's memory. Thus, the system's state represents a summary of the system's past, which, with knowledge of the system's inputs, is sufficient to uniquely determine the system's outputs. For the binary clock, the output X is a state variable (and is also the state); for the 8-bit counter, the set of output variables X_0, X_1, and X_2 make up the system's state.

4.1.3 Sequential Logic versus Combinational Logic

Dynamic relationships between switching variables, in which *time* is an essential factor, cannot be implemented without the use of memory devices. Therefore, in any inherently dynamic situation, a sequential-logic design is unavoidable. On the other hand, a combinational-logic system can always be replaced by a sequential-logic system, provided that a time delay can be tolerated between the time the inputs are applied and the time the outputs are generated.

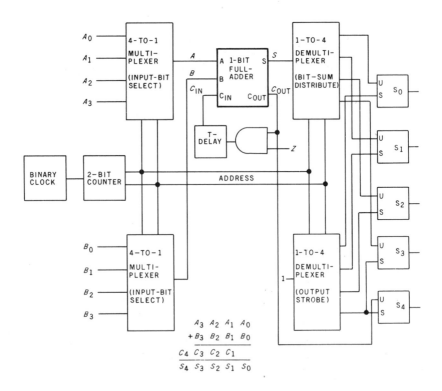

Figure 4.8: *Sequential-logic design of a four-bit full-adder using only one full-adder.*

Consider the implementation of an n-bit full-adder. Using combinational logic, an implementation of an n-bit full-adder can be realized using n 1-bit full-adders. Figure 3.15 shows a combinational-logic implementation of a 4-bit full-adder using four 1-bit full-adders. Clearly, the size of such an implementation increases in direct proportion to n. Importantly, in the combinational-logic implementation of an n-bit full-adder, the n 1-bit full-adders create a repetitive space pattern. During the operation of the combinational-logic n-bit full-adder, all n 1-bit full-adders operate simultaneously, or in *parallel*. The question that ought to be raised is whether or not an n-bit full-adder can be designed in which a *single* 1-bit full-adder is used to execute an appropriate *sequence* of operations. For an n-bit full-adder, it is a simple matter to define a sequence of 1-bit additions that would execute the n-bit addition, eg: the "0" bits are added first (ie: add A_0 and B_0 to obtain S_0 and C_0), then the "1" bits are added to the carry bit from the sum of the "0" bits (ie: add A_1 and B_1 to C_0 to obtain S_1 and C_1), and so forth. By defining an n-bit addition as a sequence of 1-bit additions, a trade-off between computing time and hardware is possible.

A sequential-logic implementation of the n-bit full-adder can be realized using only one 1-bit full-adder. However, in addition to the one 1-bit full-adder, a sequential-logic implementation requires $n + 1$ memory cells and a considerable amount of combinational logic for controlling the sequence of data to and from the only 1-bit full-adder. A sequential-logic implementation of a 4-bit full-adder, in which only one 1-bit full-adder is used, is shown in figure 4.8. This system operates as follows:

1. At time $t = -T$, the input to the T-Delay memory cell must be set LOW. This insures that the carry-in C_{in} will be 0 when the process starts at $t = 0$. This *zeroing* of the T-Delay can be achieved using an AND gate as shown: set $Z = 0$ at $t = -T$; thereafter set $Z = 1$.
2. At some time $t < 0$, say $t = -T$, the two 4-bit numbers to be added, $A_3A_2A_1A_0$ and $B_3B_2B_1B_0$, are applied as inputs to the two multiplexer terminals. These inputs are held constant throughout the addition process which starts at $t = 0$ and is $4T$ seconds long.
3. At time $t = 0$, the clock is turned ON. The clock, having a period T, drives the binary counter. Thus, the counter outputs, which are used to address the two multiplexers and the two demultiplexers, cycle through the sequence 00, 01, 10, 11 every $4T$ seconds. The following sequence of operations, making up the 4-bit addition process, now begins:

    (a) At $t = 0$: The inputs to the 1-bit full-adder are $A(0) = A_0$, $B(0) = B_0$, and $C_{in}(0) = C_0 = 0$. The sum $S(0) = S_0$ is stored in strobed-memory cell S_0. The carry-out $C_{out}(0) = C_1$ is the input to the T-Delay.
    (b) At $t = T$: The inputs to the 1-bit full-adder are $A(t) = A_1$, $B(T) = B_1$, $C_{in}(T) = C_1$. The sum $S(T) = S_1$ is stored in strobed-memory cell S_1. The carry-out $C_{out}(T) = C_2$.

(c)   At $t = 2T$: $A(2T) = A_2$, $B(2T) = B_2$, and $C_{in}(2T) = C_2$; $S(2T) = S_2$ is stored in memory cell S_2, and $C_{out}(2T) = C_3$.

(d)   At $t = 3T$: $A(3T) = A_3$, $B(3T) = B_3$, and $C_{in}(3T) = C_3$; $S(3T) = S_3$ is stored in memory cell S_3, and $C_{out}(3T) = C_4$ goes to memory cell S_4.

During the final period of the addition process (ie: from $t = 3T$ to $t = 4T$), the 5-bit sum of the two 4-bit numbers, $A_3A_2A_1A_0$ and $B_3B_2B_1B_0$, appears as the output of the memory cells S_4, S_3, S_2, S_1, and S_0. If the sum is to be used at some later time, the output demultiplexer used to strobe the bit-sum memory cells should be disabled during the final period by setting its input to 0. This would keep the sum S in the $S_4S_3S_2S_1S_0$ memory cells thereafter. Another possibility is to transfer the sum to another set of memory cells during this period. This would free the 4-bit adder for further use.

If a combination-logic design, as shown in figure 4.9a, contains many identical combinational-logic subsystems F in a loop-free interconnection, then a sequential-logic implementation can be realized using only one implementation of the subsystem F (see figure 4.9b). In the case of a 4-bit adder, where the repeated subsystem F is a 1-bit full-adder, replacing the combinational-logic 4-bit adder (ie: the 4-bit *parallel* adder) by the sequential-logic 4-bit adder (ie: the 4-bit *serial* adder) is obviously not worthwhile. The amount of hardware used in the combinational-logic implementation of the 4-bit adder (ie: the four 1-bit full-adders) is considerably less than the amount of hardware required to control the flow of data through the one 1-bit adder in the sequential-logic implementation. However, it is not difficult to imagine a situation in which the subsystem F is so enormously large and complex that the sequential-logic implementation is more economical. For example, in a typical general-purpose digital computer, which is a sequential-logic system, a highly sophisticated *arithmetic/logic unit* (ALU) is used repetitively to solve arithmetic and logic problems sequentially and, thus, the need for having many arithmetic/logic units operating in parallel is avoided.

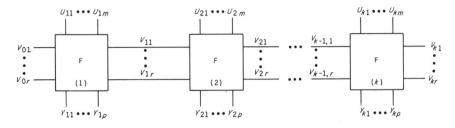

(a) COMBINATIONAL LOGIC (ie: PARALLEL LOGIC)

Figure 4.9: *Combinational logic versus sequential logic.*

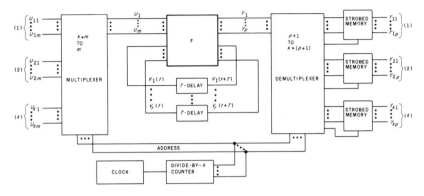

(b) SEQUENTIAL LOGIC

Figure 4.9 cont.

4.1.4 General-Purpose Sequential-Logic Systems: Introduction to Programming

In any system of combinational logic, the outputs are uniquely defined for every possible combination of input values and, thus, the relationship between each output and the inputs can be completely defined by either a truth table or a well-formed switching-algebra formula. Consider the case of a combinational-logic system having one output Y and m inputs U_1, $U_2, ..., U_m$ as shown in figure 4.1 and modeled by the equation

$$Y = F(U_1, U_2, ..., U_m)$$

where F defines a well-formed formula of switching algebra involving the input variables $U_1, U_2, ..., U_m$ and the AND, OR, and NOT operators $\bullet$, $+$, and $\overline{}$. Such a well-formed formula represents at least one sequence of operations on the variables $U_1, U_2, ..., U_m$ which, when executed, results in the evaluation of Y. Such a well-defined executable sequence of operations is called a *program*.

To illustrate the relationship between a well-formed formula and a program for evaluating the formula, consider the specific formula

$$Y = (\overline{U_1} + \overline{U_2} + U_3) \bullet U_4 \bullet U_2 \bullet \overline{U_3}$$

The correct value of Y can be obtained by executing the following sequence of operations:

Sequence 1:

(a) $V_1 = \overline{U_2}$ (ie: negate $\overline{U_2}$ and call the negation V_1)
(b) $V_2 = U_1 + V_1$
(c) $V_3 = V_2 + U_3$
(d) $V_4 = \overline{V_3}$
(e) $V_5 = V_4 \cdot U_4$
(f) $V_6 = V_5 \cdot U_2$
(g) $V_7 = \overline{U_3}$
(h) $Y = V_6 + V_7$

Sequence 1 corresponds to the interconnection of primitive-logic gates shown in figure 4.10a; each operation in the sequence corresponds to a primitive-logic gate in the interconnection, and vice versa. However, sequence 1 is not the only sequence that will give the correct value of Y, eg:

Sequence 2:

(a) $V_1 = U_1 + U_3$
(b) $V_2 = \overline{U_2}$
(c) $V_3 = V_1 + V_2$
(d) $V_4 = \overline{V_3}$
(e) $V_5 = V_4 \cdot U_4$
(f) $V_6 = V_5 \cdot U_2$
(g) $V_7 = \overline{U_3}$
(h) $Y = V_6 + V_7$

Sequence 2 corresponds to the interconnection of primitive-logic gates shown in figure 4.10b. Clearly, although a well-formed formula of switching algebra $Y = F(U_1, U_2, ..., U_m)$ defines a unique value Y for each combination of variable values $U_1, U_2, ..., U_m$, a well-formed formula does not define a unique sequence of operations for evaluating the value Y.

Reverse Polish notation (RPN) provides a format for writing well-formed formulas of switching algebra in such a way that the sequence of operations (ie: the program) for evaluating the formula is uniquely specified. For example, in RPN the formula representing sequence 1 is

$$Y = U_2 \sim U_1 + U_3 + \sim U_4 U_2 U_3 \sim + \qquad (4.1)$$

The character string on the right-hand side of the equation defines the sequence. The character string is interpreted as follows: Start at the left of the string and scan to the right until the first operator is encountered. If a NOT operator (the symbol $\sim$) is encountered, simply negate the variable im-

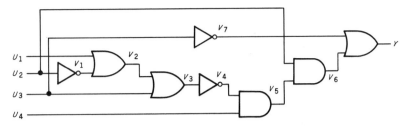

(a) INTERCONNECTION CORRESPONDING TO SEQUENCE 1

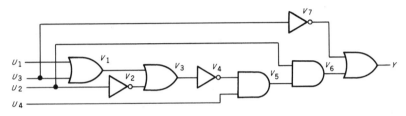

(b) INTERCONNECTION CORRESPONDING TO SEQUENCE 2

Figure 4.10: *Implementations of* $Y = (U_1 + \overline{U_2} + U_3) \cdot U_4$.

mediately to the left of the operator, then replace that variable and the NOT operator with a variable representing the negated value, and thus obtain a shortened string; if an AND or OR operator is encountered, AND or OR the two variables immediately to the left of the AND or OR operator, then replace the two variables and the AND or OR operator with a variable representing the result of the AND or the OR, and again obtain a shortened string. The process is then repeated, ie: scan the shortened string from left to right, and so forth. The process is repeated until only one variable remains; this variable represents the value of the evaluated formula. (This notation is called *reverse* because the operation follows the two operators in the formula. It is called *Polish* because, apparently, few people can remember either how to pronounce or spell the originator's name, J. Leikasawitz.)

Applying this process to equation (4.1) results in the following sequence:

(a) $Y = U_2 \sim U_1 + U_3 + \sim U_4 U_2 U_3 \sim +$

(b) $Y = V_1 U_1 + U_3 + \sim U_4 U_2 U_3 \sim +$ $\qquad V_1 = \overline{U_2}$

(c) $Y = V_2 U_2 + \sim U_4 U_2 U_3 \sim +$ $\qquad V_2 = V_1 + U_1$

(d) $Y = V_3 \sim U_4 U_2 U_3 \sim +$ $\qquad V_3 = V_2 + U_3$

(e) $Y = V_4 U_4 U_2 U_3 \sim +$ $\qquad V_4 = \overline{V_3}$

(f) $Y = V_5 U_2 U_3 \sim +$ $\qquad V_5 = V_4 \cdot U_4$

(g) $Y = V_6 U_3 \sim +$ $\qquad V_6 = V_5 \cdot U_2$

(h) $Y = V_6 V_7 +$ $\qquad V_7 = \overline{U_3}$

(i) $Y = Y$ $\qquad Y = V_6 + V_7$

Note that the above sequence corresponds to sequence 1. Similarly, sequence 2 can be represented in RPN by

$$Y = U_1 U_3 + U_2 \sim + \sim U_4 U_2 U_3 \sim + \qquad (4.2)$$

It is possible to design a sequential-logic system that will execute any defined sequence of logical operations. Since RPN provides concise descriptions of sequences of logical operations, it can serve as a basis for the design of such a system. Moreover, a concise notation for defining sequences, such as reverse Polish notation, is especially important in the design of universal sequential-logic systems which can be used in the evaluation of *any* switching-algebra formula. In such systems, the values of the variables to be used in the evaluation of the formula and, also, the inputs defining the sequence of operations to be executed must be provided.

4.1.4.1 Design of Sequential-Logic Systems from Sequences

To design a sequential-logic system, it is necessary to specify the desired output sequence for each of the possible input sequences. For an m-input system in which the input sequences are k bits long, the number of different input sequences possible is 2^{km}. Clearly, as k or m gets large, an exhaustive listing of output sequences corresponding to each input sequence becomes impractical. Furthermore, the fact that the output sequence of a sequential-logic system depends not only upon the input sequence, but also upon the system's initial state, increases the dimension of the problem. However, the state-transition equations provide a concise description of the I/O relationships of a sequential-logic system; that is, the output sequence resulting from the application of any input sequence can be generated from the state-transition equations. For example, if the initial value $X(0)$ is given, the state-transition equation

$$X(t + T) = S(t) + \bar{S}(t) \cdot \bar{R}(t) \cdot X(t)$$

can be used to generate the output sequence $X(T)$, $X(2T)$,... for any combination of input sequences $R = R(0)$, $R(T)$, $R(2T)$,... and $S = S(0)$, $S(T)$, $S(2T)$,... The values $X(0)$, $R(0)$, and $S(0)$ are sufficient to generate $X(T)$; the values $X(T)$, $R(T)$, and $S(T)$ are sufficient to generate $X(2T)$; and so forth.

When the state-transition equation is given, the sequential design is straightforward. To illustrate, the above state-transition equation can be rewritten as follows:

$$V(t) = S(t) + \bar{S}(t) \cdot \bar{R}(t) \cdot X(t)$$

$$X(t + T) = V(t)$$

By introducing the new system variable $V(t)$, the state-transition equation is split into two equations: the first equation can be implemented by a

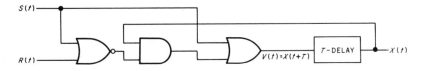

Figure 4.11: *Implementation of* $X(t + T) = S(t) + \overline{S}(t) \cdot \overline{R}(t) \cdot X(t)$.

combinational-logic system; the second equation can be implemented by a digital T-Delay. Figure 4.11 shows such an implementation. Thus, once a description of the output sequences has been obtained in the form of state-transition equations, the sequential-logic design problem reduces to a combinational-logic design problem. Incidentally, this particular sequential-logic system is a fundamental digital circuit commonly known as the *set-reset flip-flop* (also known, somewhat incongruously, as the RS flip-flop).

Although state-transition equations can be derived to describe any sequence of operations, it is not often easy to do so. For example, again consider the sequence defined by the RPN formula given in equation (4.2), ie:

$$Y = U_1 U_3 + U_2 \sim + \sim U_4 U_2 U_3 \sim +$$

The sequence defined by this formula (ie: sequence 2) is rewritten in table 4.1. However, in this version the time argument is introduced to index the variables to denote the time at which each operation is executed.

$$X(0) = U_1$$
$$X(T) = U_3$$
$$X(2T) = X(0) + X(T)$$
$$X(3T) = \overline{U_2}$$
$$X(4T) = X(2T) + X(3T)$$
$$X(5T) = \overline{X(4T)}$$
$$X(6T) = X(5T) \cdot U_4$$
$$X(7T) = X(6T) \cdot U_2$$
$$X(8T) = \overline{U_3}$$
$$Y = X(9T) = X(7T) + X(8T)$$

Table 4.1: *The sequence corresponding to* $Y = U_1 U_3 + U_2 \sim + \sim U_4 U_2 U_3 \sim +$

Examination of this sequence reveals that although the value of X at any given time is a function of past values of X, this dependency never goes back further than the last two values of X, ie: although $X(t + 2T)$ is a function of $X(t + T)$ and $X(t)$, $X(t + 2T)$ can be determined without knowing $X(t - T)$, $X(t - 2T)$, and so forth. Thus, only two memory cells are required for the implementation of a sequential-logic system which generates the sequence $X(0)$, $X(T)$, $X(2T)$,..., $X(9T)$. Specifically, two T-Delays can store the values $X(t + T)$ and $X(t)$ until they are used at time $t + 2T$ to determine $X(t + 2T)$. However, unlike the binary counter and the set-reset flip-flop, this sequence of operations for evaluating a formula of switching algebra has no discernible repetitive pattern, and a concise state-transition equation characterization of the sequence is not possible. The difficulty stems from the fact that the relationship between $X(t + 2T)$ and the set of variables $X(t)$, $X(t + T)$, U_1, U_2, U_3, and U_4 varies with time, eg: at $t = 0$, $X(0) = U_1$; at $t = T$, $X(T) = U_3$; at $t = 2T$, $X(2T) = X(0) + X(T)$; etc. Clearly, there is no discernible pattern to indicate how the operations vary. Thus, it is difficult to obtain a characterization of this sequence that is more concise than an exhaustive listing of the sequence. Compare this to the sequence defined for an n-bit full-adder where the same 1-bit addition process is repeated n times. Nevertheless, state-transition equations generating sequence 2, though not elegant and concise, can be written. The sequence can be characterized by an equation of the form

$$X(t + 2T) = F(X(t), X(t + T), U_1, U_2, U_3, U_4, t)$$

It is significant that $X(t + 2T)$ is a function of time t, as well as $X(t)$, $X(t + T)$, and U_1, U_2, U_3, and U_4. Specifically,

$$\begin{aligned}
X(t + 2T) = {} & (X(t) + X(t + T)) \cdot T_0(t) + \overline{U_2} \cdot T_1(t) \\
& + (X(t) + X(t + T)) \cdot T_2(t) + \overline{X}(t + T) \cdot T_3(t) \\
& + (X(t + T) \cdot U_4) \cdot T_4(t) + (X(t + T) \cdot U_2) \cdot T_5(t) \\
& + \overline{U_3} \cdot T_6(t) + (X(t) + X(t + T)) \cdot T_7(t) \quad\quad (4.3)
\end{aligned}$$

where T_i, $i = 0, 1,..., 7$, is a switching variable, such that

$$T_i(t) = \begin{cases} 1, \text{ for } t = iT \\ 0, \text{ otherwise} \end{cases} \quad i = 0, 1, 2, 3, 4, 5, 6, 7$$

Because the variables $X(t)$ and $X(t + T)$ must be known at the time $X(t + 2T)$ is evaluated, they comprise the state of the sequential-logic system generating the sequence $X(0)$, $X(T)$,..., $X(9T)$. In addition to the two memory cells required to store $X(t)$ and $X(t + T)$, a multiplexer addressed by a clock-driven counter is also used in the sequential-logic implementation. Figure 4.12 shows such an implementation. A_2, A_1, and A_0 are the multiplexer address inputs. Thus,

$$T_0(t) = \overline{A_2}(t) \cdot \overline{A_1}(t) \cdot \overline{A_0}(t)$$
$$T_1(t) = \overline{A_2}(t) \cdot \overline{A_1}(t) \cdot A_0(t)$$
$$T_2(t) = \overline{A_2}(t) \cdot A_1(t) \cdot \overline{A_0}(t)$$

.
.
.

The last operation in the sequence is defined as

$$Y = X(9T) = X(7T) + X(8T)$$

The solution Y appears as the system output only during the ninth clock period, starting at $t = 9T$. If it were necessary to save Y for use at a later time, it could be stored in a strobed-memory cell by making $X(t)$ an input of the strobed-memory cell and strobing the cell at some time t during the ninth clock period such that $9T < t < 10T$. Equation (4.3) can be written in the standard state-transition form (see section 4.1.2) by defining

$$X_D(t) = X(t + T)$$

Thus,

$$X_D(t + 2T) = X(t + 3T)$$

and the state-transition equations follow:

$$X(t + T) = X_D(t)$$
$$X_D(t + T) = (X(t) + X_D(t) \cdot T_0(t) + U_2 \cdot T_1(t) + (X(t) + X_D(t)) \cdot T_2(t)$$
$$+ \overline{X_D}(t) \cdot T_3(t) + (X_D(t) \cdot U_4) \cdot T_4(t) + (X_D(t) \cdot U_2) \cdot T_5(t)$$
$$+ (\overline{U_3}) \cdot T_6(t) + (X(t) + X_D(t)) \cdot T_7(t)$$

for $t = 0, 1T, ..., 9T$.

Figure 4.10b shows a combinational-logic implementation for evaluating the formula $Y = U_1U_3 + U_2 \sim + \sim U_4U_2U_3 \sim +$. Of course, no sequence results from a combinational-logic implementation; the output is the correct value of Y for as long as the correct inputs are applied. In terms of computing the value of Y, the combinational-logic circuit is considerably faster than the corresponding sequential-logic circuit. In the combinational-logic circuit, the delay between the time that the inputs are applied and the time that the correct output appears is determined only by the switching times of the logic gates being used. For example, if TTL gates are used, the total delay is on the order of 60 nanoseconds: each gate has a response time of approximately 10 nanoseconds, and the longest cascade of gates between input and output is six. In the sequential-logic implementation, the clock period T determines the delay between the application of the inputs and the appearance of the output. In this case, where the sequence is of length 10, the delay is $9T$. The shortest clock period T that can be used is determined by the maximum delay one expects to encounter in executing the necessary combination-logic functions at each time $0, T, 2T, ...$. A safety margin must be included to insure that the proper state has been reached during one period before beginning the next transition.

Clearly, the combinational-logic system results in a faster circuit than the sequential-logic system. Furthermore, just a glance at the combinational-

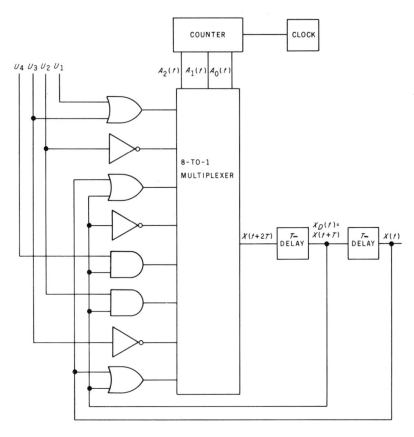

Figure 4.12: *Sequential-logic implementation of a sequence defined by*
$Y = U_1U_3 + U_2 \sim + \sim U_4U_2U_3 \sim +$.

logic system of figure 4.10b and the sequential-logic system of figure 4.12 reveals that the combinational-logic system is considerably simpler. In fact, all eight gates used in the combinational-logic system are also used in the sequential-logic system. In addition, the sequential-logic system includes a multiplexer, two digital T-Delays, a counter, and a clock. In such a comparison, little can be said in favor of the use of the sequential-logic system for evaluating a switching-algebra formula. However, if a sequential-logic system could be realized in which only one AND gate, one OR gate, and one NOT gate were used in the evaluation of *any* switching-algebra formula, then for large systems, the balance could shift in favor of a sequential-logic design.

4.1.4.2   A Programmable General-Purpose Sequential-Logic System

The main drawback in the sequential-logic design of figure 4.12 is that each of the eight primitive-logic gates used in the evaluation of Y is used only once during the sequence of operations. For example, the OR gate, which executes the operation $X(0) + X(T)$ at time $t = 2T$, is not used at any other time. Importantly, this OR gate is idle at the times $t = 4T$ and $t = 9T$, when other OR gates are executing the operations $X(2T) + X(3T)$ and $X(7T) + X(8T)$, respectively. Because no two of the eight logic gates are used simultaneously, it is possible to design a general-purpose sequential-logic system such that the same primitive-logic gate is used at any time such a logic gate is needed.

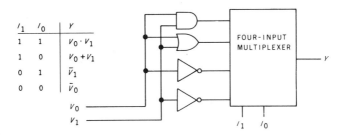

I_1	I_0	Y
1	1	$V_0 \cdot V_1$
1	0	$V_0 + V_1$
0	1	$\bar{V}_1$
0	0	$\bar{V}_0$

Figure 4.13: *A central-logic-unit (CLU) implementation of a universal-logic function.*

The main component in the design of a general-purpose sequential-logic system is a controlled two-input, one-output *logic unit*, ie: the *central logic unit (CLU)*. The CLU, on the basis of control signals applied to it, outputs either the AND or the OR of its two inputs, or the NOT of one of them. A *universal logic function* suitable for implementation as a CLU follows:

$$Y = I_1 I_0 (V_0 \cdot V_1) + I_1 \bar{I}_0 (V_0 + V_1) + \bar{I}_1 I_0 (\overline{V_1}) \text{ or } \bar{I}_1 \bar{I}_0 (\overline{V_0})$$

or, equivalently,

$$Y = \begin{cases} V_0 \cdot V_1 & \text{if } I_1 I_0 = 1 \ 1 \\ V_0 + V_1 & \text{if } I_1 I_0 = 1 \ 0 \\ \overline{V_1} & \text{if } I_1 I_0 = 0 \ 1 \\ \overline{V_0} & \text{if } I_1 I_0 = 0 \ 0 \end{cases}$$

A combinational-logic implementation of this function is shown in figure 4.13. The remainder of the general-purpose sequential-logic system is designed to control the flow of data to and from the CLU.

Clearly, a sequential-logic system capable of evaluating *any* switching-algebra formula must have inputs which include not only the values of the variables in the formula (eg: U_1, U_2, U_3, or U_4), but also all the information necessary to define the sequence of operations to be performed by the CLU.

One possibility is to provide a set of inputs, equivalent to the RPN formula, which defines the sequence. For example, a binary-coded equivalent of the RPN formula of equation (4.2) is the *P-array* shown in figure 4.14. Note that the RPN formula can be reconstructed from the P-array simply by starting in the first row, proceeding down the table, and reading I_1, I_0, and U in each row. Each row is decoded as follows: $I_1 I_0 = 11$ means AND; $I_1 I_0 = 10$ means OR; $I_1 I_0 = 01$ means NOT and is applied to original input data preceding it in the string; $I_1 I_0 = 00$ also means NOT but is applied to the result of the last logic operation*; # is ignored.

i	I_1	I_0	U
*	#	#	U_1
**	#	#	U_3
0	1	0	U_2
1	0	0	#
2	1	0	#
3	0	1	U_4
4	1	1	U_2
5	1	1	U_3
6	0	0	#
7	1	0	#

Figure 4.14: *The P-array corresponding to* $Y = U_1 U_3 + U_2 \sim + \sim U_4 U_2 U_3 \sim +$.

In terms of a sequential-logic implementation, each row of the P-array, starting with the $i = 0$ row, corresponds to a primitive-logic operation; the i-th row corresponds to the operation performed at time iT. A method for decoding the P-array that leads to an efficient sequential-logic implementation is now detailed:

1. Define U_D as U delayed by T, ie:

$$U_D(t + T) = U(t)$$

2. Define X_D as X delayed by T, ie:

$$X_D(t + T) = X(t)$$

---

*Note that in terms of reconstructing the RPN formula, it is not necessary to distinguish between a NOT on original data and a NOT on the result of a previous operation. However, in terms of an implementation of a general-purpose sequential-logic system, this distinction is quite useful.

3. Set the initial values of the variables V_0 and V_1 in accordance with the first two rows of the P-array:

$$V_0(0) = X(0) = U_1$$
$$V_1(0) = X_D(0) = X(T) = U_3$$

Table 4.2 shows the sequence of operations defined for the central logic unit by each row of the P-array. The solution Y is $X(9T)$, the last term in the

i	t	V_0-SELECT S	P-ARRAY I_1	I_0	U	SEQUENCE OF OPERATIONS
			#	#	U_1	$X(0) = V_0(0) = U_1$ $\Big\backslash$ INITIALIZE INPUTS
			#	#	U_3	$X(T) = V_1(0) = U_3$ $\Big/$ TO CLU
0	0	1	1	0	U_2	$X(2T) = X(T) + X(0)$
1	T	0	0	0	#	$X(3T) = \bar{U}(0),\ U(0) = U_2$
2	$2T$	1	1	0	#	$X(4T) = X(3T) + X(2T)$
3	$3T$	1	0	1	U_4	$X(5T) = X(4T)$
4	$4T$	0	1	1	U_2	$X(6T) = X(5T) \cdot U(3T),\ U(3T) = U_4$
5	$5T$	0	1	1	U_3	$X(7T) = X(6T) \cdot U(4T),\ U(4T) = U_2$
6	$6T$	0	0	0	#	$X(8T) = \bar{U}(5T),\ U(5T) = U_3$
7	$7T$	1	1	0	#	$Y = X(9T) = X(8T) + X(7T)$

Table 4.2: *The sequence of operations defined by the P-array.*

sequence $X(0)$, $X(T)$,..., $X(9T)$. Note that this is the same sequence previously obtained (table 4.1). Examination of this sequence reveals that the CLU operations at any time t are either $X(t + T) \cdot X(t)$, $X(t + T) \cdot U(t - T)$, $X(t + T) + X(t)$, $X(t + T) + U(t - T)$, $\overline{X(t + T)}$, or $\overline{U}(t - T)$. It is significant that the CLU is always operating on either one or two of the three values $X(t + T)$, $X(t)$, and $U(t - T)$. Also, except for the one case in which only the single value $U(t - T)$ is operated upon, the CLU always operates on the value $X(t + T)$. A fairly simple design results from defining the $V_1(t)$ input of the CLU to be always $X(t + T)$. A switching arrangement can then be used to set the $V_0(t)$ input of the CLU to either $X(t)$ or $U(t - T)$. To implement such a switching arrangement, a *select variable S*, which will be used to select the V_0 input to the CLU, is defined:

$$S = \begin{cases} 1 & \text{if } V_0(t) = X(t) \\ 0 & \text{if } V_0(t) = U(t - T) \end{cases}$$

Thus, at any given time, the select variable S determines whether or not the operation being executed by the CLU includes original input data (ie: $U(t - T)$) or is based only upon results of previous operations (ie: $X(t)$ and $X(t + T)$). The truth table of table 4.3 defines how, at any time t, the CLU

$S(t)$	$I_1(t)$	$I_0(t)$	$V_1(t)$	$V_0(t)$	$X(t+2T)$
1	1	1	$X(t+T)$	$X(t)$	$X(t+T) \cdot X(t)$
1	1	0	$X(t+T)$	$X(t)$	$X(t+T) + X(t)$
1	0	1	$X(t+T)$	$X(t)$	$\bar{X}(t+T)$
1	0	0	$X(t+T)$	$X(t)$	$\bar{X}(t)$
0	1	1	$X(t+T)$	$U(t-T)$	$X(t+T) \cdot U(t-T)$
0	1	0	$X(t+T)$	$U(t-T)$	$X(t+T) + U(t-T)$
0	0	1	$X(t+T)$	$U(t-T)$	$\bar{X}(t+T)$
0	0	0	$X(t+T)$	$U(t-T)$	$\bar{U}(t-T)$

Table 4.3: *Defining the CLU inputs and operations in terms of control signals $S(t)$, $I_1(t)$, and $I_0(t)$.*

operation to be executed and the CLU inputs are determined from the values $I_1(t)$, $I_0(t)$, and $S(t)$. The P-array and the resulting sequence of operations defined in table 4.2 provide the basis for the implementation of a *programmable* general-purpose sequential-logic system that can be used to evaluate *any* switching-algebra formula. Such a system is shown in figure 4.15. Note

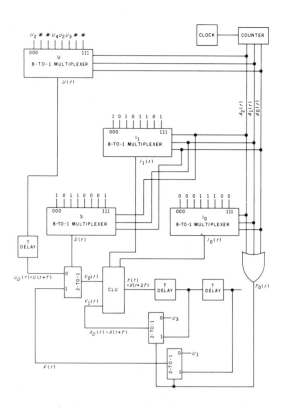

Figure 4.15: *A programmable sequential-logic system.*

that the binary-coded RPN formula derived from the P-array forms the input of the three multiplexers U, I_1, and I_0; a fourth multiplexer S provides the select signals. Thus, at time t, the variables $I_1(t)$ and $I_0(t)$ define the operation being executed by the CLU, while the select signal $S(t)$ determines whether the CLU input $V_0(t)$ is to be $U(t - T)$ or $X(t)$. Note that the two 2-to-1 multiplexers are used to set the initial values on the CLU inputs. This corresponds to the first two rows of the array in table 4.2. These multiplexers are addressed by $T_0(t)$, which is 0 only when $t = 0$.

4.2 Clock Structures

Most sequential-logic systems, including virtually all digital computers, are synchronous systems and require a clock signal. In this section, several approaches to the design of clocks are considered.

A simple clock can be constructed using four TTL inverters (eg: the 7404 IC package contains six TTL inverters), as shown in figure 4.16a. This interconnection, like the comparable interconnection of figure 3.3 in which three inverters are in a loop, is unstable. No combination of voltage levels in the loop simultaneously satisfies all three inverters. As a result, the inverters are in a continuous transient state, and oscillations result. This simple clock

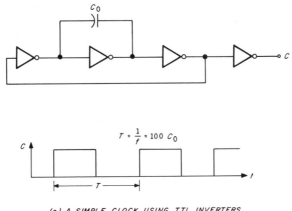

(a) A SIMPLE CLOCK USING TTL INVERTERS

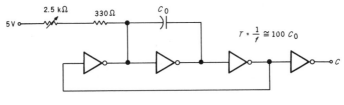

(b) A VARIABLE SIMPLE CLOCK

Figure 4.16: *Simple TTL clocks.*

gives a rather clean waveform and is suitable in applications where a precise frequency is not required. The following formula can be used for selecting the approximate value of the capacitor C_0 in terms of the clock period T:

$$C_0 = \frac{T}{100}$$

Thus, for example, if a clock period of 1 millisecond is required, the above formula indicates that a capacitor of 10 μF should be used for C_0.

For situations in which clock frequency must be more precisely controlled, the addition of a variable resistor, as shown in figure 4.16b, proves helpful. By varying the variable resistor, the frequency of the clock signal can be varied within a small range of the frequency computed for the clock of figure 4.16a. The main disadvantage of the clock structures of figures 4.16a and 4.16b is that they are not well-suited to generating low-frequency clock signals. For example, if a frequency of 100 Hz is required, a capacitor of 100 μF must be used for C_0. Unfortunately, most reasonably priced capacitors of 1 μF or more are electrolytic capacitors which can be used only in situations where the polarity of voltage across the capacitor never changes. In these simple TTL clock structures, the polarity of the voltage across the capacitor alternates during each clock period and, thus, regardless of how the capacitor is placed in the circuit, the polarity constraint of an electrolytic capacitor will be violated.

For many applications, it is important to generate clock signals with narrow clock pulses. Figure 4.17a shows a simple circuit that can be used to convert clock signals with wide pulses to clock signals with narrow pulses. This circuit generates narrow clock pulses coincident with the *rising edges* (ie: the positive edges) of the original clock signal; hence, it is called a *positive-edge triggered* pulse generator. Figure 4.17b shows the waveforms generated. Narrow clock pulses coincident with the *falling edges* (ie: the negative edges) of the original clock signal can be generated with the same circuit by first inverting the clock signal, as shown in figure 4.17c. For both circuits, the width of the generated clock pulses is approximately two-thirds of the time constant. Thus, for the case that $C = 500$ pF and $R = 330$ Ω, the width of the output pulses is approximately 100 nanoseconds.

Perhaps the most widely used IC in the construction of clocks and other timing devices is the eight-pin 555 timer. Because of its widespread acceptance, the 555 timer is widely available at low cost. Some insight into the operation of the 555 timer can be obtained from the block diagram of figure 4.18. In this diagram, the numbers within the small squares correspond to the pin numbers of the eight-pin DIP housing the 555 timer.

(a) POSITIVE-EDGE TRIGGERED PULSE GENERATOR

Figure 4.17: *Edge-triggered pulse generators.*

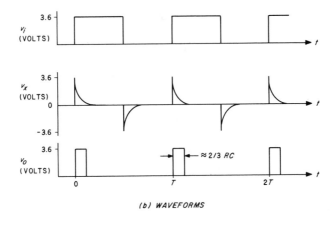

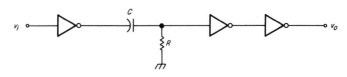

(b) WAVEFORMS

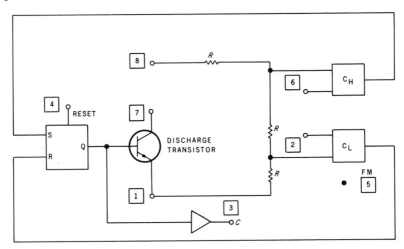

(c) NEGATIVE-EDGE TRIGGERED PULSE GENERATOR

Figure 4.17 cont.

The two blocks marked C_H and C_L in figure 4.18 are *analog comparators*. Although a study of the operation of the analog comparator is beyond the scope of this text, the function of the analog comparator is simple and easily

Figure 4.18: *The 555 timer.*

described. For the comparator shown in figure 4.19, the input voltages v_1 and v_2 are analog voltages; the comparator output V_0 is a digital output (ie: a HIGH or a LOW). The relationship between the output V_0 and the inputs v_1 and v_2 is such that

$$V_0 = \begin{cases} \text{HIGH} & \text{if } v_1 \geq v_2 \\ \text{LOW} & \text{if } v_1 < v_2 \end{cases}$$

The two analog comparators C_H and C_L in the 555 timer are of this type. Specifically, comparator C_H is such that when the voltage on pin 6 is greater than two-thirds the voltage on pin 8, its output is HIGH; comparator C_L is such that when the voltage on pin 2 is less than one-third the voltage on pin 8, its output is HIGH.

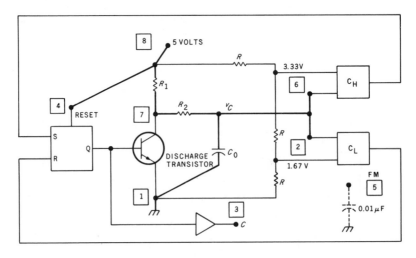

Figure 4.19: *An analog comparator.*

To construct a clock using the 555 timer, external components must be connected to it. One possibility for a clock design is shown in figure 4.20a; the external components and connections are shown in boldface. In this configuration, whenever voltage v_C is less than 1.67 V, the output of C_L

(a) CONSTRUCTION

Figure 4.20: *A 555 timer-based clock.*

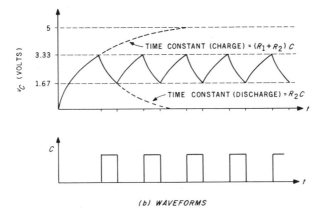

(b) WAVEFORMS

Figure 4.20 cont.

goes HIGH, Q is set LOW, and the discharge transistor is cut OFF. This initiates the charging of capacitor C_0 through resistors R_1 and R_2. The charging continues until v_C goes above 3.33 V. At this point, C_H goes HIGH, Q is set HIGH, and the discharge transistor turns ON. This initiates the discharge of capacitor C_0 through R_2 and the collector-to-emitter path of the discharge transistor to ground. When the voltage v_C again drops below 1.67 V, the charge-discharge cycle is repeated. Figure 4.20b shows the waveforms on pin 2 (voltage v_C) and on pin 3 (the clock signal C); capacitor C is initially uncharged (ie: $v_C(0) = 0$).

Note that an electrolytic capacitor can be used for capacitor C_0 because one terminal of the capacitor C_0 is connected to ground, and because the voltage v_C on the other terminal is always positive with respect to ground. The following formulas can be used to select the external components for the clock configuration of figure 4.20a:

Period: $\qquad\qquad\qquad T = 0.685(R_1 + 2R_2)C_0$

Frequency: $\qquad\qquad\qquad f = \dfrac{1}{T}$

Duty Cycle: $\dfrac{\text{Time HIGH}}{\text{Time LOW}} = \dfrac{R_1 + R_2}{R_2}$

Charge Time: $\qquad\qquad T_C = 0.685(R_1 + R_2)C_0$ $\left.\rule{0pt}{40pt}\right\}$ $T = T_C + T_D$

Discharge Time: $\qquad\qquad T_D = 0.685\,R_2C_0$

The following limits on component values should be observed:

$[R_1 + R_2]_{max} = 3.3\ \mathrm{M\Omega}$

$[R_1]_{min} = [R_2]_{min} = 1\ \mathrm{k\Omega}$

$$[C_0]_{min} = 500 \text{ pF}$$

$[C_0]_{max}$ is determined by the quality of the capacitor (ie: by the leakage currents). Note that electrolytic capacitors may be used.

An extremely stable and precise clock-signal source is provided by a *crystal-controlled clock*. Certain crystals, such as quartz, exhibit the *piezoelectric* effect. When a piezoelectric crystal is physically stressed, as for example by applying forces to its surfaces, a voltage is generated between its surfaces. Conversely, when a voltage is applied across two surfaces of a piezoelectric crystal, the crystal becomes physically stressed. Thus, in a piezoelectric crystal, physical stress can generate voltages, and voltages can generate physical stress. Figure 4.21a shows a graphical representation of a piezoelectric crystal. In the same way that the physical dimensions of a tuning fork determine the frequency at which the tuning fork will vibrate after being struck, the dimensions to which a crystal is cut determine the frequency at which the crystal will vibrate after a force impulse (or, importantly, a voltage impulse) is applied to it. However, because mechanical vibrations are the result of varying internal stresses, a piezoelectric crystal produces an oscillatory voltage across its surfaces when it is vibrating. Because the vibration frequency of a crystal is determined by the physical characteristics of the crystal (mass, dimensions, mounting, etc) and is relatively insensitive to temperature variations, a piezoelectric crystal provides an extremely stable frequency source.

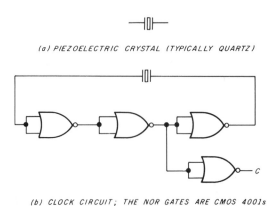

(a) PIEZOELECTRIC CRYSTAL (TYPICALLY QUARTZ)

(b) CLOCK CIRCUIT; THE NOR GATES ARE CMOS 4001s

Figure 4.21: *A crystal-controlled clock.*

Crystal vibrations, caused by physical or electrical excitation, eventually die out due to friction. If a crystal is to be used as the source of a stable clock frequency, a method must be devised to sustain the vibrations. There are many circuits used to sustain crystal vibrations. The basic principle underlying all these circuits is the *regenerative-feedback* principle, in which oscillations in the crystal itself control the frequency at which the crystal takes energy from the circuit to sustain the vibrations. Figure 4.21b shows a simple circuit for a crystal-controlled clock. This circuit operates in the range of 0.5 to 10 MHz, and the frequency is stable to within 0.2 percent, even with power supply variations up to 50 percent and with temperature variations from $-50\,°C$ to $+70\,°C$. Note that the NOR gates are from the CMOS 4001 (quad NOR). Therefore, one should be careful in loading this clock. With parallel inputs, as shown, this clock can drive one regular TTL load.

4.3 Memory

Sequential-logic systems differ from combinational-logic systems in that sequential-logic systems have memory. This section shows how various memory devices can be constructed by interconnecting simple combinational-logic gates. *Two-state* logic devices are fundamental in the construction of memory devices. In a two-state device, it is possible for at least one output to be either in the LOW or the HIGH state for at least one input combination, ie: at any given time, knowledge of the input values is not sufficient information from which to determine the outputs.

4.3.1 Debounced Switch

An ordinary switch consists of two metal contacts which can be brought together to complete a circuit path. Consider the circuit shown in figure 4.22a containing switch S. With switch S open, voltage v_o is 0 V; with switch S closed, voltage v_o is 5 V. Figure 4.22b shows the waveform of voltage v_o for the case that switch S is an *ideal switch*. Real switches, however, do not respond quite like this. When the two hard metallic surfaces that make up the switch contacts are brought together with a finite velocity, *bounce* occurs, and the circuit closes and opens several times before a stable closed circuit is finally achieved. A waveform, typical of what might be observed at V_o when a real switch S is thrown closed, is shown in figure 4.22c. The duration and frequency of the switch bounce depends upon the physical characteristics of the particular switch being used; 5 to 50 milliseconds is typical for the duration of switch bounce.

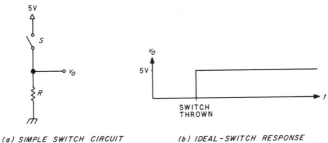

(a) SIMPLE SWITCH CIRCUIT   (b) IDEAL-SWITCH RESPONSE

Figure 4.22: *Switch bounce.*

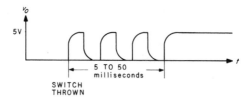

(c) REAL-SWITCH RESPONSE

Figure 4.22 cont.

For many applications, the existence of switch bounce is of little consequence. However, in certain applications, particuarly where counting is involved, switch bounce cannot be tolerated. In such cases, the switch must be electronically *debounced*. Figure 4.23a shows one possibility for debouncing a switch. This debounced switch utilizes a two-position switch (ie: a single-pole double-throw (SPDT) switch). Note the presence of the two-state logic circuit formed by the two inverters in a loop. In this circuit, if the output voltage v_o is HIGH, it can be made LOW only by touching the

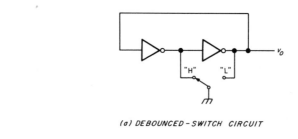

(a) DEBOUNCED-SWITCH CIRCUIT

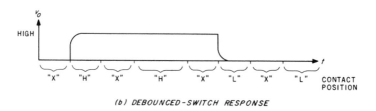

(b) DEBOUNCED-SWITCH RESPONSE

Figure 4.23: *Debouncing a switch.*

switch blade to contact "L"; similarly, if v_o is LOW, it can be made HIGH only by touching the switch blade to contact "H." Importantly, breaking contact with "L" does not result in v_o going HIGH, and breaking contact with "H" does not result in v_o going LOW. As a result the effect of switch bounce is not observed at v_o. Figure 4.23b shows the waveform of voltage v_o as the switch is thrown alternately from position "H " to position "X" (denoting that the switch blade is somewhere between contacts "H" and "L," but touching neither), then to position "L."

4.3.2 Two-State Logic

A simple two-state logic device can be realized by connecting two inverters in a loop, as shown in figure 4.24a. This two-state logic circuit, similar to that used in the construction of the debounced switch, has two mechanical inputs S and R (the two single-pole single-throw (SPST) switches) and two electrical outputs Q and θ. Consider the case in which both switches S and R are of the type that are *normally* open, ie: each switch is always in the "O" position unless a force is applied to it; therefore, push to close and release to open. *Assuming that both switches are never closed at the same time,* the circuit remembers which switch was the last to be closed: if switch S is the last to be closed, then Q is *set* to 1; if switch R is the last to be closed, then Q is *reset* to 0. Therefore, this circuit is a fundamental 1-bit memory cell. If $S \cdot R \neq 1$ (ie: if both switches are not closed simultaneously), then the output $\theta = \overline{Q}$.

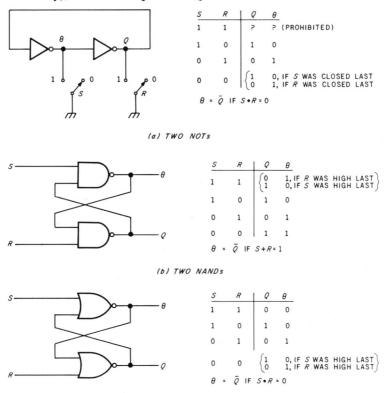

(a) TWO NOTs

(b) TWO NANDs

(c) TWO NORs

Figure 4.24: *Examples of two-state logic.*

If both switches are closed simultaneously, then both the input and the output of the two inverters are forced LOW, and the NOT relationship that the inverters are trying to maintain is violated. In fact, if TTL inverters (eg: 7404s) are used in this circuit, closing both switches simultaneously could destroy the inverters. Specifically, grounding the inverter input turns ON the upper transistor Q_4 of the totem-pole output (see figure 2.19e). However, with the inverter output also grounded, transistor Q_4 conducts maximum collector-to-emitter current, in effect vainly trying to charge a short-circuited capacitive load. As seen in figure 2.21, during the LOW-to-HIGH transition, a current spike with a peak of approximately 30 mA occurs when transistor Q_4 is trying to charge an uncharged capacitive load. With the output grounded, this peak current is maintained on a continuous basis and can very well burn out one of the components in that current path.

The possibilities for designing two-state logic circuits for use as primitive-memory cells are endless. Figures 4.24b and 4.24c show two two-state logic circuits, made from interconnections of NANDs and NORs, respectively. These two circuits differ from the two-state circuit made from an interconnection of inverters (figure 4.24a), in that the inputs S and R are electrical rather than mechanical. Thus, these circuits are suitable for use as memory cells in high-speed applications, as are typical in a digital computer. Unlike the interconnection of inverters, there are no input combinations that can cause the gates in these circuits to burn out. However, the $S = 0$, $R = 0$ combination for the NAND interconnection, and the $S = 1$, $R = 1$ combination for the NOR interconnection should be avoided if Q and θ are to be inverses of each other. But, if it is not necessary for Q and θ to be inverses of each other, these input combinations need not be avoided.

4.3.3   Flip-Flop

A *flip-flop* is a 1-bit memory cell. The essential property of a flip-flop is that it is a two-state logic device, ie: for at least one input combination there are two possible output states. It is common for flip-flops to have two outputs, and for one output to be the inverse of the other. Some of the most widely used flip-flop types are introduced in the following sections.

4.3.3.1   RS Flip-Flop

The *RS flip-flop* (or the *set-reset flip-flop*) is a two-input, two-output device defined by the truth table in figure 4.25. The essential characteristic of the RS flip-flop is that it remembers which of its two inputs, S or R, was the last to be HIGH; the two inputs are never allowed to go HIGH simultaneously. Because the output responds to input changes whenever the inputs are applied, this RS flip-flop is called an *asynchronous flip-flop*.

Synchronous flip-flops respond to input changes only in synchronism with a clock input C, and are appropriate for use in clocked systems (ie: in

S	R	Q	$\bar{Q}$
1	1	DISALLOWED	
1	0	1	0
0	1	0	1
0	0	$\begin{Bmatrix} 1 \\ 0 \end{Bmatrix}$	$\begin{matrix} 0 \text{, IF } S \text{ WAS HIGH LAST} \\ 1 \text{, IF } R \text{ WAS HIGH LAST} \end{matrix}$

Figure 4.25: *An asynchronous RS flip-flop.*

synchronous systems). Figure 4.26a shows how a synchronous RS flip-flop can be constructed from an asynchronous flip-flop and two AND gates; figure 4.26b shows a typical representation of a synchronous RS flip-flop; and figure 4.26c shows how a synchronous RS flip-flop can be implemented with four NAND gates. The synchronous flip-flop remembers which of the two inputs, S or R, was the last to be HIGH in synchronism with a HIGH clock input C. Thus, the state of the synchronous RS flip-flop output can be changed only by applying inputs while the clock is HIGH.

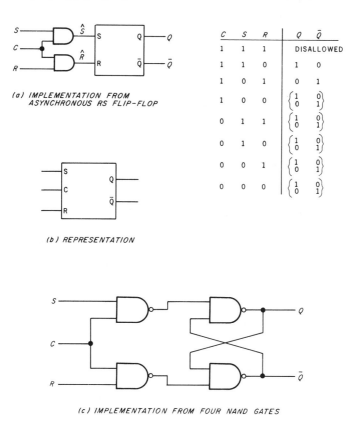

(a) IMPLEMENTATION FROM
ASYNCHRONOUS RS FLIP-FLOP

C	S	R	Q	$\bar{Q}$
1	1	1	DISALLOWED	
1	1	0	1	0
1	0	1	0	1
1	0	0	$\begin{Bmatrix} 1 \\ 0 \end{Bmatrix}$	$\begin{Bmatrix} 0 \\ 1 \end{Bmatrix}$
0	1	1	$\begin{Bmatrix} 1 \\ 0 \end{Bmatrix}$	$\begin{Bmatrix} 0 \\ 1 \end{Bmatrix}$
0	1	0	$\begin{Bmatrix} 1 \\ 0 \end{Bmatrix}$	$\begin{Bmatrix} 0 \\ 1 \end{Bmatrix}$
0	0	1	$\begin{Bmatrix} 1 \\ 0 \end{Bmatrix}$	$\begin{Bmatrix} 0 \\ 1 \end{Bmatrix}$
0	0	0	$\begin{Bmatrix} 1 \\ 0 \end{Bmatrix}$	$\begin{Bmatrix} 0 \\ 1 \end{Bmatrix}$

(b) REPRESENTATION

(c) IMPLEMENTATION FROM FOUR NAND GATES

Figure 4.26: *A synchronous RS flip-flop.*

Figure 4.27a is a timing diagram which shows the waveforms of the various signals of the synchronous RS flip-flop (figure 4.26a). This timing diagram shows the flip-flop's response to a particular sequence of inputs, R and S, for the case that the clock signal is a periodic pulse train having

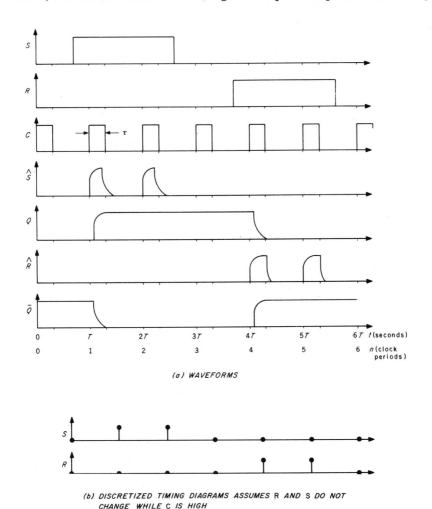

(a) WAVEFORMS

(b) DISCRETIZED TIMING DIAGRAMS ASSUMES R AND S DO NOT CHANGE WHILE C IS HIGH

$S(t)$	$R(t)$	$Q(t+T)$
1	1	X (DISALLOWED)
1	0	1
0	1	0
0	0	$Q(t)$

(c) TRUTH TABLE

Figure 4.27: *Synchronous RS flip-flop timing.*

period T and pulse width τ. Neither of the flip-flop inputs, S or R, is permitted to change during any time interval in which the clock C is HIGH, ie:

$$\left.\begin{array}{l} S(nT + d) = S(nT) \\ R(nT + d) = R(nT) \end{array}\right\} \; d < \tau, n = 1, 2,...$$

If the inputs R and S do not change while the clock C is HIGH, then a simple sequential model of the synchronous RS flip-flop can be obtained by agreeing to observe all input and output signals only at the discrete times 0, T, $2T$,... (ie: only during the *rising*, or *positive edges* of the clock pulses). A timing diagram showing the discretized input and output signals is shown in figure 4.27b. For the discretized model, the relationship between the inputs and the outputs of the RS flip-flop is straightforward and is summarized in the truth table of figure 4.27c. Therefore,

$$Q(t + T) = S(t) \cdot \overline{R}(t) + \overline{S}(t) \cdot \overline{R}(t) \cdot Q(t) + x \cdot S(t) \cdot R(t)$$

where $t = nT$
$\qquad n = 0, 1, 2,...$

Because we do not allow $S(t)$ and $R(t)$ to be HIGH simultaneously (ie: $S(t) \cdot R(t) \neq 1$), the above expression can be simplified further:

$$Q(t + T) = S(t) + \overline{S}(t) \cdot \overline{R}(t) \cdot Q(t)$$

where $S(t) \cdot R(t) \neq 1$
$\qquad t = nT$
$\qquad n = 0, 1, 2,...$ \hfill (4.4)

The time index of a switching-algebra variable is often denoted in the variable subscript rather than in the variable argument. For example, the value of variable Q at time nT can be denoted by Q_n instead of by $Q(nT)$. Thus, equation (4.4), characterizing the RS flip-flop, can be written as

$$Q_{n+1} = S_n + \overline{S}_n \cdot \overline{R}_n \cdot Q_n$$

where $S_n R_n \neq 1$

4.3.3.2 D Flip-Flop (T-Delay)

A device producing a delay of one clock period T is called a *D flip-flop* (or a *T-Delay*). Figure 4.28a shows a representation of a D flip-flop and gives the defining truth table. Thus, for the D flip-flop,

$$Q_{n+1} = D_n$$

Therefore, a D flip-flop stores an input bit for T seconds before outputting

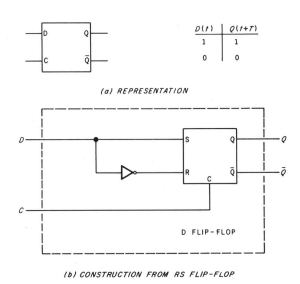

(a) REPRESENTATION

(b) CONSTRUCTION FROM RS FLIP-FLOP

Figure 4.28: *D flip-flop (T-Delay).*

it. A D flip-flop is easily constructed from an RS flip-flop (see figure 4.28b). It is easy to verify that this construction realizes a D flip-flop; for the RS flip-flop,

$$Q_{n+1} = S_n + \overline{S_n} \cdot \overline{R_n} \cdot Q_n$$

Since $S_n = D_n$ and $R_n = \overline{D_n}$, it follows that

$$Q_{n+1} = D_n + \overline{D_n} \cdot D_n \cdot Q_n$$

Therefore, since $\overline{D_n}D_n = 0$,

$$Q_{n+1} = D_n$$

4.3.3.3   Master-Slave Flip-Flop and Edge-Triggered Flip-Flops

Because equation (4.4) is derived from the timing diagram of figure 4.27b, this equation is a valid model of the synchronous RS flip-flop only if the inputs S and R do not change while the clock is HIGH. Specifically, because the inputs are observed only at the discrete times corresponding to the positive edge of the clock pulse, it is possible for input changes occurring after the positive edge of the clock pulse, and while the clock is still HIGH, to produce output changes which are not predictable from the *observed* inputs.

When a synchronous RS flip-flop, such as that of figure 4.26, is used in a cascade of similar flip-flops, it is not possible to guarantee that its inputs, which are generated by the other flip-flops, will not change while the clock is HIGH. For example, consider the two cascaded synchronous RS flip-flops of figure 4.29. If equation (4.4) were applicable to both flip-flops, then the following input/output (I/O) relationships would apply:

$$Q_1(t + T) = U(t)$$
$$Y(t + T) = Q_1(t)$$

and the relationship between the cascade input and the cascade output would be

$$Y(t + 2T) = U(t)$$

However, it is unlikely that this relationship, which indicates a delay of $2T$ seconds between input and output, would apply for the cascaded flip-flops. As can be seen from the waveforms in figure 4.27a, the outputs of the first flip-flop, Q_1 and $\overline{Q_1}$, which are the inputs to the second flip-flop, S_2 and R_2, may complete their transitions before the clock signal C goes LOW. If this were to occur, the relationship between the input and output would be

$$Y(t + T) = U(t)$$

and a delay of only T seconds would exist between the input and output of the cascaded flip-flops. In this event, a *race* condition is said to exist, in which the response to an input propagates through the cascade during a single clock pulse. In long cascades involving many such flip-flops, an input would start to propagate down the cascade on the rising edge of a clock pulse and continue down the cascade until the clock went LOW. The switching delays of the logic gates used in constructing the individual flip-flops would determine the number of flip-flops in the cascade that would be affected by an input during one clock pulse. There are many important applications of flip-flops that require them to be cascaded, and in these cases race conditions must be avoided.

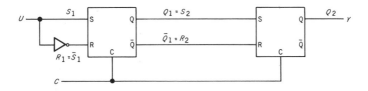

Figure 4.29: *Cascading synchronous flip-flops.*

The *RS master-slave flip-flop*, designed to eliminate the possibility of race conditions, is always well modeled by the synchronous RS flip-flop model given by equation (4.4), regardless of the digital-logic network in which the flip-flop is used. Figure 4.30a shows how an RS master-slave flip-flop can be constructed from two simple RS flip-flops; figure 4.30b shows a D master-slave flip-flop constructed from two simple D flip-flops. The important feature of the master-slave flip-flop is that its outputs Q and $\overline{Q}$ cannot change unless the clock C is LOW. The master flip-flop can respond to input changes occurring only when the clock C is HIGH; the slave flip-flop can respond to input changes only when the clock C is LOW. Thus, race conditions are impossible, and regardless of how master-slave flip-flops are cascaded, equation (4.4) always provides a valid model for each flip-flop.

Because the output of a master-slave flip-flop does not change while the clock is HIGH, it provides a suitable input for other flip-flops. However, there is a serious problem in modeling the master-slave flip-flop when its inputs change while the clock is HIGH. This generally occurs when the inputs are generated by external sources which are not constrained by the clock. If the inputs change while the clock is HIGH, equation (4.4) is not a valid model of the flip-flop.

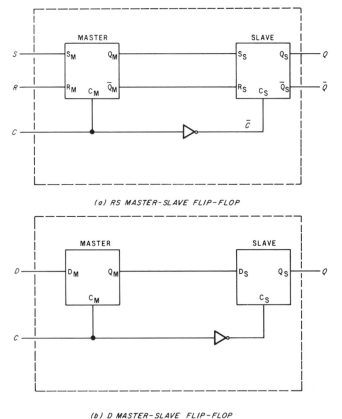

(a) RS MASTER-SLAVE FLIP-FLOP

(b) D MASTER-SLAVE FLIP-FLOP

Figure 4.30: *Master-slave and edge-triggered flip-flops.*

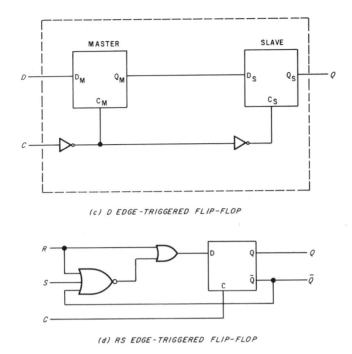

(c) D EDGE-TRIGGERED FLIP-FLOP

(d) RS EDGE-TRIGGERED FLIP-FLOP

Figure 4.30 cont.

Equation (4.4) indicates that the flip-flop will be set or reset on the basis of the values of the inputs S and R during the positive clock edge. This is true, however, only if the inputs do not change after the positive clock edge while the clock is HIGH. In fact, since the master flip-flop can respond to inputs only while the clock is HIGH, the slave flip-flop sets or resets on the basis of the master flip-flop's output values during the negative clock edge. However, the master flip-flop's outputs during the negative clock edge are determined by whether the last input, coincident with a HIGH clock, was a set or a reset. An exception to this occurs in situations where the master flip-flop's inputs change immediately before the negative clock edge occurs, and the switching delays of the logic gates making up the master flip-flop are sufficiently long to keep the output from changing before the clock goes LOW. In either case, unless the inputs are constrained to be constant during a HIGH clock, the master-slave flip-flop output may not reflect the inputs applied to it during the last positive clock edge. In such cases, equation (4.4) does not provide a valid model of the flip-flop.

An *edge-triggered flip-flop* is designed to respond only to inputs applied during the positive clock edge. Figure 4.30c shows how an edge-triggered D flip-flop can be constructed from two simple D flip-flops. At any given time, the output of this flip-flop is determined by the value of the input applied during the last positive clock edge. The edge-triggered D flip-flop can be used in the construction of other edge-triggered flip-flops. For example, figure 4.30d shows how an edge-triggered D flip-flop is used in the implementation of an edge-triggered RS flip-flop. Equation (4.4) provides the basis for this implementation; the combinational logic generating the input to the D flip-flop is a realization of the right-hand side of equation (4.4).

4.3.3.4 T Flip-Flop (Toggle)

A *T flip-flop*, or a *toggle flip-flop*, is a one-input flip-flop such that a HIGH input causes the flip-flop output to change, after a *T*-second delay, ie: a HIGH input "toggles" the output. Figure 4.31 shows a representation of a T flip-flop and gives its defining truth table. Thus, for the T flip-flop,

$$Q_{n+1} = \overline{T_n} \cdot Q_n + T_n \cdot \overline{Q_n}$$

Equivalently,

$$Q_{n+1} = T_n \oplus Q_n$$

where $\oplus$ is the exclusive-OR.

A T flip-flop can be easily constructed from an RS flip-flop, as shown in figure 4.31b. Note the feedback in this construction where the flip-flop outputs are used to generate the flip-flop inputs. To prevent signals from racing around the feedback loops while the clock is HIGH, it is essential that the RS flip-flop used be a master-slave flip-flop. If an ordinary RS flip-flop were

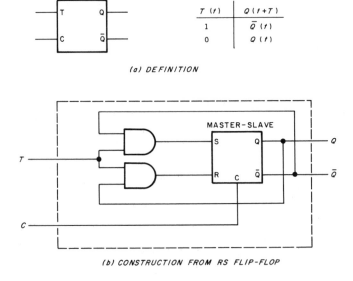

Figure 4.31: *The T (toggle) flip-flop.*

used instead of a master-slave RS flip-flop, an analysis of the resulting system would be virtually impossible. With a master-slave RS flip-flop,

$$Q_{n+1} = S_n + \overline{S_n} \cdot \overline{R_n} \cdot Q_n$$

The output of the ANDs provides the flip-flop inputs: $R_n = Q_n \cdot T_n$, and $S_n = \overline{Q_n} \cdot T_n$.
Therefore,

$$Q_{n+1} = \overline{Q_n} \cdot T_n + (\overline{\overline{Q_n} \cdot T_n}) \cdot (\overline{Q_n \cdot T_n}) \cdot Q_n$$

$$= \overline{Q_n} \cdot T_n + (Q_n + \overline{T_n}) \cdot (\overline{Q_n} + \overline{T_n}) \cdot Q_n$$

$$= \overline{Q_n} \cdot T_n + Q_n \cdot \overline{Q_n} + Q_n \cdot \overline{T_n} + \overline{T_n} \cdot \overline{Q_n} \cdot Q_n + Q_n \cdot \overline{T_n}$$

and so,

$$Q_{n+1} = \overline{Q_n} T_n + Q_n \overline{T_n} = Q_n \oplus T_n$$

4.3.3.5 JK Flip-Flop

Perhaps the most widely used flip-flop is the *JK flip-flop* (JK does not stand for anything in particular, eg: as T stands for "toggle"). Its operation is identical to that of the RS flip-flop, except that the forbidden input condition, in which both $R = 1$ and $S = 1$, is allowed. Figure 4.32a shows a representation of the JK flip-flop and gives the defining truth table. Thus, for the JK flip-flop,

$$Q_{n+1} = J_n \cdot \overline{K_n} + J_n \cdot K_n \cdot \overline{Q_n} + \overline{J_n} \cdot \overline{K_n} \cdot Q_n \qquad (4.5)$$

Equation (4.5) can be simplified to

$$Q_{n+1} = \overline{K_n} \cdot Q_n + J_n \cdot \overline{Q_n} \qquad (4.6)$$

Therefore, the JK flip-flop can be toggled by setting both inputs HIGH. The JK flip-flop is frequently used in applications requiring either an RS flip-flop, a D flip-flop, or a T flip-flop (figure 4.32d).

$J(t)$	$K(t)$	$Q(t+T)$
1	1	$\overline{Q}(t)$
1	0	1
0	1	0
0	0	$Q(t)$

(a) DEFINITION

Figure 4.32: *The JK flip-flop.*

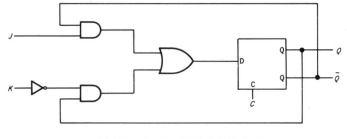

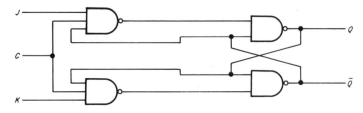

(b) CONSTRUCTION FROM D FLIP-FLOP

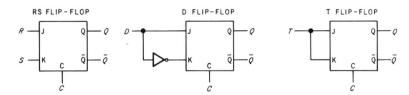

(c) CONSTRUCTION FROM FOUR NAND GATES

RS FLIP-FLOP   D FLIP-FLOP   T FLIP-FLOP

(d) CONSTRUCTION OF OTHER FLIP-FLOPS FROM JK FLIP-FLOP

Figure 4.32 cont.

Although a JK flip-flop can be constructed from an RS flip-flop or from a D flip-flop, such constructions are neither straightforward nor efficient. For example, figure 4.32b shows the construction of a JK flip-flop using a D flip-flop. Recall that the D flip-flop (ie: the T-Delay) can be used as the basic dynamic element in the design of any synchronous sequential-logic system. In this case, the design hinges on the implementation of a combinational-logic system which realizes the right-hand side of equation (4.6); the output of this combinational-logic system provides the input to the D flip-flop. However, a more fundamental design of the JK flip-flop can be realized by using four NAND gates as shown in figure 4.32c.

4.3.3.6   Preset and Clear

Many commercial flip-flops have two additional inputs which allow the state of the flip-flops to be set independently of the clock and the normal inputs. An input that allows the state of the flip-flop to be set HIGH, independently of the clock, is called a *preset* input; an input that allows the state of the flip-flop to be set LOW, independently of the clock, is called a *clear* input. Figure 4.33a shows how preset and clear inputs can be im-

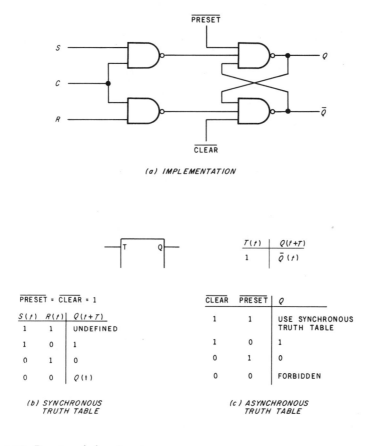

(a) IMPLEMENTATION

$T(t)$	$Q(t+T)$
1	$\bar{Q}(t)$

PRESET = CLEAR = 1

$S(t)$	$R(t)$	$Q(t+T)$
1	1	UNDEFINED
1	0	1
0	1	0
0	0	$Q(t)$

(b) SYNCHRONOUS TRUTH TABLE

CLEAR	PRESET	Q
1	1	USE SYNCHRONOUS TRUTH TABLE
1	0	1
0	1	0
0	0	FORBIDDEN

(c) ASYNCHRONOUS TRUTH TABLE

Figure 4.33: *Preset and clear inputs.*

plemented in the design of an RS flip-flop. Note that in this implementation, the preset and clear inputs are active LOW (hence the bars: $\overline{\text{PRESET}}$, $\overline{\text{CLEAR}}$); this is particularly useful in TTL implementations where, in the absence of connections to the $\overline{\text{PRESET}}$ and $\overline{\text{CLEAR}}$ inputs, those inputs would naturally go HIGH, and the flip-flop would function as an ordinary RS flip-flop. The truth table of figure 4.33b defines the flip-flop when the $\overline{\text{PRESET}}$ and $\overline{\text{CLEAR}}$ inputs are HIGH and the flip-flop is functioning as an ordinary synchronous RS flip-flop; hence the *synchronous truth table*. Figure 4.33c shows the *asynchronous truth table* which defines the flip-flop's response to the various $\overline{\text{CLEAR}}$-$\overline{\text{PRESET}}$ input combinations.

4.4 Applications of Flip-Flops

Some important applications of flip-flops are now examined. Special emphasis is placed upon the construction of registers, latches, and counters.

4.4.1 Registers

An n-bit register is a collection of n flip-flops used to store an n-bit number. Figure 4.34 shows a 3-bit *parallel-load* register constructed from three JK flip-flops. Whenever the *enable E* is HIGH the 3-bit number $U_2U_1U_0$ will be stored in the register. The contents of the register can be determined by observing $Q_2Q_1Q_0$. This register is called a parallel-load register because all 3 bits U_2, U_1, and U_0 are loaded into the register simultaneously (ie: in parallel).

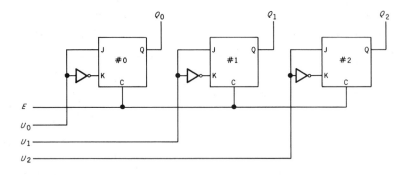

Figure 4.34: *A 3-bit parallel-load register constructed from three JK flip-flops.*

A bit of data stored in one JK flip-flop is easily transferred to another JK flip-flop. Figure 4.35a shows an arrangement where a HIGH on the enable input causes the 1 bit of data to be transferred from flip-flop #1 to flip-flop #2. Note that the enable signal is applied to the clock input of flip-flop #2. This allows the data transfer to take place without disturbing the contents of flip-flop #1. By applying the enable signal to the clock inputs of both flip-flops, a data shift takes place. For example, a HIGH on the enable input of

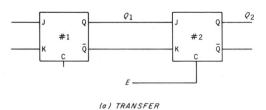

(a) TRANSFER

Figure 4.35: *Data transfer using JK flip-flops.*

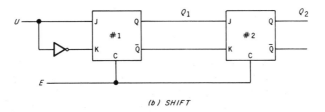

(b) SHIFT

Figure 4.35 cont.

the two flip-flop system of figure 4.35b also causes the 1-bit data transfer from flip-flop #1 to flip-flop #2. However, in this case, the contents of flip-flop #1 are also changed: Q_0 shifts to Q_1, and Q_1 shifts to Q_2. Because the data transfer of figure 4.35b involves the cascading of the two flip-flops, it is necessary that the flip-flops (at least flip-flop #1) be master-slave types. This scheme for data transfer provides the basis for construction of the *shift register*.

A 3-bit shift register, constructed from three JK flip-flops, is shown in figure 4.36a. The discrete timing diagram of figure 4.36b shows how the in-

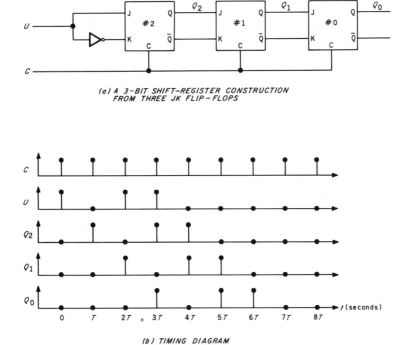

(a) A 3-BIT SHIFT–REGISTER CONSTRUCTION
FROM THREE JK FLIP–FLOPS

(b) TIMING DIAGRAM

Figure 4.36: *Shift registers.*

put U propagates down the shift register, transferring 1 bit of data from one flip-flop to the next during each clock period. Thus, it takes three clock periods to load the shift register with a 3-bit word $U_2 U_1 U_0$; the 3 bits U_0, U_1, and U_2 must be input sequentially, starting with bit U_0, coincident with three consecutive clock pulses. The shift register is modeled by the following equations:

$$Q_2(t + T) = U(t)$$
$$Q_1(t + T) = Q_2(t)$$
$$Q_0(t + T) = Q_1(t)$$

The above three delay equations can be combined to give

$$Q_0(t + 3T) = U(t)$$

Thus, the 3-bit shift register can be used to obtain a delay of three clock periods.

It is generally convenient to use abbreviated graphical representations of registers. Figure 4.37a shows a 3-bit parallel-load register; figure 4.37b shows a 3-bit shift register; figure 4.37c shows a 1-bit shift register, called a delay, which simply provides a one-clock-period delay.

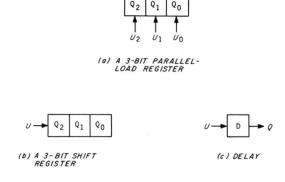

*(a) A 3-BIT PARALLEL-
LOAD REGISTER*

*(b) A 3-BIT SHIFT
REGISTER*

(c) DELAY

Figure 4.37: *Register representations.*

As an example of an application of a shift register, consider the design of the 4-bit *serial* (sequential-logic) adder shown in figure 4.38a. Recall that a *parallel* (combinational-logic) 4-bit adder requires four full-adders. By using two 4-bit shift registers and a delay, the 4-bit adder can be implemented using only one full-adder. To add two 4-bit numbers, the two numbers are initially (eg: at $t = 0$) parallel-loaded into the two 4-bit shift registers A and B, and the delay D is cleared. The system is then allowed to run. At time $t = 4T$, the sum will appear in register A, provided there is no overflow (ie:

provided the sum is not a 5-bit number); delay D provides the high-order bit of the 5-bit sum. The table in figure 4.38b shows the contents of the two registers and the delays during the process of adding the two 4-bit numbers 1011 and 1111. In comparison to the parallel adder, the serial adder is slow, requiring n clock periods to complete the addition of the two n-bit numbers. However, the serial adder uses only one full-adder compared to the n full-adders required to implement an n-bit parallel adder.

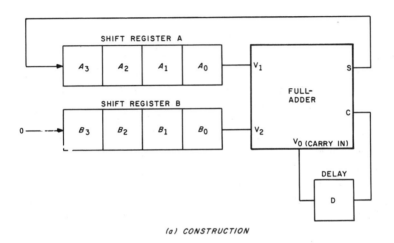

(a) CONSTRUCTION

t	D	A_3	A_2	A_1	A_0	B_3	B_2	B_1	B_0
0	0	1	0	1	1	1	1	1	1
T	1	0	1	0	1	0	1	1	1
$2T$	1	1	0	1	0	0	0	1	1
$3T$	1	0	1	0	1	0	0	0	1
$4T$	1	1	0	1	0	0	0	0	0

SUM $= D(4T)\ A_3(4T)\ A_2(4T)\ A_1(4T)\ A_0(4T) = 11010$

(b) SEQUENCE OF SIGNALS

Figure 4.38: *A 4-bit serial adder.*

Compare this sequential-logic design of a 4-bit adder to that of figure 4.8. In particular, note how the use of the shift registers eliminates the need for the four demultiplexers.

4.4.2 Latching

Most complex digital devices, such as digital computers, are sequential-logic devices in which relatively sophisticated logic and arithmetic units are used iteratively to solve a single problem. Although sequential-logic implementations are generally more hardware-efficient than combinational-logic implementations, the implications on the type of outputs generated are severe. Specifically, because a sequential-logic system time-shares the hardware, the solution data may appear as a set of observable signals only for the duration of a single clock pulse. For example, in the serial adder of figure 4.38, the sum of the two 4-bit numbers being added appears in the 4-bit register A (the fifth bit of the sum appears in delay D) during the clock pulse starting at time $4T$. Recall that register A initially contained one of the two 4-bit numbers being added.

For even moderately slow sequential-logic implementations, the solution data may be available as observable signals for only a fraction of a microsecond. In cases where it is necessary for the solution data to be available for longer periods of time, either for observation by slower devices (such as humans) or for future reference, it is necessary to *latch* the desired data signals into a storage device (ie: a register) at the precise time that the desired solution data are present.

Thus, a latch is a register, generally a parallel-load register, in which data are accepted only upon command. Synchronous flip-flops make excellent latches because the clock input can be used as a store command. The TTL 7475 IC, a quad D flip-flop, is frequently used to construct output latches (see figure 4.39a for pin connections). It is not a master-slave flip-flop and is, thus, relatively inexpensive. Although the 7475 cannot be used in logic designs in which flip-flops are to be cascaded, this limitation is of no consequence in applications where the 7475 is used as an output latch.

Figure 4.39a shows a system in which four D flip-flops (eg: one 7475) are used to latch a 4-bit number $D_3D_2D_1D_0$ from four wires constituting a 4-bit *bus*. The 4-bit number to be latched must be placed on the 4-bit bus coincident with a store command pulse. In this case, the 4-bit number is a BCD

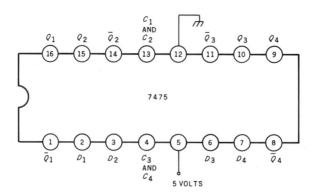

(a) PIN CONNECTIONS FOR TTL 7475
QUAD D FLIP-FLOP

Figure 4.39: *Latching.*

number that is to be displayed on a seven-segment LED display where it can be observed. Figure 4.39c shows a timing diagram illustrating the operation of the 4-bit latch.

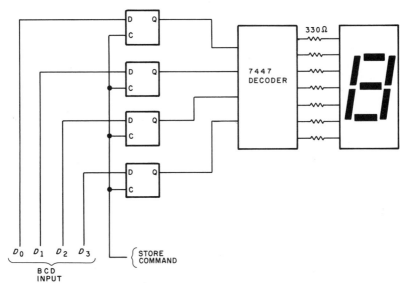

(b) BCD LATCH TO SEVEN-SEGMENT LED DISPLAY

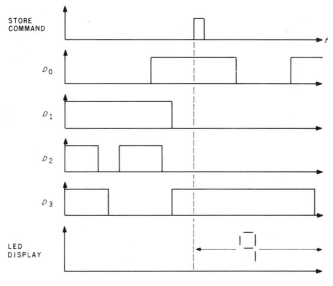

(c) TIMING DIAGRAM

Figure 4.39 cont.

4.4.3 Counters

A *counter* is a single-input device that counts input pulses. Although the pulses may denote the occurrence of random events (such as cars passing a toll station), in many sequential-logic systems where it is necessary to keep track of time in terms of multiples of the clock period, the pulses denote the beginning or end of a clock period. For example, in the serial adder of figure 4.38, the sum appears in register A and delay D at time $4T$. Therefore, it would be important to keep track of time, so that the solution can be observed at the time it appears.

A divide-by-n counter is a device which, when driven by a clock signal with period T, produces a periodic output with period nT. Thus, the equation characterizing a divide-by-n counter, whose output is Q, is

$$Q(t + nT) = Q(t) \qquad \text{for all } t$$

and

$$Q(t + iT) \neq Q(t) \qquad \text{for any } i < n \text{ and for all } t$$

This section illustrates some standard approaches to counter design.

A rather simple and obvious approach to designing a divide-by-n counter involves the use of an n-bit shift register in a simple feedback configuration. Such counters are called *shift counters* or, more commonly, *ring counters*. Figure 4.40a shows a divide-by-5 counter, in which the 5-bit ring register is constructed from a cascade of five flip-flops having $\overline{\text{PRESET}}$ and $\overline{\text{CLEAR}}$ inputs. At $t = 0$, the output state of each flip-flop is set using the $\overline{\text{PRESET}}$ and $\overline{\text{CLEAR}}$ inputs. This initial setting of the five flip-flops determines the waveform of the counter output. Figure 4.40b shows the counter output for one particular set of initial conditions:

$$Q_0(0) = 1 \quad \text{and} \quad Q_1(0) = Q_2(0) = Q_3(0) = Q_4(0) = 0$$

Ring counters are generally inefficient in terms of the number of flip-flops used in an implementation. For cases where n is an integral power of 2, a particularly simple and efficient design scheme applies, in which a divide-by-n counter can be realized using only $\log_2(n)$ flip-flops. The fundamental

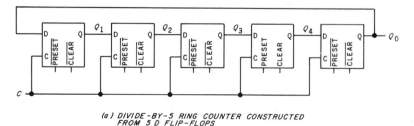

(a) *DIVIDE-BY-5 RING COUNTER CONSTRUCTED FROM 5 D FLIP-FLOPS*

Figure 4.40: *Ring counters.*

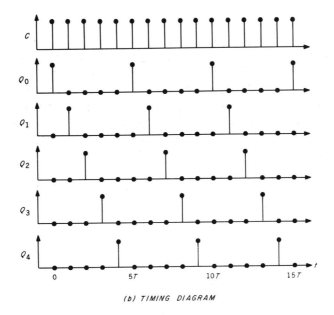

(b) TIMING DIAGRAM

Figure 4.40 cont.

building block in such a design is the T flip-flop. Therefore, such counters are called *toggle counters*. The popular JK flip-flop is generally used in applications requiring a T flip-flop. Recall that a T flip-flop is obtained from a JK flip-flop simply by applying the toggle input T to both the J and K inputs.

Figures 4.41a thru 4.41d show implementations of divide-by-2 (ie: 2^1), divide-by-4 (ie: 2^2), divide-by-8 (ie: 2^3), and divide-by-16 (ie: 2^4) counters.

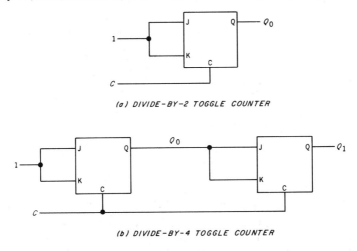

(a) DIVIDE-BY-2 TOGGLE COUNTER

(b) DIVIDE-BY-4 TOGGLE COUNTER

Figure 4.41: *Toggle counters.*

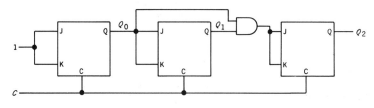

(c) DIVIDE-BY-8 TOGGLE COUNTER

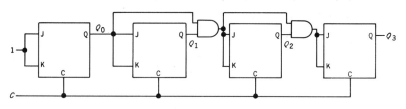

(d) DIVIDE-BY-16 TOGGLE COUNTER

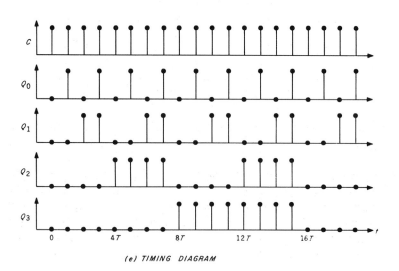

(e) TIMING DIAGRAM

Figure 4.41 cont.

The pattern is clear. The essence of these designs lies in the special cascading of the T flip-flops, so that the input to each flip-flop is the AND of all the outputs of the previous flip-flops in the cascade; the input to the first flip-flop in the cascade is always HIGH. Thus, for the first flip-flop,

$$Q_0(t + T) = \overline{Q}_0(t)$$

Clearly, this is the characterizing equation for the divide-by-2 counter. For the second flip-flop,

$$Q_1(t + T) = Q_0(t) \oplus Q_1(t)$$

This is the characterizing equation for the divide-by-4 counter. Similarly, for the divide-by-8 and divide-by-16 counters, respectively,

$$Q_2(t + T) = (Q_0(t) \cdot Q_1(t)) \oplus Q_2(t)$$

$$Q_3(t + T) = (Q_0(t) \cdot Q_1(t) \cdot Q_2(t)) \oplus Q_3(t)$$

Figure 4.41e shows the timing diagrams of Q_0, Q_1, Q_2, and Q_3 relative to the clock signal C.

A simple divide-by-n counter is essentially a single-input, single-output device in which the frequency of the output signal is $1/n$-th of the frequency of the input signal. In applications where it is necessary to keep a running count of the clock, a one-output, divide-by-n counter is not useful. For example, if one were designing a digital clock, it might be necessary to display seconds elapsed on a two-digit seven-segment LED. If a clock signal with a period of 1 second were available, a divide-by-60 counter could be used to generate a signal with a 1-minute period. It would be especially useful if this divide-by-60 counter had, in addition to the single output used to time 60-second intervals, a set of outputs that could be decoded to provide all intermediate counts from 1 to 60. Counters having such a set of outputs are called *decoding counters*, or *weighted counters*.

Decoding either a ring counter, such as that shown in figure 4.40, or a toggle counter, such as those shown in figure 4.41, is a fairly straightforward matter. In the case of a divide-by-n ring counter, if the initial values of the D flip-flops are set such that $Q_0(0) = 1$, and $Q_1(0) = Q_2(0) = \ldots = Q_{n-1}(0) = 0$, then the count at any time t is determined by observing which of the flip-flop outputs is HIGH, ie: if Q_i is HIGH, then iT seconds have elapsed since the output Q_0 was last HIGH. In the case of a divide-by-n toggle counter, if the initial values of all the flip-flops are set to 0, then the count is determined from the binary number formed from the flip-flop outputs (eg: for the divide-by-16 counter of figure 4.41d, the count at any time t is determined from the binary number $Q_3Q_2Q_1Q_0$).

Because a toggle counter is significantly more hardware-efficient than a ring counter, practically all commercial counters are toggle counters. Figure 4.42 shows a diagram used to represent a weighted divide-by-16 toggle

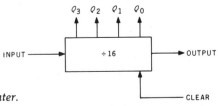

Figure 4.42: *A divide-by-16 weighted counter.*

counter. Such counters generally have a single input, which allows all flip-flops to be cleared simultaneously for initialization purposes.

There seems to be no limit to the number of ingenious schemes that can be used to design divide-by-n counters, in cases where n is not an integral power of 2. Figure 4.43 shows two rather efficient designs for divide-by-3

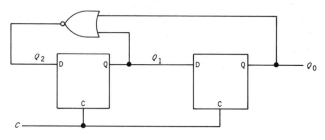

(a) CONSTRUCTION USING D FLIP-FLOPS

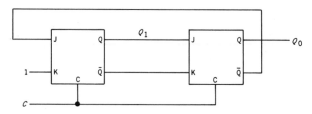

(b) CONSTRUCTION USING JK FLIP-FLOPS

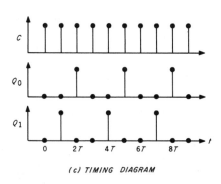

(c) TIMING DIAGRAM

Figure 4.43: *Divide-by-3 counters.*

counters. The design of figure 4.43a uses two D flip-flops. Note that since

$$Q_0(t + 2T) = Q_1(t + T) = Q_2(t)$$

and since

$$Q_2(t) = \overline{Q_1}(t) \cdot \overline{Q_0}(t)$$

and

$$Q_1(t) = Q_0(t + T)$$

that

$$Q_0(t + 2T) = \overline{Q_0}(t) \cdot \overline{Q_0}(t + T) \tag{4.7}$$

Figure 4.43c shows the timing diagram for this counter for the case that

$$Q_0(0) = Q_1(0) = 0$$

The design shown in figure 4.43b uses two JK flip-flops. Note that for a JK flip-flop whose K input is always HIGH,

$$Q(t + T) = J(t) \cdot \overline{Q}(t)$$

Thus, the output of the first JK flip-flop is given by

$$Q_1(t + T) = \overline{Q_0}(t) \cdot \overline{Q_1}(t)$$

The second JK flip-flop is wired as a D flip-flop. Thus,

$$Q_0(t + T) = Q_1(t)$$

Therefore, the characterizing equation is

$$Q_0(t + 2T) = \overline{Q_0}(t) \cdot \overline{Q_0}(t + T)$$

This is the same as equation (4.7) and, thus, provides the basis for the construction of a divide-by-3 counter.

A divide-by-n weighted counter can always be used as the basic component in designing other counters with periods less than nT. One such scheme is illustrated in figure 4.44, which shows a divide-by-11 counter constructed

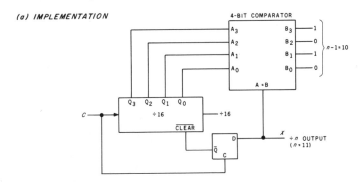

Figure 4.44: A divide-by-11 counter.

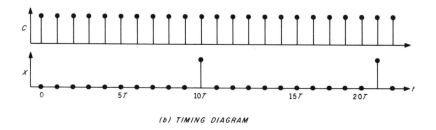

(b) TIMING DIAGRAM

Figure 4.44 cont.

from a weighted divide-by-16 counter (eg: the TTL 7493) and a 4-bit comparator (eg: the TTL 7485). Simply by setting the B input of the comparator to $n - 1$ (ie: $B_3B_2B_1B_0 = n - 1$), this circuit can be used for any n, such that $n \le 16$.

Weighted counters are often used in driving multiplexers and demultiplexers. For example, figure 4.45 shows how two weighted divide-by-8 counters could be used in a data-transmission system in which a data line and a clock line are used to transmit 8 bits of data.

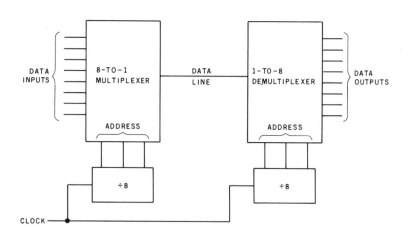

Figure 4.45: *Use of weighted counters in data transmission.*

Weighted counters are frequently used to drive encoders. For example, figure 4.46 shows how two weighted divide-by-10 counters can be used to obtain a decimal display of a binary clock signal on two seven-segment LED displays; clock counts up to 99 can be displayed.

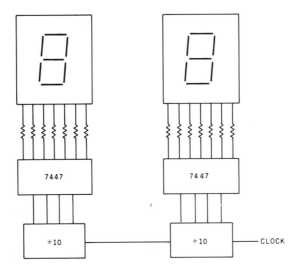

Figure 4.46: *Use of weighted counters in driving encoders.*

An interesting application of a weighted counter is shown in figure 4.47a where a binary clock count (up to a count of 15) is converted to an analog voltage which is proportional to the count. A weighted divide-by-16 counter is used. The output voltage is given by

$$v_o = \frac{v_H}{R/R_L + 15} (Q_0 + 2Q_1 + 4Q_2 + Q_3)$$

where v_H is the HIGH output voltage and $Q_i = 1$ or 0, $i = 0, 1, 2,$ or 3, depending upon whether the i-th output is HIGH or LOW, respectively. For

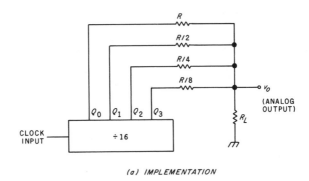

(a) IMPLEMENTATION

Figure 4.47: *Analog conversion of a digital-clock count.*

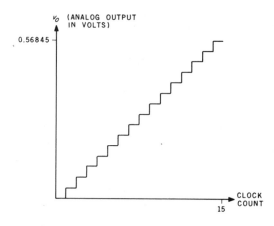

(b) INPUT/OUTPUT (I/O) CHARACTERISTICS

Figure 4.47 cont.

the case that $R/R_L >> 15$, the output voltage is approximated by

$$v_o = v_H \frac{R_L}{R} (Q_0 + 2Q_1 + 4Q_2 + 8Q_3)$$

Thus, if $R_L = 100 \ \Omega$, $R = 8$ kΩ, and $v_H = 3.6$ V, the maximum output voltage (for the case that $Q_0 = Q_1 = Q_2 = Q_3 = 1$) is 0.5685 V; the estimated maximum output voltage determined from the approximate formula is 0.675 V. Figure 4.47b shows a graph of the analog-output voltage v_o versus the clock count.

4.4.4 Read/Write Memory

The flip-flop is the basic component in the construction of *read/write memory*, meaning memory which can have its contents examined (read) or have data stored into it (written). Read/write memory has come to be known as *random-access memory*, or RAM. Because other types of memory, such as *read-only memory* (ROM), are also randomly accessible, the use of the term random-access memory, or RAM, is somewhat imprecise. Therefore, in this text this type of memory will be called read/write memory, programmable memory, user memory, or, simply, memory. The terms *programmable memory* and *user memory* refer more specifically to the memory used directly by a programmer to store programs or data. The term *read/write memory* can be used in a more general manner to refer to this entire class of memory device. Usually, however, the term *memory* will be used to mean this class of device, and other memory devices will be explicitly identified, as in *read-only memory*.

Figure 4.48 shows a representation of a basic memory cell which is used to store 1 bit. Q represents the state of the cell, ie: $Q = 1$ implies that a 1 is

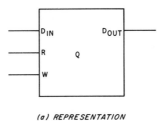

(a) REPRESENTATION

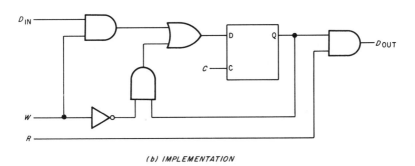

(b) IMPLEMENTATION

Figure 4.48: *A memory cell: independent read and write lines.*

stored, and $Q = 0$ implies that a 0 is stored. The specifications of this memory cell are such that the data on the input pin D_{in} are *written* into the cell whenever W is HIGH, and the data stored in the cell are *read* out onto pin D_{out} whenever R is HIGH. Thus, the following equations characterize the operation of the memory cell:

$$Q(t + T) = W(t) \cdot D_{in}(t) + \overline{W}(t) \cdot Q(t)$$

$$D_{out}(t) = R(t) \cdot Q(t)$$

A sequential-logic system realizing the above equations can be easily implemented (figure 4.48b).

By constraining a memory cell to be always in either the read or write mode, it is possible to combine the read and write inputs into a single R/W input, as shown in figure 4.49a. In this case, $R/W = 1$ implies read, and

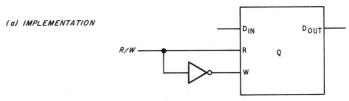

(a) IMPLEMENTATION

Figure 4.49: *A memory cell: combined read/write line.*

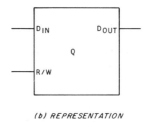

(b) REPRESENTATION

Figure 4.49 cont.

$R/W = 0$ implies write. The characterizing equations for this memory cell are:

$$Q(t + T) = \overline{R/W}(t) \cdot D_{in}(t) + R/W(t) \cdot Q(t)$$

$$D_{out}(t) = R/W(t) \cdot Q(t)$$

Figure 4.49b shows a representation of such a cell.

When large amounts of data are to be stored, the hardware implementation can often be simplified by connecting the inputs of many memory cells to a single input line which is time-shared; similar economies can be achieved by ORing the outputs to a single output line. Thus, at any given time, the input on the line is to go to no more than one cell. In such cases, it is necessary that each cell be individually accessible for reading and writing. This selection process is achieved by using a cell *enable* input E. The effect of the enable input E is such that the contents of a memory cell Q cannot be changed unless $E = 1$, and the output D_{out} is 0 whenever $E = 0$, ie: unless the enable is HIGH, one cannot read or write. Thus,

$$Q(t + T) = \overline{E}(t) \cdot Q(t) + E(t) \cdot (\overline{R/W}(t) \cdot D_{in}(t) + R/W(t) \cdot Q(t))$$

$$D_{out}(t) = E(t) \cdot (R/W(t) \cdot Q(t))$$

Figure 4.50a shows the implementation of a memory cell with a cell enable input, and figure 4.50b shows the representation of such a cell.

(a) IMPLEMENTATION

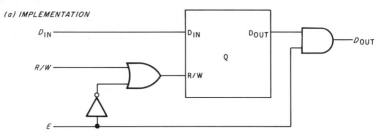

Figure 4.50: *A memory cell with a cell-enable signal.*

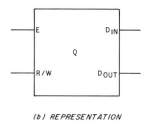

(b) REPRESENTATION

Figure 4.50 cont.

Figure 4.51a shows how the basic memory cell of figure 4.50 can be used in the construction of a memory array capable of storing four 2-bit words (ie: a 4 × 2 memory array). By inputting the proper address, the four-output demultiplexer enables the two memory cells corresponding to the 2-bit word that is to be stored or read. Because the enable signals of all cells not addressed are LOW, the outputs of cells not addressed are LOW. Thus, the outputs of all memory cells corresponding to the same bit of a word can be ORed together, as shown, and only the word selected will appear at the output.

(a) 4×2 MEMORY ARRAY CONSTRUCTION

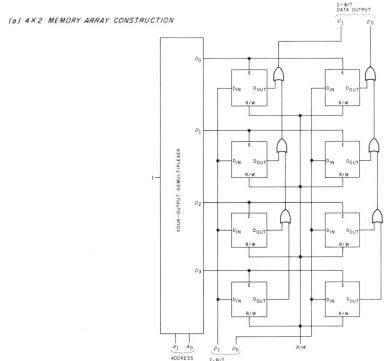

Figure 4.51: *A 4 × 2 memory array representation.*

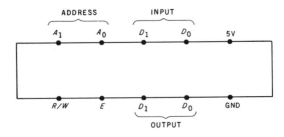

(b) REPRESENTATION

Figure 4.51 cont.

Figure 4.51b shows the representation of a 4×2 memory array. Note that if an IC were to be constructed corresponding to this 4×2 memory array, a total of ten pins would be required for this IC. This includes 5 volt and ground power-supply pins, assuming TTL construction. Using bus-structure techniques (see section 5.2), it is possible to use only one set of data pins for both data inputs and data outputs, thereby reducing the number of pins required in the IC construction.

4.4.5 Dynamic Read/Write Memory

The memory cells studied thus far are two-state logic devices constructed from interconnections of combinational-logic gates (eg: figure 4.24). In these interconnections, the two-state logic property, in which either of two stable output states can exist for one input combination, is always caused by a loop. The contents of a memory cell constructed from such a two-state logic device are associated with the state of the device. That is, if the device is in one state it is said to be storing a "1," and if it is in the other state it is said to be storing a "0." Because both states of such two-state logic devices are stable states, data can be stored indefinitely. As a result, memory cells constructed from such two-state logic devices are called *static* memory cells. In contrast, there are *dynamic* memory cells, made from single MOS transistors, in which the data stored are lost after a short time. Data which are to be stored for long periods of time in dynamic memory cells must be periodically *refreshed*.

A single MOS transistor can be used as a fundamental memory cell. In this application, the charge stored on the gate capacitor, formed by the gate, substrate, and dielectric (see figure 2.24), represents data stored in the memory cell. For example, when the gate capacitor is charged, a "1" is stored in the memory cell; when the gate capacitor is discharged, a "0" is stored in the memory cell. Figure 4.52a depicts an n-channel MOS transistor which is to be used as a memory cell; the gate capacitor C_g is shown explicitly. The data input D_i is applied to the gate terminal, and the write-select input W is applied to the source substrate terminal. To write into the memory cell, the write-select input W is set LOW. When W is set LOW, the gate capacitor C_g will either charge or discharge, depending upon whether the data input D_I is HIGH or LOW. The properties of the n-channel MOS transistor cell are summarized in the truth table of figure 4.52a: the state of the gate capacitor is denoted by Q_g, where $Q_g = 1$ implies that the gate capacitor is charged, and $Q_g = 0$ implies that the gate capacitor is discharged.

In using the p-channel MOS transistor as a memory cell (see figure 4.52b), the source-substrate terminal is the data input D_I, and the gate terminal is the write-select input W.

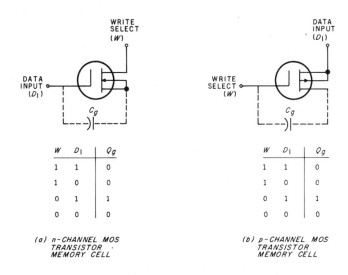

W	D_I	Q_g
1	1	0
1	0	0
0	1	1
0	0	0

W	D_I	Q_g
1	1	0
1	0	0
0	1	1
0	0	0

(a) n-CHANNEL MOS TRANSISTOR MEMORY CELL

(b) p-CHANNEL MOS TRANSISTOR MEMORY CELL

Figure 4.52: MOS transistor dynamic memory cells.

The gate capacitor, because of the thinness of the dielectric material separating the gate and substrate, has considerable leakage current when it is charged. As a result, a charged gate capacitor will discharge itself through its own dielectric. Thus, data stored in the MOS transistor as charge on the gate capacitor is lost when the capacitor discharges. Typically, the gate capacitor is very small, less than 1 pF, and will discharge itself in a few milliseconds. To store data for longer periods, the memory cell must be periodically *refreshed* by recharging the gate capacitor before it is discharged. Also, in using the MOS transistor as a fundamental memory cell in a memory array, provisions must be made for selecting a particular memory cell in the array for reading or writing.

Figure 4.53 shows how four n-channel MOS transistors can be used to construct a fundamental memory cell. In this arrangement, the gate capacitor C_g of transistor T_1 is used for data storage. When the write-select input W is HIGH, the drain-to-source resistance of transistor T_3 is 0, and the gate capacitor C_g is charged or discharged through T_3 to the data-input level D_I. Before a read of the memory cell can be initiated, capacitor C_{DD} must be

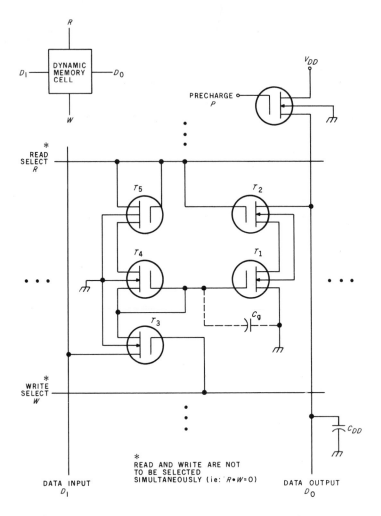

Figure 4.53: *A dynamic memory cell with read and write selects.*

charged to voltage V_{DD} by setting the precharge input P to HIGH. Now, the drain-to-source resistance of transistor T_2 can be made 0 by setting the read-select input R to HIGH. With transistor T_2 in the conducting state, the charge on the gate capacitor C_g, which represents the data stored in the memory cell, is reflected on the data-output line D_0. Specifically, when Q_g (the charge of gate capacitor C_g) is HIGH, the drain-to-source resistance of transistor T_1 is 0, C_{DD} discharges to ground through T_2 and T_1, and the data-output line D_0 goes LOW. On the other hand, if Q_g is LOW, then C_{DD} cannot discharge through transistor T_1, and the data-output line D_0 stays HIGH. Note that D_0 is the inverse of Q_g.

The memory cell can be refreshed through the read-select line R. When the read-select line R is HIGH and capacitor C_g is charged (ie: Q_g is HIGH),

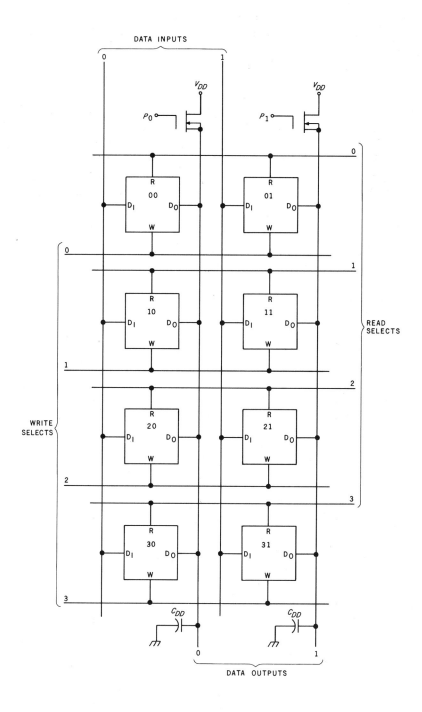

Figure 4.54: *A 4 × 2 dynamic memory array.*

the drain-to-source resistances of transistors T_4 and T_5 are 0, and capacitor C_g charges to the read-select level R. Note the circular argument reflecting the *feedback* configuration, ie: if capacitor C_g is charged, then it can be further charged by R. Thus, when the read-select line R is set HIGH, capacitor C_g will be charged to R if the capacitor is sufficiently charged to turn ON transistor T_4. If there is not sufficient charge on C_g, either because a "0" is stored in the memory cell, or because the charge associated with a "1" has discharged as leakage current through the capacitor, then setting R HIGH will not change the state of capacitor C_g. Thus, setting the read-select R HIGH will achieve the refresh operation: a HIGH will go HIGHer and a LOW will stay LOW. Note that setting the read-select HIGH will refresh an entire row of memory cells. The refresh period determines the minimum frequency at which a dynamic memory cell can be clocked. A manufacturer will, on the basis of the values of C_g and the dielectric leakage resistance, specify the minimum refresh period for a dynamic memory unit.

Figure 4.54 shows an arrangement that could be used in constructing a 4×2 dynamic memory array. The advantages of MOS dynamic memory over static memory (either bipolar or MOS) are:

- Smaller area per cell and, thus, greater cell density per chip
- Higher speeds than MOS static (but not higher than bipolar static)
- Lower power dissipation (only leakage currents flow)
- Lower cost

The disadvantages are:

- Refresh circuitry required
- Slower speeds than bipolar static
- Extra power-supply voltages often needed for refreshing

PROBLEMS

P4.1.   Use the 555 timer IC to construct the clock circuit shown in figure P4.1:

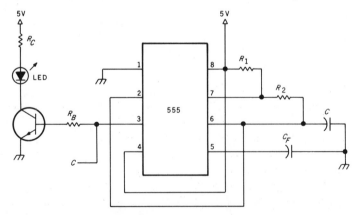

Figure P4.1.

$R_1 = 1.5$ MΩ, $R_2 = 1.5$ MΩ, $C = 1$ μF, and $C_F = 0.01$ μF. The 1-μF capacitor is an electrolytic. Be sure to observe the polarity markings.
(a) Compute the clock's period T and duty cycle.
(b) Observe the LED output and, using a watch, measure the clock's period T and duty cycle.
(c) Repeat parts (a) and (b) with $C = 2$ μF.

P4.2. Construct the 555 clock circuit of figure P4.1, where $R_1 = 2$ kΩ, $C = 0.01$ μF, $C_F = 0.01$ μF, and R_2 is made up of a series combination of a 2 kΩ resistor and a 25 kΩ potentiometer, as shown in figure P4.2.

Figure P4.2.

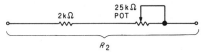

(a) Compute the minimum and maximum clock periods attainable with this circuit.
(b) Connect the clock output C (pin 3) to one channel of a dual-trace oscilloscope (the probe ground goes to pin 1). By using the oscilloscope's calibrated time base, measure the minimum and maximum clock periods and the corresponding duty cycle.
(c) Repeat parts (a) and (b) with $C = 0.047$ μF.
(d) Use both channels of the oscilloscope to simultaneously observe the clock output (pin 3) and the input to the 555 comparator (pin 2 or 6). Sketch the waveforms.

P4.3. (a) Construct a weighted divide-by-16 counter using two 7473s (dual JK level-triggered flip-flops). Figure P4.3 shows the pin connections for the 7473.

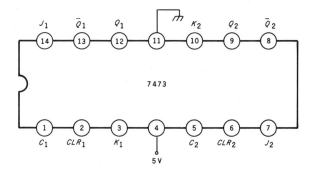

Figure P4.3.

(b) Drive this counter with a 50 kHz clock constructed with a 555 timer.
(c) Using a dual-trace oscilloscope, observe each output of the counter (ie: Q_0, Q_1, Q_2, and Q_3) simultaneously with the clock signal. Sketch the waveforms.

P4.4.   (a) Construct a circuit that converts the 4-bit number, corresponding to the outputs Q_3, Q_2, Q_1, and Q_0 of a 7493 weighted divide-by-16 counter, to an analog output. Figure P4.4 shows the pin connections for the 7493. The 7493 contains both a divide-by-2 and a divide-by-8 counter. There are two clock inputs, and the two counters can be used separately. The 7493 can be used as a divide-by-16 counter by using the divide-by-2 clock as the clock input and placing a jumper between Q_0 and the divide-by-8 clock; both zero-set inputs must be grounded.

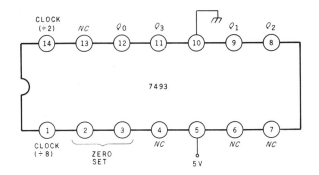

Figure P4.4.

(b) Drive the counter with the 50 kHz clock constructed in problem P4.3a, and use the dual-trace oscilloscope to determine whether or not the four counter outputs are proper.

(c) Use the dual-trace oscilloscope to observe the I/O characteristic of the count converter: display the analog output on one channel of the dual-trace oscilloscope and the Q_3 counter output on the other channel. Trigger the oscilloscope with Q_3. Sketch the waveforms.

P4.5.   Through a connecting cable from the KIM-1 microcomputer to a solderless breadboard, you have access to the following pins of a 6502 MOS Technology microprocessor:

- The clock signals (two pins: Q_1 and Q_2)
- The 16-bit address line (sixteen pins: $AB0$, $AB1$, $AB2$,..., $AB15$)
- The 8-bit data bus (eight pins: $DB0$, $DB1$, $DB2$,..., $DB7$)
- The read/write signal (one pin: R/W)

In the 6502 microprocessor, R/W is a status signal used for synchronizing the flow of data in and out of the microprocessor on the data lines $DB0$, $DB1$, $DB2$,..., $DB7$ (ie: on the data bus). Specifically, R/W is HIGH, except when the 6502 microprocessor is trying to write to external memory. This occurs during a portion of the time that the instructions STA, STX, STY, DEC, and INC are being executed. Figure P4.5a shows the relative timing of these signals during the clock cycle of the STA instruction when the data from the A register are put onto the data bus.

Consider the execution of the KIM-1 program of figure P4.5b. As a result of running this program, the hexadecimal number 34 (ie: binary 0011 0100) will be put on the data bus (ie: on $DB0$, $DB1$, $DB2$, $DB3$, $DB4$, $DB5$, $DB6$,

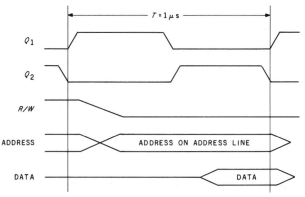

Figure P4.5.

TIMING FOR WRITING DATA TO MEMORY OR PERIPHERALS

(a)

Address	Instruction	Op Code	Comments
0100	AD	LDA	Load contents of memory
0101	00	(abs)	location 0200 into register A
0102	02		
0103	8D	STA	Write contents of register A
0104	FF	(abs)	into memory location FFFF
0105	FF		
0106	EA	NOP	No operation
0107	4C	JMP	Jump to address 0106 for the
0108	06	(abs)	next executable instruction. (A
0109	01		tight loop is formed between
			0106 and 0107)
0200	34		Number 34 is fetched during ex-
			ecution of instruction 0100

(b)

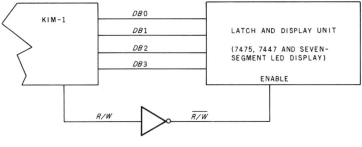

(c)

and $DB7$) during the execution of the STA instruction. The signal R/W goes LOW to signify the presence of data on the data bus. Thus, one can capture and hold this data by using eight latches (eg: eight D-type flip-flops with enable inputs such as can be obtained with two 7475s). Figure P4.5c shows how one might create an output display for the KIM-1. In this system, only the 4 least-significant bits are output — they are displayed as a BCD using a seven-segment display.

(a) Construct the latch and display unit. By using an 8-bit switch to simulate the KIM-1 signals $DB0$, $DB1$, $DB2$, $DB3$, and R/W, test the latch and display unit. *Do not use the KIM-1 microcomputer here.*

(b) Once you are certain that the latch and display unit is functioning well, interface it to the KIM-1. Load the program and run it. The number 4 should appear on the display. To further check your system, store various numbers in 0200 and run the program.

(c) Design and implement an interface similar to the above with the following exception:

The modified latch and display unit should not accept the data on the data lines unless the write instruction being executed (ie: the STA instruction) is attempting to write to a memory location whose 16-bit address begins and ends with a "1" (eg: FFFF or 8001).

Hint: Input $\overline{R/W} \cdot AB0 \cdot AB15$ to the enable pin of the display. Either the 7410 or the 7420 is convenient for implementing this logic function, in that $\overline{R/W} \cdot AB0 \cdot AB15$ can be realized by using only one IC package.

Chapter 5

Bus Structures

In the design of large systems made up of interconnections of many sub-systems, a serious practical problem arises when each subsystem must communicate with every other subsystem. To illustrate, consider the system, composed of five subsystems, shown in figure 5.1. If each subsystem is to transmit data to and receive data from every other subsystem, then each subsystem must have a data path to and a data path from every other subsystem. Figure 5.1 shows the most obvious approach to this problem: each subsystem is connected to every other subsystem by two wires, one for

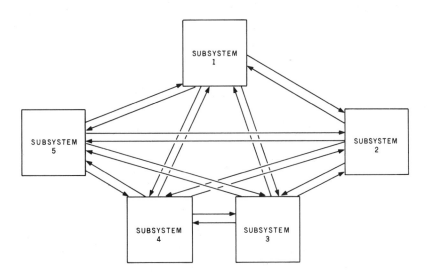

Figure 5.1: *Interconnecting subsystems with independent communication links.*

transmitting and one for receiving. In this system, a total of twenty wires is required to complete all the communication links.

Consider the general case in which a large digital system is made up of n subsystems and data is transmitted in the form of w-digit binary numbers. Using parallel data transmission (ie: data transmission where all w bits of a w-bit number are transmitted simultaneously), it takes w wires to transmit a single w-bit number. If there is two-way data transmission between all subsystems, and if each subsystem is to transmit and receive simultaneously, then there must be $2w$ wires connecting each subsystem to every other subsystem. The number of wires required to connect n subsystems so that there is only one wire between all subsystems is denoted by N_{1n}, and

$$N_{1n} = \frac{1}{2} n(n + 1)$$

The number of wires required to connect n w-bit digital systems so as to provide two-way communication between all subsystems is denoted by N_{wn}:

$$N_{wn} = wn(n - 1)$$

If this approach to connecting subsystems were used for a modest 8-bit, twenty-subsystem digital system, 3040 wires would be required; for a 16-bit, 200-subsystem digital system, 636,800 wires would be required. An alternate approach requiring fewer wires is obviously needed.

The key to reducing the number of wires between subsystems lies in the fact that most large digital systems, such as digital computers, are sequential-logic systems. As such, these systems are not always inputting and outputting data. As a result, it is possible for the various subsystems to *time share* data-transmission wires with each other; the same wires can be used for both inputting and outputting. Figure 5.2 shows how the time sharing of data-transmission wires can simplify the interconnections; compare this to the five-subsystem system shown in figure 5.1, which has independent two-way data transmission between each pair of subsystems. In this time-sharing system, all subsystems are connected to a single wire, and this single wire is used by each subsystem to both transmit and receive data to

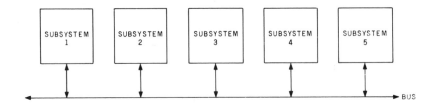

Figure 5.2: *Interconnecting subsystems with a time-shared bus.*

and from every other system. Such a wire is called a *bus*. For an 8-bit digital system, a set of eight wires is required for the parallel transmission of all 8 bits of an 8-bit word; an *8-bit bus* is needed. A bus consists of one or more wires; each wire is driven by one or more transmitters and has one or more receivers attached to it.

A typical 1-bit bus structure is shown in figure 5.3. The state of the bus can be determined by any *one* of the n transmitters attached to it; the state of the bus can be sensed by *all* m receivers attached to it. The essential characteristic required of a bus structure is that it should be possible for a selected transmitter to set the state of the bus while the other transmitters are physically connected to the bus.

By representing the state of the bus by the switching variable D, one possibility for a bus-structure design can be based upon the relationship

$$D = V_1 + V_2 + \cdots + V_n$$

If transmitters can be designed such that a bus-structure implementation of the above equation can be realized, then the bus-structure design is completed. For example, if this equation modeled the 1-bit bus structure of figure 5.3, the bus could be driven by transmitter i simply by setting all transmitter inputs other than V_i to 0 (ie: $V_j = 0$ for $j \neq i$), and the state of the bus would be determined by transmitter V_i:

$$D = V_i$$

All the receivers simply sense the data on the bus, ie:

$$D_1 = D_2 = \cdots = D_m = D$$

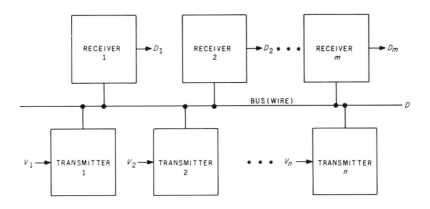

Figure 5.3: *A 1-bit bus structure.*

A simple noninverting driver (ie: a *buffer*) would serve well as a receiver. Thus, one possibility for a general bus relationship is

$$D_1 = D_2 = \cdots = D_m = V_1 + V_2 + \cdots + V_n \qquad (5.1)$$

The difficulty in bus-structure design is associated with the design of the transmitters. For use in a bus structure, transmitters must be devices that can be connected to the bus *without physically cutting the bus*. The problem is that the bus connects the outputs of all the transmitters. For example, if standard TTL gates with totem-pole outputs are used, connecting two outputs leads to an indeterminate output condition. This occurs when one gate is trying to drive the output HIGH and the other gate is trying to drive the output LOW. When two or more TTL outputs are connected, there is a risk of burning out the connected gates.

In this chapter, bus transmitters that allow data to be unambiguously transmitted on a bus are examined.

5.1 RTL-Based Bus Structures

A simple bus design is based on the RTL inverter. An RTL inverter is shown again for convenience in figure 5.4. Recall that for a properly designed inverter, a LOW input voltage v_i produces a HIGH output voltage

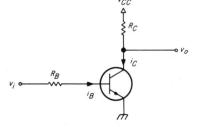

Figure 5.4: *An RTL inverter.*

v_o, and vice versa. The fundamental transistor property upon which the operation of the inverter is based is that of current gain; until the transistor saturates, the collector current is roughly proportional to base current:

$$i_C = h_{FE} \, i_B$$

Equivalently, the transistor's collector-to-emitter resistance R_{CE} can be controlled by the amount of base current i_B. When $i_B = 0$, R_{CE} is very large (eg: values of $R_{CE(OFF)} = 50 \text{ k}\Omega$ are typical). For most applications, the amount of collector current I_{CO} flowing through the 50 kΩ resistor $R_{CE(OFF)}$ is negligible (eg: typically $I_{CO} < 250 \ \mu A$ when $V_{CC} = 5$ V). R_{CE} is very small (eg:

values of $R_{CE(OFF)} = 10 \ \Omega$ are typical) when the transistor is saturated, ie: when

$$i_B > \frac{V_{CC}}{h_{FE}R_C}$$

The circuit operates as an inverter only if

$$R_{CE(ON)} \ll R_C \ll R_{CE(OFF)}$$

When these inequalities are satisfied

$$v_{o(HIGH)} = \frac{R_{CE(OFF)}}{R_C + R_{CE(OFF)}} \, V_{CC}$$

and

$$v_{o(LOW)} = \frac{R_{CE(ON)}}{R_C + R_{CE(ON)}} \, V_{CC}$$

If $R_C \cong 1000 \ \Omega$, $R_{CE(OFF)} = 50 \ k\Omega$, and $R_{CE(ON)} = 10 \ \Omega$, then

$$v_{o(HIGH)} = 0.98 \, V_{CC} \cong V_{CC}$$
$$v_{o(LOW)} = 0.0099 \, V_{CC} \cong 0$$

Consider the case in which the outputs of two RTL inverters are connected, as shown in figure 5.5a. The output voltage v_o can be determined from the equivalent circuit of figure 5.5b, in which transistors Q_1 and Q_2 are replaced by their equivalent collector-to-emitter resistances R_{CE1} and R_{CE2}. When both inputs v_1 and v_2 are low, $R_{CE1} = R_{CE2} = R_{CE(OFF)}$, and the output is HIGH:

$$v_o = \frac{R_{CE(OFF)}}{R_C + R_{CE(OFF)}} \, V_{CC} \cong V_{CC}$$

When both inputs are HIGH, $R_{CE1} = R_{CE(ON)}$, and the output is LOW:

$$v_o = \frac{R_{CE(ON)}}{R_C + R_{CE(ON)}} V_{CC} \cong 0$$

When one input is LOW (eg: $v_1 = 0$), and the other input is HIGH ($v_2 = V_{CC}$), $R_{CE1} = R_{CE(OFF)}$, and $R_{CE2} = R_{CE(ON)}$, and

$$v_o = \frac{R_{CEP}}{\frac{1}{2}R_C + R_{CEP}} \, V_{CC}$$

where R_{CEP} is the resistance of the parallel combination of $R_{CE(OFF)}$ and $R_{CE(ON)}$:

$$R_{CEP} = \frac{R_{CE(OFF)} \, R_{CE(ON)}}{R_{CE(OFF)} + R_{CE(ON)}}$$

However, for a well-designed inverter, $R_{CE(OFF)} >> R_{CE(ON)}$, and thus

$$R_{CEP} \cong R_{CE(ON)}$$

Therefore, with one input LOW and one input HIGH, the output is LOW:

$$v_o \cong \frac{R_{CE(ON)}}{\frac{1}{2}R_C + R_{CE(ON)}} V_{CC} \cong 0$$

Figure 5.5c shows a truth table summarizing the operation of this circuit for the case that $R_C = 1000\ \Omega$, $R_{CE(OFF)} = 50\ k\Omega$, and $R_{CE(ON)} = 10\ \Omega$. Note that when one input is LOW and the other input is HIGH, the output voltage is somewhat higher than it is when both inputs are HIGH. It can still be interpreted as a LOW however. Note that R_C must be selected so that $R_{CE(ON)} << R_C$ to obtain a LOW output when both inputs are HIGH. To obtain a LOW output when one input is HIGH and the other input is LOW, R_C must be selected so that $R_{CE(ON)} << \frac{1}{2}R_C$. This truth table shows that, with proper designs, connecting the outputs of two RTL inverters produces a NOR circuit:

$$V_0 = \overline{V_1 + V_2}$$

Thus, RTL inverters can be used as transmitters in designing bus structures.

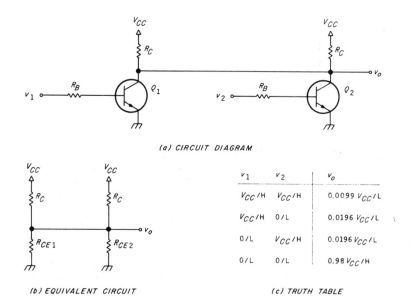

(a) CIRCUIT DIAGRAM

(b) EQUIVALENT CIRCUIT

v_1	v_2	v_o
V_{CC}/H	V_{CC}/H	0.0099 V_{CC}/L
V_{CC}/H	0/L	0.0196 V_{CC}/L
0/L	V_{CC}/H	0.0196 V_{CC}/L
0/L	0/L	0.98 V_{CC}/H

(c) TRUTH TABLE

Figure 5.5: *Connecting the outputs of two RTL inverters.*

Figure 5.6 shows a bus design using RTL inverters. For this structure the data on the bus D is related to the transmitter inputs by

$$D = \overline{V_1 + V_2 + \cdots + V_n}$$

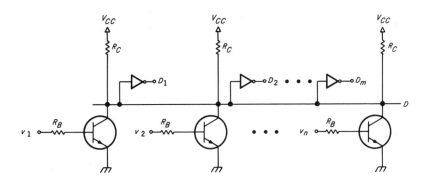

Figure 5.6: *An RTL inverter-based bus.*

Although an OR relationship was suggested earlier, the NOR relationship serves the objective just as well. By making the receivers inverters instead of buffers, the effect of the inversion is cancelled, and the desired bus relationship is obtained:

$$D_1 = D_2 = \cdots = D_m = V_1 + V_2 + \cdots + V_n$$

5.2 TTL Open-Collector Logic

Recall that standard TTL gates use the totem-pole output (see figure 5.7) to obtain higher switching speeds in the LOW-to-HIGH transitions (section 2.2.3). Unfortunately, because of the totem-pole output, the standard TTL gate is unsuitable as a bus transmitter.

The totem-pole output achieves its fast LOW-to-HIGH switching speed by using transistor Q_3 to actively drive the output HIGH, rather than passively letting the output go HIGH as in an RTL output. In terms of bus structures, an RTL inverter (figure 5.4) is not violated if the output voltage is HIGH instead of LOW when the transistor is OFF. In other words, setting the base current i_B to 0 imposes no demands on the collector-to-emitter voltage v_{CE}; all that is required is that the transistor's collector current also be 0. In an RTL inverter, setting the transistor's base current to 0 does not *drive* the output voltage HIGH. Rather, the transistor simply turns OFF (ie: collector current goes to 0), and other circuit parameters determine if v_{CE} will go HIGH or LOW.

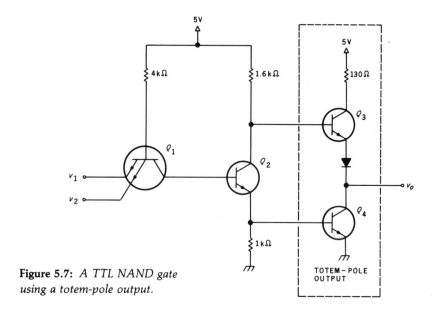

Figure 5.7: *A TTL NAND gate using a totem-pole output.*

In the case of a capacitively loaded inverter, the capacitive load is *passively* charged through resistor R_C when the transistor is turned OFF, resulting in a HIGH output voltage; the transistor plays no role in this charging process. When the outputs of two RTL inverters are connected as in figure 5.5a, the output of one inverter can be LOW even though the transistor is turned OFF. The inverter in the passive state (ie: the inverter whose transistor is turned OFF and whose output is normally HIGH) allows the inverter in the active state (ie: the inverter whose transistor is turned ON and whose output is normally LOW) to dominate, producing a LOW output voltage.

On the other hand, driving the base current HIGH turns the transistor ON, and the transistor's collector-to-emitter resistance becomes very small. The transistor uses its current gain to *actively* sink the collector terminal to the emitter potential (to ground in the case of an RTL inverter).

For the totem-pole output (figure 5.7), transistor Q_4 is active in the HIGH-to-LOW output transition, while transistor Q_3 is active in the LOW-to-HIGH output transition. The output is being actively driven both HIGH and LOW. Therefore, it is not advisable to connect two totem-pole outputs; when one totem-pole circuit tries to drive the output LOW, while the other is trying to drive the output HIGH, the output state is indeterminate, and both totem-pole output circuits may burn out.

Because of the difficulty in using standard TTL having totem-pole outputs in the design of bus structures, an alternate output structure suitable for use in bus structures has been introduced. As shown in the TTL NAND gate of figure 5.8, a simpler (but slower) output stage would simply utilize an RTL inverter instead of the totem-pole output. There is no single value for resistor R that is suitable for all potential applications and, as a result, there is no commercially available IC logic family corresponding to this cir-

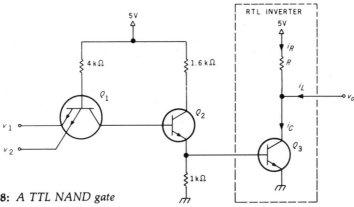

Figure 5.8: *A TTL NAND gate with RTL-inverter output.*

cuit. However, because resistor R is the only component in this circuit which is sensitive to the particular application, and because resistor R is connected between the 5 V power supply and the collector (output v_o), and because both these circuit points must be accessible as output pins on any IC devised, it is feasible to manufacture an IC corresponding to this circuit, minus resistor R; it would be the user's responsibility to insert the appropriate resistor R. There is a family of TTL devices having RTL inverter output stages, minus the collector-to-power supply resistor R. This logic family is called the *TTL open-collector* family. Figure 5.9 shows an open-collector NAND gate. Note that the user must provide the *pull-up resistor R*

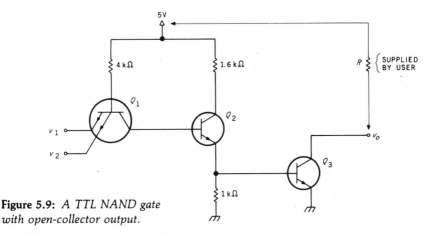

Figure 5.9: *A TTL NAND gate with open-collector output.*

and connect it between the collector of Q_3 and the 5 V power supply. The TTL 7403 IC is a quad two-input open-collector NAND package, in which each of the four NANDs is similar to the open-collector NAND gate of figure 5.9.

Figure 5.10a shows common graphical representations of the open-collector NAND and the open-collector inverter circuits. The NAND and NOT functions are achieved only when pull-up resistors have been connected as shown in figure 5.10b. These open-collector representations, in which logic components and circuit components are used in the same diagram, are somewhat awkward in that switching-algebra variables and real-algebra variables are unconventionally mixed in a single model representation. Nevertheless, these commonly used representations are descriptive of the hardware used in the implementation of a model and should cause no confusion.

Selection of an appropriate value for R depends upon two particular categories of applications. In the first category, open-collector logic devices are used as standard TTL devices to drive other TTL devices. In the second category, open-collector logic devices are used as bus drivers.

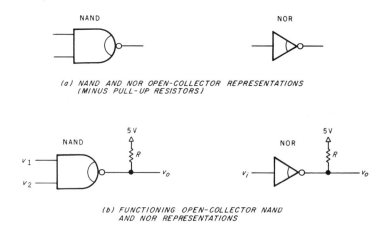

(a) NAND AND NOR OPEN-COLLECTOR REPRESENTATIONS
(MINUS PULL-UP RESISTORS)

(b) FUNCTIONING OPEN-COLLECTOR NAND
AND NOR REPRESENTATIONS

Figure 5.10: *Open-collector representations.*

5.2.1   Use of Open-Collector Logic Devices to Drive Other TTL Devices

In figure 5.11 an open-collector NAND gate is used to drive m TTL devices. The designer's problem is to determine the range of acceptable values for register R that allows the open-collector NAND to function as a NAND gate.

When the output v_o is LOW (ie: the open-collector transistor Q_3 is turned

ON), there is no upper bound on the value of R. Increasing the value of R decreases the collector current i_C ($i_C = i_R + i_L$), and decreasing the collector current simply reduces the minimum base current i_B required to saturate the

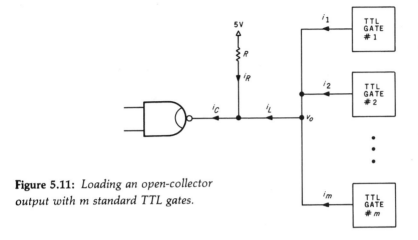

Figure 5.11: *Loading an open-collector output with m standard TTL gates.*

transistor. On the other hand, R can be decreased to the point that the collector current becomes large enough to drive transistor Q_3 out of saturation, and a LOW output v_o cannot be guaranteed. To insure that the output v_o is in the LOW state, R must be greater than a certain minimum value $R_{(min)}$:

$$R_{(min)} = \frac{V_{CC(max)} - v_{CES(min)}}{i_{CS(min)} - i_{LLOW(max)}}$$

where $i_{CS(min)}$ = the minimum collector-current that might drive Q_3 out of saturation, and $i_{LLOW(max)}$ = the maximum current that the m TTL gates loading the output can sink to ground through the collector of the open-collector transistor Q_3. For standard TTL,

$$V_{CC(max)} = 5.5 \text{ V}$$
$$v_{CES(min)} = 0.2 \text{ V}$$
$$i_{CS(min)} = 16 \text{ mA}$$
$$i_{LLOW(max)} = 1.6m \text{ mA}$$

Thus,

$$R_{(min)} = \frac{5.5 - 0.2}{(16 - 1.6m) \ 10^{-3}}$$

For example, if an open-collector NAND is driving three TTL loads (ie: $m = 3$), then

$$R_{(min)} = \frac{5.5 - 0.2}{(16 - 4.8) \ 10^{-3}} = 473 \ \Omega$$

When the output v_o is HIGH (ie: the open-collector transistor Q_3 is turned OFF), there is no lower bound on the value of R. Decreasing the value of R simply decreases the voltage drop across R and thus brings the value of v_o closer to V_{CC}. Conversely, increasing R can reduce the value of v_o below the minimum value specified for a HIGH. To insure that v_o is in the HIGH state, R must be less than a certain maximum value $R_{(max)}$:

$$R_{(max)} = \frac{V_{CC(min)} - v_{oHIGH(min)}}{I_{CO(max)} + |i_{LHIGH(max)}|}$$

where $v_{oHIGH(min)}$ = the minimum voltage, which will be interpreted as a HIGH; $I_{CO(max)}$ = the maximum leakage current I_{CO} through the open-collector transistor Q_3 when it is turned OFF; and $i_{LHIGH(max)}$ = the maximum current drawn by the m TTL gates loading the output. For standard TTL,

$$\begin{aligned} V_{CC(min)} &= 4.5 \text{ V} \\ v_{oHIGH(min)} &= 2.4 \text{ V} \\ I_{CO(max)} &= 250 \ \mu\text{A} \\ i_{LHIGH(max)} &= -40m \ \mu\text{A} \end{aligned}$$

Thus,

$$R_{(max)} = \frac{4.5 - 2.4}{(250 + 40m) \ 10^{-6}}$$

For the case that $n = 3$,

$$R_{(max)} = 5676 \ \Omega$$

If an open-collector gate is loaded with three TTL gates, the value of the pull-up resistor R must be such that

$$473 < R < 5676$$

5.2.2 Open-Collector Bus Drivers

Consider the situation in which n open-collector inverters are used as transmitters to drive a bus having m TTL inverters connected to it as receivers (figure 5.12). A single pull-up resistor R is connected between the bus and the 5 V source to serve all n open-collector inverters connected to the bus. Again, the designer's problem is to determine the range of acceptable values for resistor R. Proceeding as before, $R_{(min)}$ is determined when $v_o = $ LOW:

$$R_{(min)} = \frac{V_{CC(max)} - v_{CES(min)}}{i_{CS(min)} - i_{LLOW(max)}}$$

$$= \frac{5.5 - 1.2}{(16 - 1.6m) \ 10^{-3}}$$

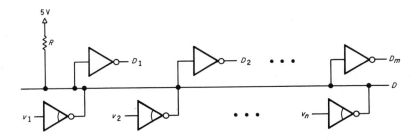

Figure 5.12: *An open-collector bus driver: n transmitters and m receivers.*

Therefore,

$$R_{(min)} = \frac{3312}{10 - m}$$

For example, if there are five receivers (ie: $m = 5$), then

$$R_{(min)} = 663 \ \Omega$$

$R_{(max)}$ is determined with $v_o = $ HIGH:

$$R_{(max)} = \frac{V_{CC(min)} - v_{oHIGH(min)}}{nI_{CO(max)} + |i_{LHIGH(max)}|}$$

$$= \frac{4.5 - 2.4}{(250n + 40m) \ 10^{-6}}$$

Therefore,

$$R_{(max)} = \frac{2.1 \times 10^5}{25n + 4m}$$

For example, if there are five transmitters (ie: $n = 5$) and five receivers (ie: $m = 5$), then

$$R_{(max)} = 1448 \ \Omega$$

Thus, if an open-collector bus has five transmitters and five receivers connected to it, the value of the pull-up resistor R must be such that

$$663 < R < 1448$$

5.3 TTL Tristate

Now, consider the possibility of using standard TTL gates with totem-pole outputs (figure 5.7) in the design of bus structures. For purposes of determining the output voltage v_o, the TTL totem-pole output circuit can be replaced by the simpler equivalent circuits shown in figure 5.13. Figure 5.13a shows the equivalent circuit for the case that v_o is LOW (ie: the lower totem-pole transistor Q_3 is ON, and the upper totem-pole transistor Q_4 is OFF), and figure 5.13b shows the equivalent circuit for the case that v_o is HIGH (ie: Q_3 is OFF and Q_4 is ON). Resistor R_{OFF} represents a transistor's collector-to-emitter resistance when that transistor is OFF; for the totem-pole transistors Q_3 and Q_4,

$$R_{OFF} \cong 50 \text{ k}\Omega$$

Resistor R_3 represents transistor Q_3's collector-to-emitter resistance when ON:

$$R_3 \cong 10 \ \Omega$$

Resistor R_4 represents the *total* resistance in the collector-to-emitter current path of Q_4. This includes the collector-to-emitter resistance of transistor Q_4 when ON, the conducting resistance of diode D, and the 125 Ω resistor:

$$R_4 \cong 150 \ \Omega$$

Voltage v_D is the diode-conducting voltage, and voltage v_T is the collector-to-emitter voltage of transistor Q_4 when ON (remember that when the output is HIGH, Q_4 is ON but not saturated):

$$v_D \cong 0.7 \text{ V}$$
$$v_T \cong 0.7 \text{ V}$$

Voltage v_{CES} is the collector-to-emitter saturation voltage of transistor Q_4:

$$v_{CES} \cong 0.3 \text{ V}$$

Using the above values in the equivalent circuits of figure 5.13 shows that

$$v_{o(HIGH)} \cong 3.6 \text{ V}$$
$$v_{o(LOW)} \cong 0.3 \text{ V}$$

Now suppose two totem-pole outputs are connected, and one is trying to drive the output HIGH while the other is trying to drive the output LOW. This situation can be analyzed by using the totem-pole equivalent LOW and HIGH circuits of figures 5.13a and 5.13b, as shown in figure 5.13c. The currents through the two 50 kΩ resistors are negligible compared with the currents through the 150 kΩ and 10 Ω resistors. Therefore, in terms of this analysis, the 50 kΩ resistors are considered to be open circuits. The only significant current path in this equivalent circuit is the one through the

150 Ω and 10 Ω resistors, as shown in figure 5.13c. The current i through the path can be easily computed:

$$i = \frac{5 - 1.4 - 0.3}{150 + 10} \cong 20.6 \text{ mA}$$

A current of this magnitude flowing for any extended period is sufficient to burn out both transistors Q_3 and Q_4. Even if transistor Q_3 does not burn out, a current of more than 16 mA may drive transistor Q_3 out of the saturated state and invalidate the assumption that voltage source $v_{CES} = 0.3$ V. Transistor Q_4 is normally not saturated when it is conducting, and its response to attempts to drive large currents through it, while simultaneously lowering its emitter voltage, would be difficult to predict. Even if transistors Q_3 and Q_4 do not burn out, it is difficult to predict voltage v_o. Totem-pole outputs obviously should not be connected.

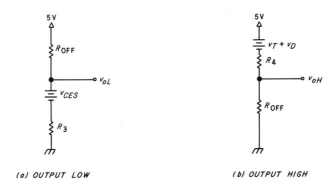

(a) OUTPUT LOW

(b) OUTPUT HIGH

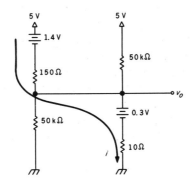

(c) HIGH AND LOW OUTPUTS CONNECTED TOGETHER

Figure 5.13: *Totem-pole output equivalent circuits.*

Another possibility is modifying the TTL NAND gate so that it is possible to turn OFF *both* totem-pole transistors Q_3 and Q_4 simultaneously. Figure 5.14a shows the equivalent circuit for the totem-pole output for the case that both transistors Q_3 and Q_4 are OFF, a case not possible with a standard TTL gate. Although the resulting output voltage v_o is theoretically 2.5 V, a transistor's collector-to-emitter cutoff resistance R_{OFF} is not a precisely specified parameter and varies significantly even among transistors of the same type. When both transistors Q_3 and Q_4 are turned OFF, the output voltage v_o is not predictable. As will be seen, this is of little consequence. Because the output terminal v_o is isolated from both the 5 V power supply and ground, with the only path to either being through a high-resistance R_{OFF}, this state of the totem-pole output, in which both transistors Q_3 and Q_4 are turned OFF, is called the *High-Z output* state.*

Of particular concern in the design of bus structures is the effect of connecting a totem-pole High-Z output to a standard totem-pole output. Such an interconnection can be analyzed by using the totem-pole equivalent circuits: figure 5.14b shows the equivalent circuit corresponding to a High-Z output connected to a LOW output; figure 5.14c shows the equivalent circuit corresponding to a High-Z output connected to a HIGH output.

Figure 5.14: *The totem-pole High-Z output state.*

(a) EQUIVALENT CIRCUIT FOR
HIGH-Z OUTPUT

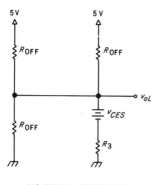

(b) HIGH-Z CONNECTED
TO A LOW

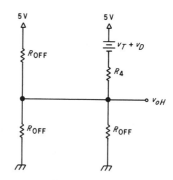

(c) HIGH-Z CONNECTED TO A HIGH

---

*Z is the symbol used for *impedance.* Impedance is a generalization of resistance that is applicable in the analysis of dynamic circuits in which the voltages and currents are time-varying. In DC circuit analysis and in resistive circuits, impedance and resistance are equivalent.

Analysis of these circuits is straightforward and results in

$$v_{o(LOW)} = 0.3 \text{ V}$$
$$v_{o(HIGH)} = 3.6 \text{ V}$$

Note that connecting the totem-pole High-Z output to a standard totem-pole output does not affect the standard totem-pole output in either the LOW or HIGH state. Therefore, a totem-pole High-Z output connected to a bus, driven by a standard TTL gate with a totem-pole output, is ignored by the bus. A TTL gate having a totem-pole output which could be put into the High-Z state would make an excellent transmitter for a bus structure.

The standard TTL NAND gate with a totem-pole output can be easily modified to provide the High-Z output capability. This involves the addition of two transistors, a diode, and a 4 kΩ resistor, as shown in bold in figure 5.15a. With such a modification, the TTL NAND gate has *three* output states: HIGH, LOW, and High-Z; hence, *tristate*. When the enable input e is HIGH, the totem-pole output is in the High-Z state, regardless of the two regular inputs v_1 and v_2; figures 5.15b and 5.15c show the conducting paths for the tristate NAND when the enable is HIGH. When the enable input e is LOW, the totem-pole output is either HIGH or LOW, depending upon the NAND of inputs v_1 and v_2; figures 5.15d and 5.15e show the conducting paths for the tristate NAND when the enable is LOW.

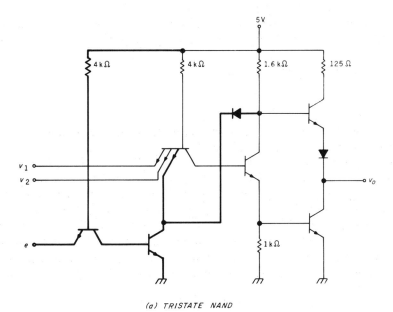

(a) TRISTATE NAND

Figure 5.15: *Construction of a tristate TTL NAND gate.*

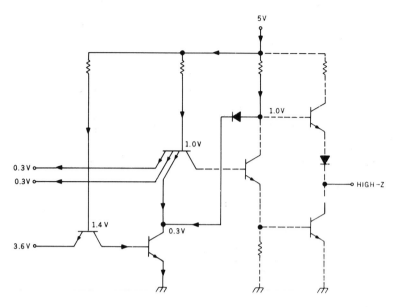

(b) CONDUCTING PATHS: INPUTS LOW, ENABLE HIGH

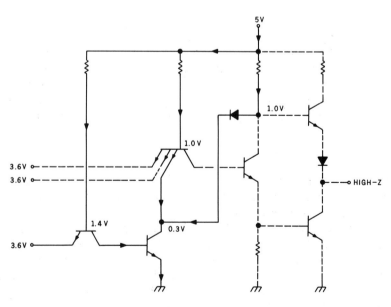

(c) CONDUCTING PATHS: INPUTS HIGH, ENABLE HIGH

Figure 5.15 cont.

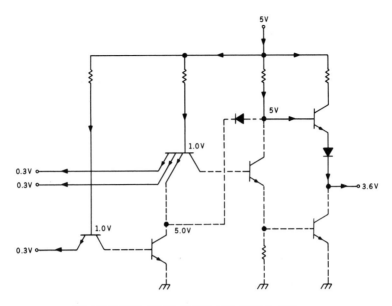

(d) CONDUCTING PATHS: INPUTS LOW, ENABLE LOW

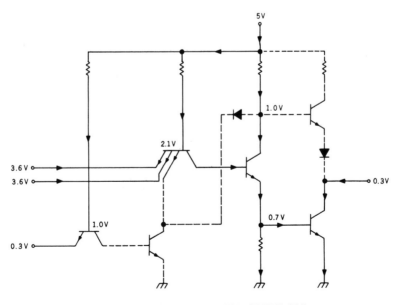

(e) CONDUCTING PATHS: INPUTS HIGH, ENABLE LOW

Figure 5.15 cont.

The graphical representation of a tristate inverter is shown in figure 5.16a. For the case that $E = 0$, the device is a standard TTL inverter. For the case that $E = 1$, regardless of the input V_i, both transistors Q_3 and Q_4 in the totem-pole output are turned OFF, and a High-Z output exists. The enable switching variable E may be thought of as representing a switch which selects either a standard TTL inverter or a High-Z output (see figure 5.16b). In terms of modeling digital systems, the utmost caution must be employed in using *2-state* switching algebra to model digital circuits which include *tristate logic* devices.

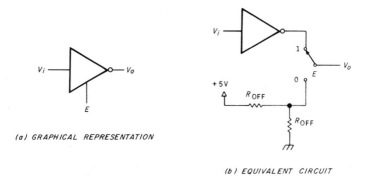

(a) GRAPHICAL REPRESENTATION

(b) EQUIVALENT CIRCUIT

Figure 5.16: *Tristate inverter.*

It is quite simple to create bus structures with tristate logic devices. Figure 5.17 shows a bus structure in which the transmitters are tristate buffers. In this bus structure, the bus is driven by one of the n transmitters, say transmitter i. In this case,

$$E_i = 0$$
$$E_j = 1 \quad j \neq i$$

All transmitters except the ith one are in the passive High-Z output state.

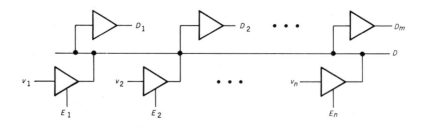

Figure 5.17: *A tristate bus structure.*

In using a tristate bus structure, it is important to take the necessary precautions to assure that no two tristate transmitters are enabled simultaneously. Enabling two transmitters is equivalent to connecting two standard totem-pole outputs and can give rise to the troublesome situation in which one or both gates may be burned out.

5.4 CMOS Tristate Logic

As with standard TTL, it is not advisable to connect the outputs of two standard CMOS logic gates. In CMOS logic circuits, the HIGH and LOW outputs are obtained by using the MOS transistors to create low-resistance paths from the output terminal to V_{DD} and to ground, respectively. For example, in the CMOS inverter of figure 2.29, a HIGH output state occurs when the upper (p-channel) MOS transistor presents a low resistance from the output terminal to V_{DD}; a LOW output state occurs when the lower (n-channel) MOS transistor presents a low resistance from the output terminal to ground. Now suppose that the output terminals of two CMOS inverters are connected, as shown in figure 5.18. If one inverter tries to drive the output HIGH, while the other inverter tries to drive the output LOW, the result is a low-resistance path from V_{DD} to ground through the p-channel MOS transistor of the HIGH-driving inverter and the n-channel MOS transistor of the LOW-driving inverter. Because the MOS transistor resistances are not precisely specified, the output state would be, at best, indeterminate. At the worst, the current through these transistors would be sufficiently large to burn them out. The outputs of standard CMOS logic gates should not be connected.

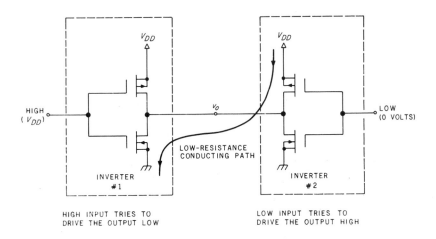

Figure 5.18: *Connecting standard CMOS logic outputs, resulting in either an indeterminate output state or a burning out of the transistors.*

Any standard CMOS logic gate can be converted to a tristate logic gate with the addition of two MOS transistors. By placing one MOS transistor in the line from the logic gate to the voltage source V_{DD} and placing the other MOS transistor in the line from the logic gate to ground, the entire logic gate can be isolated from both V_{DD} and ground upon command. Figure 5.19 shows how a standard CMOS logic gate can be converted into a tristate logic gate. The logic gate's V_{DD} terminal is connected to the V_{DD} source

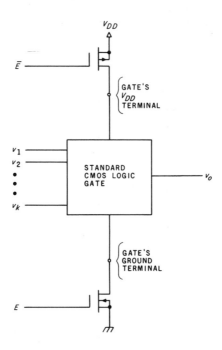

Figure 5.19: *Converting a standard CMOS logic gate to a tristate CMOS logic gate (High-Z when $E = 0$).*

through a p-channel MOS transistor, and the logic gate's ground terminal is connected to ground through an n-channel MOS transistor. The enable signal E is applied to the gate of the n-channel MOS transistor, and its inverse $\overline{E}$ is applied to the gate of the p-channel MOS transistor. A LOW enable (ie: $E = 0$) puts the gate's output into the High-Z state. Figure 5.20 shows the details of a tristate conversion for the case that the standard CMOS logic gate is an inverter. Note that this approach can be used to convert an entire standard CMOS IC package to tristate operation. For example, all four NANDs of the CMOS 4011 (quad two-input NAND) can be converted to tristate NANDs by connecting the two MOS transistors, as shown in figure 5.21. Of course, the enable signal E affects all four NAND gates in the package, and it would not be possible to control each gate separately.

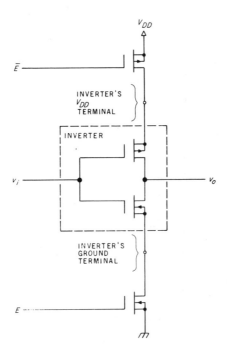

Figure 5.20: *Tristate CMOS inverters (High-Z when E = 0).*

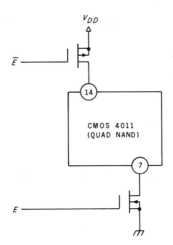

Figure 5.21: *Power supply connections to convert standard CMOS 4011 quad NAND to tristate quad NAND (High-Z when E = 0).*

5.5   Tristate Logic Applications

5.5.1   Memory Design

An example of an application of tristate logic in bus design is the use of bus concepts to reduce the number of pins required for the 4 × 2 memory array (section 4.4.4) by using the same pins for both data input and data output. Recall that the basic memory cell, shown again here in figure 5.22a, was designed such that

$$Q(t + T) = \overline{E}(t)\, Q(t) + E(t)\, [\,\overline{R/W}(t)\, D_{in}(t) + R/W(t)\, Q(t)]$$
$$D_{out}(t) = E(t)\, [R/W(t)\, Q(t)]$$

In designing a data-input, data-output bus structure, it is desirable to have a basic memory cell in which only one pin is used for both input and output; the combination of the D_{in} and D_{out} pins into a single pin is called the input/output (I/O) pin. A representation of such a memory cell is shown in figure 5.22b. When $E \cdot \overline{R/W} = 1$, the I/O pin is used as an input pin, and when $E \cdot R/W = 1$, the I/O pin is used as an output pin,

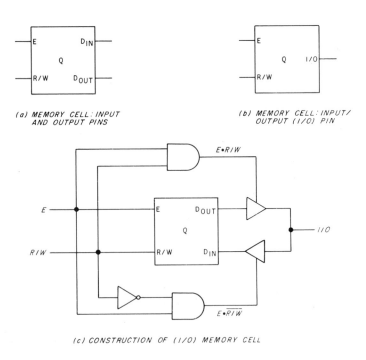

(a) MEMORY CELL: INPUT
AND OUTPUT PINS

(b) MEMORY CELL: INPUT/
OUTPUT (I/O) PIN

(c) CONSTRUCTION OF (I/O) MEMORY CELL

Figure 5.22: *Basic read/write memory cells.*

$$Q(t + T) = \overline{E}(t)\, Q(t) + E(t)\, [\overline{R/W}(t)\, I/O(t) + R/W(t)\, Q(t)]$$
$$\text{I/O used as input}$$

$$I/O(t) = \begin{cases} Q(t) & \text{if } E(t)\, R/W(t) = 1 \quad \text{and} \quad \text{I/O used as output} \\ \text{High-Z} & \text{if } E(t) = 0 \end{cases}$$

Figure 5.22c shows the design of such a memory cell using the basic cell of figure 5.22a.

Designing a 4 × 2 memory array is a straightforward matter using the basic memory cell of figure 5.22c. Such a design is shown in figure 5.23a.

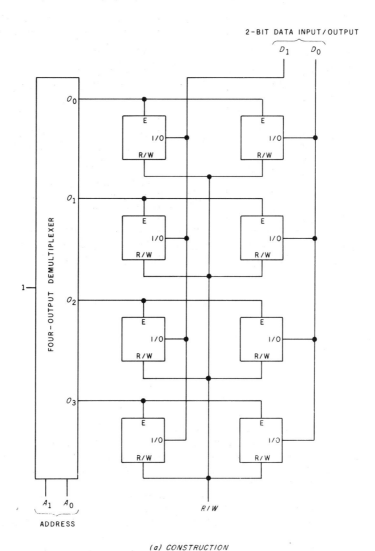

(a) CONSTRUCTION

Figure 5.23: *A 4 × 2 memory array.*

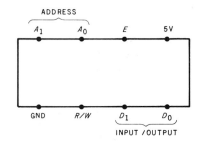

Figure 5.23 cont.

(b) PIN CONNECTIONS

Compare the simple 2-bit bus structure here with the input/output (I/O) arrangement of the 4 × 2 memory array of figure 4.39a. Figure 5.23b shows the output pins that would be required for an IC implementation of this 4 × 2 memory array of figure 5.23a.

5.5.2   Bi-Bus Drivers

By using tristate logic devices, it is relatively simple to design a single logic device that can act alternately as a transmitter and a receiver. Such a device is called a *transceiver*, or a *bi-bus driver*. The function of a transceiver is defined with reference to figure 5.24. Specifically, if $E_1 = 1$ and $E_2 = 0$, then transceiver #1 functions as a transmitter (and thus drives the bus), and transceiver #2 functions as a receiver. Therefore, an input applied to transceiver #1 is transmitted on the bus and appears as an output on transceiver #2. Conversely, if $E_1 = 0$ and $E_2 = 1$, the roles of the two transceivers are reversed; an input applied to transceiver #2 is transmitted on the bus and appears as an output on transceiver #1. Figure 5.25a shows how a transceiver can be implemented by using two tristate buffers and an inverter. A graphical representation of a transceiver is shown in figure 5.25b.

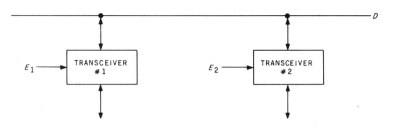

Figure 5.24: *Transceiver bus structure.*

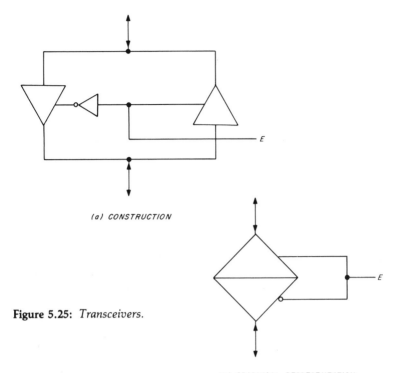

(a) CONSTRUCTION

(b) GRAPHICAL REPRESENTATION

Figure 5.25: *Transceivers.*

PROBLEMS

P5.1. (a) Construct an interface to the KIM-1 microcomputer to *externally* compare two 8-bit numbers. The two numbers to be compared are stored in memory locations 0000 and 0001. They are sequentially put onto the data bus by running the program of figure P5.1a. Note that when number A is put on the data bus, as a result of executing the store instruction STA at 0123, AB15 goes HIGH; when number B is put on the data bus, AB14 goes HIGH. Thus, the latch circuit used to store number A can be enabled with $\overline{R/W} \cdot AB15 \cdot \overline{AB14} \cdot \overline{AB13}$; the latch circuit used to store number B can be enabled with $\overline{R/W} \cdot \overline{AB15} \cdot AB14 \cdot \overline{AB13}$; AB13 provides increased redundancy, and AB13 is used in part (b). Use three LEDs to display the result of the comparison: LED #1 lights up if $A < B$; LED #2 lights up if $A = B$; LED #3 lights up if $A > B$. Two 7485s should be used to construct an 8-bit comparator, and a pair of 7475s should be used to latch each of the two numbers to be compared. The diagram of figure P5.1b suggests such an interface.

(b) The interface circuit of part (a) provides the basis for this exercise. Design and construct the appropriate tristate bus interface, so that the result of the external comparison of the two 8-bit numbers, A and B, is input to the KIM-1 on lines DB7 (HIGH when $A < B$), DB6 (HIGH when $A = B$), and DB5 (HIGH when $A > B$) of the data bus whenever a read-memory instruction (eg: LDA) is executed in which the memory location being read is such that AB13 = 1. The diagram of figure P5.1c suggests such an interface.

A KIM-1 program has been written, and it is listed in figure P5.1d.

1. Put the two numbers to be compared (ie: the numbers stored in 0000 and 0001) onto the data bus: A is on the data bus when $\overline{R/W} \cdot AB15 \cdot \overline{AB14} \cdot \overline{AB13}$ is HIGH; B is on the data bus when $\overline{R/W} \cdot \overline{AB15} \cdot AB14 \cdot \overline{AB13}$ is HIGH.
2. Display the result of the external comparison on the KIM-1 six-digit LED display, as shown in figure P5.1e. The KIM-1 timing used for reading data from memory or peripherals during the execution of a STA instruction is shown in figure P5.1f.

Address	Instruction	Op Code	Comments
0120 0121 0122	AD 00 00	LDA (abs)	Load contents of memory location 0000 into Register A
0123 0124 0125	8D 00 8F	STA (abs)	Store contents of Register A into memory location 8F (ie: 10001111)
0126 0127 0128	AD 01 00	LDA (abs)	Load contents of memory location 0001 into Register A
0129 012A 012B	8D 00 4F	STA (abs)	Store contents of Register A into memory location 4F (ie: 01001111)
012C	EA	NOP	No operation
012D 012E 012F	4C 2C 01	JMP (abs)	Jump to 012C forming a tight loop between 012C and 012D
0000 0001	## ##		Number A is stored here Number B is stored here

Figure P5.1a.

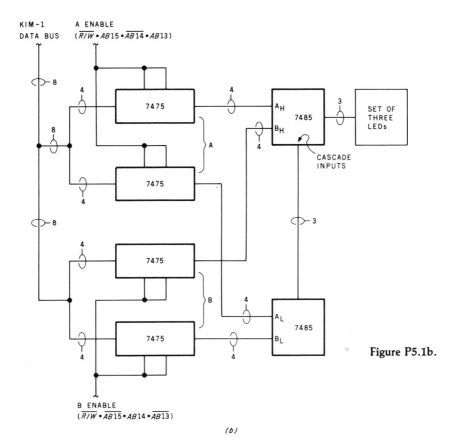

Figure P5.1b.

(b)

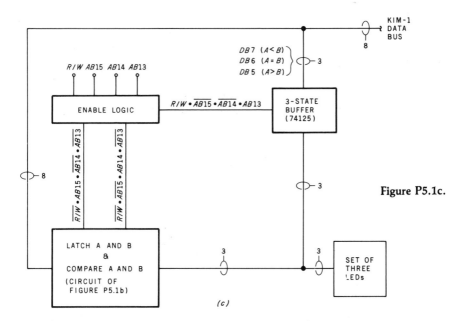

Figure P5.1c.

(c)

KIM-1 Program to display result of external comparison

Address	Instruction	Op Code	Comments
0120	AD	LDA	
1	00	(abs)	
2	00		
3	8D	STA	Write: Put number A
4	00	(abs)	on data bus
5	8F		
6	AD	LDA	
7	01	(abs)	
8	00		
9	8D	STA	Write: Put number B
A	00	(abs)	on data bus
B	4F		
C	AD	LDA	Read: Result of comparison
D	00	(abs)	put on data bus
E	2F		
F	30	BMI	
0130	1B		
1	0A	ASL	
2	30	BMI	
3	27		
4	AD	LDA	
5	00	(abs)	
6	00		
7	8D	STA	
8	FB	(abs)	
9	00		
A	AD	LDA	
B	01	(abs)	
C	00		
D	8D	STA	
E	FA	(abs)	
F	00		
0140	AD	LDA	
1	02		
2	00		
3	8D	STA	
4	F9	(abs)	
5	00		

Figure P5.1d.

Address	Instruction	Op Code	Comments
6	20	JSR	SCANDS subroutine in
7	1F		KIM-1 ROM starting at
8	1F		address 1F1F*
9	4C	JMP	
A	46	(abs)	
B	01		
C	AD	LDA	
D	00	(abs)	
E	00		
F	8D	STA	
0150	FA	(abs)	
1	00		
2	AD	LDA	
3	01	(abs)	
4	00		
5	8D	STA	
6	FB	(abs)	
7	00		
8	4C	JMP	
9	40	(abs)	
A	01		
B	AD	LDA	
C	03	(abs)	
D	00		
E	8D	STA	
F	FA	(abs)	
0160	00		
1	8D	STA	
2	FB	(abs)	
3	00		
4	AD	LDA	
5	00	(abs)	
6	00		

Figure P5.1d cont.

*The KIM-1 display consists of six seven-segment LED displays, as shown in figure P5.1g. The four leftmost LED displays are identified as a_3, a_2, a_1, and a_0; the two rightmost LED displays are identified as d_1 and d_0. The LEDs are controlled by the KIM-1 subroutine SCANDS located in read-only memory starting at address 1F1F. Calling SCANDS results in the following:

- The contents of address 00F9 are displayed in d_1 and d_0
- The contents of address 00FA are displayed in a_1 and a_0
- The contents of address 00FB are displayed in a_3 and a_2

To sustain the display, subroutine SCANDS must be included in a fast loop.

Address	Instruction	Op Code	Comments
7	8D	STA	
8	F9	(abs)	
9	00		
A	4C	JMP	
B	46	(abs)	
C	01		
0000	##		Number A is stored here
0001	##		Number B is stored here
0002	AA		AA is stored here
0003	EE		EE is stored here

Figure P5.1d cont.

● *IF THE NUMBERS ARE NOT EQUAL*

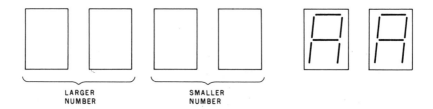

LARGER NUMBER   SMALLER NUMBER

● *IF THE NUMBERS ARE EQUAL*

THE NUMBER

(e)

Figure P5.1e.

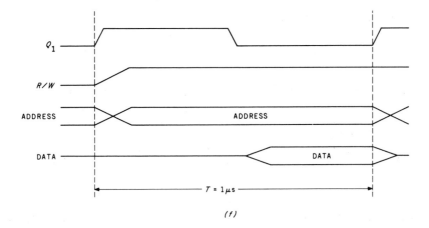

(f)

Figure P5.1f.

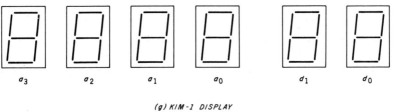

(g) KIM-1 DISPLAY

Figure P5.1g.

Chapter 6

Computer Architecture

Perhaps the most sophisticated of all sequential-logic systems is the digital computer. A general-purpose digital computer can be programmed to execute a variety of sequential-logic functions. Whether or not a specific sequential-logic function can be executed by a given digital computer is determined by the size of the computer's memory. Theoretically, a general-purpose digital computer with infinite memory could be programmed to execute *any* sequential-logic function. Practically, however, a digital computer is limited not only by the size of its memory, but also by the computer's speed in accessing memory and in evaluating primitive logic functions. Although it may be theoretically possible for a digital computer to execute a specified sequential-logic function, the length of time required to do so may be practically prohibitive. In addition to the size of a computer's memory, computer speed is an important figure of merit used in evaluating the effectiveness of a digital computer.

Also of practical concern is the ease with which a digital computer can be programmed. Although a digital computer may be capable of executing a specified sequential-logic function at high speed, it may still be impractical to use the digital computer for this function if the programming effort is exceedingly time consuming. For example, in programming a digital computer to execute a specified sequential-logic function which includes a large number of 8-bit additions, it would be simpler for the programmer if he could avoid having to repeatedly program each 8-bit addition in terms of a sequence of the primitive logic operators (ie: ANDs, ORs, and NOTs). Including a combinational-logic 8-bit adder as an integral part of the digital computer would result in higher speed as well as simpler programming. Alternatively, the programming of a primitive digital computer (ie: one that allows the execution of combinational logic corresponding only to the primitive logic operators) could be simplified by storing a program for an

8-bit addition within the computer's memory as a *subroutine*. In this way, a program involving many 8-bit additions could be written so as to refer to this stored subroutine whenever an 8-bit addition is to be executed. Use of a subroutine simplifies the programming task, but does not improve computing speed.

Although a digital computer's speed is ultimately limited by the switching speeds of the electronic logic circuits used in constructing the computer, the *architectural* structure of a digital computer is also an important factor in determining its speed. For example, the addition of hardware corresponding to a combinational-logic 8-bit adder as an integral part of a digital computer results in significantly higher computer speeds in executing arithmetic functions. The architecture of a digital computer refers to the characteristics of the major functional units of the computer, and how they are interconnected. The architecture of a digital computer determines its capabilities, its speed, and its ease of use. These are important considerations. This chapter introduces the basic architectural structures used in most microcomputers.

6.1   Architectures

The basic architectural units of a general-purpose digital computer are the *central processing unit* (CPU), the *main memory*, the *input and output units* (I/O), and the *bus structures*. Figure 6.1 shows a block diagram representation of a digital computer.

The CPU is generally considered to consist of two subunits:

- the *control unit* (CU) which controls the flow of data between I/O, memory, and the registers contained in the CPU
- the *arithmetic and logic unit* (ALU) which processes data contained in the CPU registers

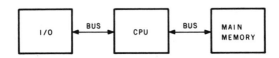

Figure 6.1: *A block diagram representation of a digital computer.*

A *program*, which is typically stored in memory, controls the sequence of actions executed by the CPU.

The computer's main memory is generally considered to be divided into two blocks:

- the CPU registers, which play a major role in determining the architecture of the CPU (and thus its speed and effectiveness)

- the external addressable memory, consisting of both read-only memory (ROM), in which initializing programs and other often-used programs are permanently stored, and read-write memory, which provides temporary storage to be used at the discretion of the programmer

The I/O units generally provide the interface between the user and the CPU. For example, an input device such as a keyboard can be used to enter a program into memory (under control of the CPU), and an output device such as a printer can be used to observe the contents of memory after a program has been executed. The distinction between an I/O device and memory is often not well defined. A mass-memory device, such as an audio-cassette recorder, may be thought of either as external or secondary memory or as an I/O device.

Bus structures interconnect the various architectural units of the digital computer. The type of bus used in a specific digital computer is determined primarily by the architecture of the CPU.

In a *microcomputer*, the CPU is generally implemented on a single chip and packaged as a single IC, although sometimes a microprocessor may be distributed over two or three ICs. An IC implementation of a CPU is called a *microprocessor*. (From here on, we shall use the term *processor* instead of CPU when we refer to the microprocessor.) Therefore, the architecture of a microcomputer is determined primarily by the particular microprocessor used. The designs of most microprocessors now being marketed are based upon von Neumann-type architecture.

6.2 Von Neumann Architecture

In von Neumann-type architecture, a program is an ordered set of instructions which is stored in addressable memory: hence, a *stored-program* computer. A program stored in memory is indistinguishable from data stored in memory; therefore, a program in memory can be manipulated by the processor as data. The control unit steps through the instructions in a program, executing each instruction as it goes.

An instruction consists of one or more words; a word is an ordered set of bits which a computer treats as a single unit. In large computers having long word lengths (such as 32-bit words), an instruction usually consists of only one word. In small computers, such as microcomputers, which typically have shorter word lengths, for example, 8-bit words, two-word and three-word instructions are common. As the technology for manufacturing LSI advances, microprocessor word lengths generally increase (eg: 16-bit word microprocessors are now common), and the distinction between large computers and microcomputers in terms of word length becomes increasingly obscure.

An instruction in a simple von Neumann architecture has two parts: the *operator* and the *operand* (see figure 6.2). The operator portion of an instruction specifies the operation to be executed by the processor (eg: ADD, SHIFT, JUMP, TRANSFER). The operand portion of an instruction either specifies the location or the *address* of the data to be operated upon or *is* that data. When the operand specifies the address of the data, the instruction is an *absolute addressing* mode instruction; when the operand *is* the data, the instruction is an *immediate addressing* mode instruction. An input or output device can be considered to be part of memory and, thus, addressable as a location in memory. There are some instructions in which the location of the data to be operated upon is implicit in the instruction itself and for which no operand is necessary. Such instructions generally refer to data stored in the registers of the processor.

Information which is either stored or transmitted within a digital computer falls into one of three categories:

- data (this includes program instructions)
- addresses, which identify the location of data
- control signals, which control the processing and transmission of data

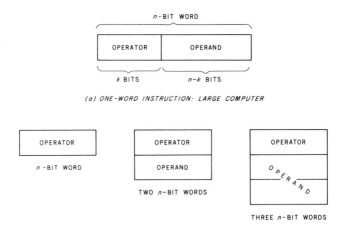

Figure 6.2: *Instruction structures.*

A bus structure that has proved to be particularly effective in many architectures is one that distinguishes between data, addresses, and control signals. Figure 6.3 depicts a general computer architecture using such a bus structure.

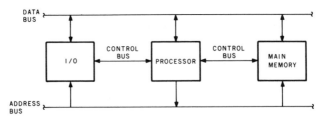

Figure 6.3: *A simple computer bus structure.*

6.2.1 A Simple Processor Architecture

A simple processor architecture that is particularly effective in implementing a von Neumann-type machine is presented here. Again, it is convenient to divide the processor into two subsystems: the control unit (CU) and the arithmetic and logic unit (ALU).

A simple CU consists of an instruction decoder and an array of registers. The register array includes the *accumulator*, usually called the A register; the *instruction register*, sometimes called the I register; the *program counter*, also known as the PC or the P register; and the *data counter*, also called the D register. The ALU consists of the necessary digital logic to perform specified arithmetic and logic operations on data input to it. Even the simplest ALU must be capable of performing the three primitive logic operations, AND, OR, and NOT; more sophisticated ALUs perform additional logic operations such as ADD, SUBTRACT, SHIFT, and so forth.

The architecture for a simple processor is shown in figure 6.4. Note that this processor is a three-bus system. Data which are to be processed and data representing instructions are transferred on the *data bus*. The data bus is a bidirectional bus in that it can be used for data transfers in and out of the processor. Address data, which identifies the memory location (or the I/O device) where data are to be read or stored, are transferred on the *address bus*. The address bus is generally a unidirectional bus in that address data is transmitted only from the processor to external memory and I/O devices. Data controlling the operation of the processor (eg: timing references, interrupts, and halt/wait signals) and data reflecting the state of the processor (eg: clock signals, read and write signals) are transferred to and from the processor on the *control bus*. Each line in the control bus is generally unidirectional. Some control lines are input lines which carry data to the processor, while others are output lines and carry data from the processor.

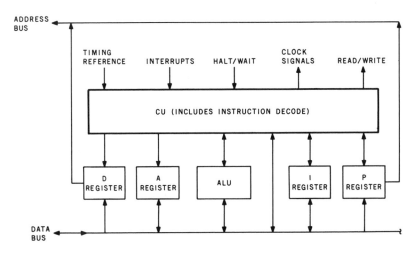

Figure 6.4: *A simple processor architecture.*

6.2.2   Program Execution

Although an instruction may correspond to a processor action that is quite complex, that processor action can be resolved into a sequence of primitive actions, where each primitive action is executed during a single *machine cycle*. A machine cycle is defined by a clock signal derived from an external timing reference. It is convenient to divide the set of primitive actions into three categories:

- READ: During a READ machine cycle, the data stored at an external memory location are transferred on the data bus to a processor register; during the execution of the READ, the address bus identifies that external memory location.
- WRITE: During a WRITE machine cycle, the data stored in a processor register are transferred on the data bus to an external memory location; during the execution of the WRITE, the address bus identifies that external memory location.
- INTERNAL OPERATION: During an internal operation, the processor processes data contained in one or more of its registers, and there is no activity on the data bus.

An instruction is a sequence of two or more primitive actions and is always at least two machine cycles in duration. During the first machine cycle, in which an instruction is being executed, the processor *fetches* (ie: READs) the instruction from external memory. The address of the instruction being fetched is in the program counter (processor register P), and during the fetch cycle the contents of the program counter are placed on the address bus. In the remaining one or more machine cycles of the instruction, other primitive actions are executed in accordance with the particular instruction being executed.

A program consists of a sequence of instructions. In a von Neumann-type architecture, the instructions are stored contiguously in external memory. A typical processor sequence of actions for executing one instruction of a program is the following:

1. Fetch the instruction stored at the memory address indicated by the program counter.
2. Increment the contents of the program counter by 1.
3. Decode the instruction fetched in step 1 and execute it.
4. Return to step 1.

6.2.3   Register Notation

In describing the operation of a digital computer, it is convenient to introduce a brief notation to represent registers, the contents of registers, and the transfer of data. In the following text, a single capital letter is used to identify a register: A represents the accumulator (register A), P represents the program counter (register P), and so forth. A captial letter enclosed in square brackets denotes the contents of the register indicated by the capital letter: [A] denotes the data stored in register A, [P] denotes the data stored is register P, and so forth. A transfer of data is denoted by an arrow: [A]→[I] denotes that the contents of register A are transferred to register I (the contents of register A remain unchanged); [P]+1→[P] denotes that the contents of register P are incremented by 1.

Each word in external memory is identified by its address. In the following text, a single lowercase letter is used to represent an address in external memory; for example, [P]=m denotes that the program counter P contains address m.

The operator portion of an instruction is represented by an *operation code* (op code) consisting of a three-letter mnemonic; the operand portion of an instruction is enclosed in parentheses and is concatenated to the operator, eg: the instruction SRA(m) has the operator SRA and the operand m.

Consider the following examples corresponding to the simple processor of figure 6.4, where A and I are 8-bit registers, and P and D are 16-bit registers.

- [A] = 01010101   This statement says that the 8-bit binary number 01010101 is stored in the accumulator.
- m = 0000111100001111   This statement says that variable m is referring to external memory address 0000111100001111.
- [m] = 11100111   This statement says that the 8-bit number 11100111 is stored in memory location m.
- [P] = m   This statement says that the 16-bit address defined by variable m is stored in the program counter.
- [[P]] = SRA(m)   This statement says that the instruction SRA(m) is located at the memory location whose address is stored in the program counter.
- [m]→[A]   This statement says that contents of memory location m are transferred to the accumulator; the contents of memory location m remain unchanged.
- [A]→[q]   This statement says that the contents of the accumulator are transferred to memory location q; the contents of the accumulator remain unchanged.

Consider using this notation to describe the sequence of processor actions that occurs when one instruction of a program is executed. In particular, consider the case of a two-word instruction, in which the first word is the operator and the second word is the operand:

1. [[P]]→[I]   Fetch the operator portion of the instruction at the address indicated by the program counter, and store the operator in the instruction counter.
2. [[P]+1]→[D]   Fetch the operand portion of the instruction, which is

stored immediately following the operator (ie: at address [P]+1), and store the operand in the data counter.

3. [[P]+2]→[P]   Increment the program counter so that it *points* to the operator of the next instruction. In this case, where the instruction consists of two words, the program counter must be incremented by 2.

4. At this point, [I] = operator and [D] = operand (ie: the address of data upon which to be operated). Decode operator [I], and accordingly, operate upon the data stored in external memory location [D].

5. Return to step 1.

6.2.4   A Simple Instruction Set

A basic, though not minimal, instruction set for the simple processor of figure 6.4 is defined in table 6.1. It is convenient to use op codes to identify the operators in defining the instructions. However, it is understood that *machine language* instructions are binary numbers. Also, it is assumed that the operator and the operand are each one word long. This instruction set is used later to illustrate various processor characteristics.

Instruction (Op Code)	Machine Cycle	Processor Action	Comments
SRA(m)	1 2 3	SRA→[I] m→[D] [A]→[m]	Fetch the operator. Fetch the operand. Store (absolute addressing): contents of the accumulator are stored in memory location m.
LDA(m)	1 2 3	LDA→[I] m→[D] [m]→[A]	Fetch the operator. Fetch the operand. Load (absolute addressing): contents of memory location m are loaded into the accumulator.
LDI(m)	1 2	LDI→[I] m→[A]	Fetch the operator. Load (immediate addressing): the operand m is loaded into the accumulator.

Table 6.1: *A simple instruction set.*

Instruction (Op Code)	Machine Cycle	Processor Action	Comments
ADA(m)	1 2 3	ADA→[I] m→[D] [m]+[A]→[A]	Fetch the operator. Fetch the operand. Add (absolute addressing): contents of memory location m are added to the contents of the accumulator, and the result is loaded into the accumulator.
ADI(m)	1 2	ADI→[I] m+[A]→[A]	Fetch the operator. Add (immediate addressing): the operand m is added to the contents of the accumulator, and the result is loaded into the accumulator.
JMP(m)	1 2	JMP→[I] m→[P]	Fetch the operator. Jump (unconditional): the operand m is loaded into the program counter P. Thus, the next instruction to be executed will be that instruction stored in memory location m, rather than the instruction immediately following JMP(m).
BRP(m)	1 2	BRP→[I] If [A]>0 then m→[P]	Fetch the operator. Branch on the positive accumulator: test the contents of the accumlator. If positive, load the operand m into the program counter, thus causing a jump to the instruction stored at memory location m. If not positive, do nothing, and the instruction immediately following BRP(m) will be executed.

Table 6.1 cont.

Instruction (Op Code)	Machine Cycle	Processor Action	Comments
DEC(m)	1	DEC→[I]	Fetch the operator.
	2	m→[D]	Fetch the operand.
	3		
	4 }	$[m]-1$→$[m]$	The contents of memory location m are decremented by 1. This takes three machine cycles: one cycle is used to read $[m]$ from external memory into the ALU; one cycle is used by the ALU to decrement $[m]$; one cycle is used to write the decremented value back into m.
	5		

Table 6.1 cont.

6.2.5   Program Execution

Consider the timing sequence of the simple processor, defined by the architecture of figure 6.4, when executing the following two-instruction program:

Address	Instruction	Processor Action
r	SRA	
$r+1$	m }	$[A]$→$[m]$
$r+2$	LDA	
$r+3$	n }	$[n]$→$[A]$

For illustrative purposes, assume the simplest possible processor clock structure in which the external timing-reference signal and the clock signal are identical, and in which the clock period defining a machine cycle is T. Note that each instruction consists of two words. At time $t = 0$, the program counter P is set to r, the address of the first word in the program, and the execution of the program proceeds. Figure 6.5 details the timing sequence in executing this two-instruction program.

As an example of a more sophisticated program, consider the problem of summing a set of data which is stored in n contiguous memory locations, starting at address q. An efficient program for executing this computation will involve a *loop* in which the same instructions in the program are executed repeatedly in sequencing through the data. Suppose the program written to do this is stored in memory, starting at address r. It is necessary to be sure that the program and the data do not overlap in memory. While sequencing through the data during a program run, memory location s is

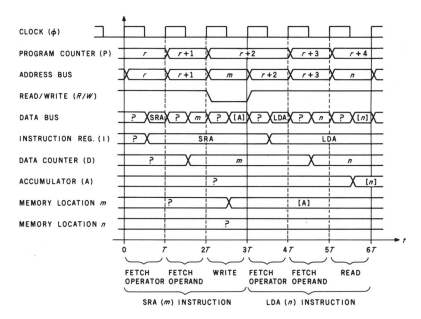

Figure 6.5: *A simple-processor timing sequence.*

used to store the partial sum. To reflect the new datum read from memory, the contents of *s* are updated during each pass through the loop. After running this program, the final sum will be stored in memory location *s*. Memory location *y* is used as a counter to keep track of how much data is yet to be added to the sum. A representation of how the data, the program, the sum, and the counter might be located in external memory is given in figure 6.6a. A flowchart detailing the algorithm used to sum the data appears in figure 6.6b, and figure 6.6c gives a listing of the program.

An important characteristic of this program that reflects the architectural limitations of this simple processor is that the program is continuously modifying itself during a run. Specifically, the add instruction, located at memory locations $r + 18$ and $r + 19$, is altered during the execution of the program. The function of the store instruction SRA$(r + 19)$, located at memory locations $r + 14$ and $r + 15$, is to change the operand at memory location $r + 19$ during program execution. A computer's capability to modify a program while running that program is a consequence of the von Neumann architectural feature which allows no distinction to be made between stored data and stored programs. In this program it is the capability to increment the operand of the add instruction that makes it possible to program a loop that efficiently sequences through the data. There is, however, a serious problem associated with a program's modifying itself while running: the program must be loaded into memory each time it is to be run. If the program is to be run ten times, it must be loaded into memory ten times, once before each run. This problem is solved in most present-day processors by introducing *indirect addressing* modes and/or *index registers*.

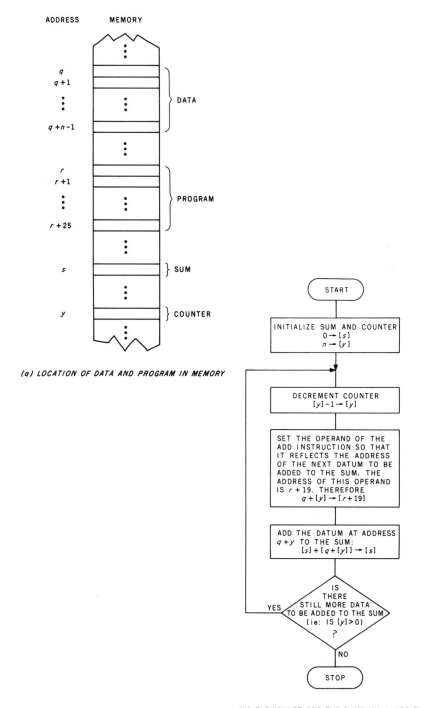

(a) LOCATION OF DATA AND PROGRAM IN MEMORY

(b) FLOWCHART FOR THE SUMMING ALGORITHM

Figure 6.6: *A program to sum data stored in memory.*

Address	Instruction	Comments
r	LDI	
$r + 1$	n	Initialize
$r + 2$	SRA	counter $n \rightarrow [y]$
$r + 3$	y	
$r + 4$	LDI	
$r + 5$	0	Initialize
$r + 6$	SRA	sum $0 \rightarrow [s]$
$r + 7$	s	
$r + 8$	DEC	Decrement
$r + 9$	y	counter $[y] - 1 \rightarrow [y]$
$r + 10$	LDA	
$r + 11$	y	
$r + 12$	ADI	Set operand of add
$r + 13$	q	instruction
$r + 14$	SRA	$q + [y] \rightarrow [r + 19]$
$r + 15$	$r + 19$	
$r + 16$	LDA	
$r + 17$	s	Add next datum to sum
$r + 18$	ADA	$[s] + [q + [y]] \rightarrow [s]$
$r + 19$	***	The contents of $r + 19$ can
$r + 20$	SRA	be anything to begin with.
$r + 21$	s	
$r + 22$	LDA	Check if there is more
$r + 23$	y	data to be added. If $[y] > 0$
$r + 24$	BRP	go to instruction at $r + 8$.
$r + 25$	$r + 8$	

Figure 6.6 cont.   (c) THE PROGRAM

6.2.6 Indirect Addressing

In executing an instruction in the indirect addressing mode, the operand is interpreted neither as actual data to be processed (ie: immediate addressing), nor as the address of the data to be processed (ie: absolute addressing). Rather, in indirect addressing, the operand identifies the address of the memory location in which the *address* of the data to be processed is located. Consider augmenting the instruction set of the simple processor (figure 6.4, table 6.1) to include the indirect addressing instructions defined in table 6.2.

For comparative purposes, the indirect addressing instructions are used again to write a program to add the n numbers stored in memory, starting at address q; a listing of such a program is given in figure 6.7. In this program, memory locations s and y are used as before (ie: the partial sum is

stored in s), and the amount of data yet to be added to the sum is stored in
y. However, in this program an additional memory location is used: the address of the datum to be added to the sum is stored in t. Thus, t is the indirect address referred to in the indirect-add instruction at locations $r + 20$
and $r + 21$.

By using the indirect-add instruction, it is not necessary to increment the
operand of any instruction in the program in order to implement the loop
required for the iterative computation. This program is never altered during
a run, and once the program is loaded it can be run any number of times
without having to reload it.

Instruction (Op Code)	Machine Cycle	Processor Action	Comments
SRN(m)	1	SRN→[I]	Fetch the operator.
	2	m→[D]	Fetch the operand.
	3	[A]→[[m]]	Store (indirect address-ing): contents of the ac-cumulator are stored in memory location [m].
LDN(m)	1	LDN→[I]	Fetch the operator.
	2	m→[D]	Fetch the operand.
	3	[[m]]→[A]	Load (indirect addressing).
ADN(m)	1	ADN→[I]	Fetch the operator.
	2	m→[D]	Fetch the operand.
	3	[A]+[[m]]→[A]	Add (indirect addressing).

Table 6.2: *Indirect addressing instructions.*

Address	Instruction	Comments
r	LDI	
r + 1	n	n → [y]
r + 2	SRA	
r + 3	y	
r + 4	LDI	
r + 5	q	
r + 6	ADA	n + q → [t]
r + 7	y	
r + 8	SRA	
r + 9	t	
r + 10	LDI	
r + 11	0	0 → [s]
r + 12	SRA	
r + 13	s	
r + 14	DEC	[y] − 1 → [y]
r + 15	y	
r + 16	DEC	[t] − 1 → [t]
r + 17	t	
r + 18	LDA	
r + 19	s	
r + 20	ADN	[s] + [[t]] → [s]
r + 21	t	
r + 22	SRA	
r + 23	s	
r + 24	LDA	
r + 25	y	If [y] > 0 go to
r + 26	BRP	r + 14
r + 27	r + 14	

Figure 6.7: *Indirect addressing: a program for summing data stored in memory.*

6.2.7 Index Registers

Another approach to varying an address within a loop without modifying the program itself is to add another register to the processor register array and to augment the instruction set with an appropriate set of instructions related to this register. This additional register is called the *index register* (or register X). Figure 6.8 shows a processor with an index register, and table 6.3 defines a set of instructions involving the index register.

For comparative purposes, a program is written using this augmented instruction set to again add the *n* numbers stored in memory, starting at address *q*; a listing of such a program is given in figure 6.9. Note that the index register and the instructions associated with it make certain efficiencies possible. Most importantly, the program itself is never altered during a run.

Therefore, the program can be run any number of times without having to reload it into memory before each run. In addition, because the index register is used to sequence through the data, and because the index register can be decremented and tested directly (using the DEX and BXP instructions, respectively) without affecting the contents of the accumulator, the accumulator can be used to store the partial sum throughout the entire computation. This eliminates the need for continuously transferring the partial sum in and out of external memory during each iteration of the computation. The introduction of an index register and a set of instructions for its control allows repetitive computations to be programmed and executed simply and efficiently.

Instruction (Op Code)	Machine Cycle	Processor Action	Comments
SAX(m)	1	SAX → [I]	Fetch the operator.
	2	m → [D]	Fetch the operand.
	3	A → [m + [X]]	Store (indexed addressing): contents of the accumulator are stored in memory location m + [X].
LAX(m)	1	LAX → [I]	Fetch the operator.
	2	m → [D]	Fetch the operand.
	3	[m + [X]] → [A]	Load (indexed addressing).
AAX(m)	1	AAX → [I]	Fetch the operator.
	2	m → [D]	Fetch the operand.
	3	[A] + [m + [X]] → [A]	Add (indirect addressing).
BXP(m)	1	BXP → [I]	Fetch the operator.
	2	If [X] > 0 then m → [P]	Branch on the positive index register.
DEX	1	DEX → [I]	Fetch the operator.
	2	[X] − 1 → [X]	Decrement the index register.
LDX(m)	1	LDX → [I]	Fetch the operator.
	2	m → [X]	Load the X register (immediate addressing).

Table 6.3: *Indexed addressing instructions.*

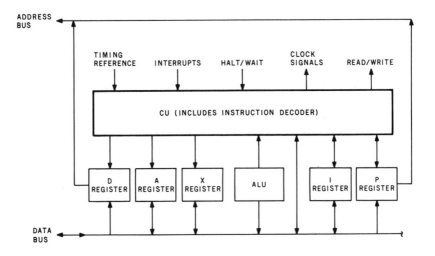

Figure 6.8: *The addition of an index register to the processor.*

Address	Instruction	Comments
r	LDX	Initialize index
$r + 1$	n	register: $n \rightarrow [X]$
$r + 2$	LDI	
$r + 3$	0	Initialize sum: $0 \rightarrow [A]$
$r + 4$	DEX	Decrement index register: $[X] - 1 \rightarrow [X]$
$r + 5$	AAX	Add next datum to sum:
$r + 6$	q	$[q + [X]] + [A] \rightarrow [A]$
$r + 7$	BXP	Check is there is more data to be
$r + 8$	$r + 4$	added. If $[X] > 0$ go to instruction at $r + 4$.
$r + 9$	LDA	Store final sum in memory location s.

Figure 6.9: *Indexed addressing: a program for summing data stored in memory.*

6.2.8 Subroutines and Stacks

A *subroutine* is a program that can be called upon and executed from any point in another program. A subroutine can be called from another subroutine. There are many levels of subroutines. The need for a subroutine generally arises in situations where a particular sequence of instructions must be executed many times in a program, but where there is no discernable repetitive pattern with which this particular sequence is executed (ie: where it is not obvious how to include this sequence in a loop). By defining a sequence as a subroutine, the sequence is stored only once in memory.

Where there is an obvious repetitive pattern with which a particular sequence of instructions is executed, such as in the case of summing numbers stored in contiguous locations in memory, a simple loop suffices.

The major problem in using subroutines stems from the fact that the contents of important processor registers (eg: the program counter, the accumulator, and the index register) may be lost while executing the subroutine. In many situations, it would be absolutely essential that the processor registers be restored before control is returned to the program from which the subroutine was called. A simple, standard solution to this problem is to use a *stack* to store important register data before executing a subroutine. The stack is then used to restore the registers after the subroutine has been executed and before control is transferred back to the main program.

A stack is a last-in, first-out data structure. A simple stack can be accessed by only two operations: the *push* and the *pop*. As a result of executing a push, a new datum is placed at the top of the stack, thus increasing the size of the stack. Executing a pop removes the datum from the top of the stack, thus decreasing the size of the stack. Figure 6.10 illustrates the push and pop operations. A stack can be constructed either by appropriately interconnecting registers (a hardware stack) or by setting aside a portion of memory to be used as a stack (a software stack).

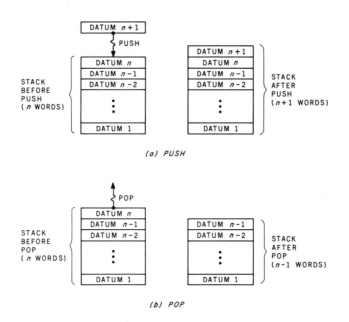

Figure 6.10: *Stack operations: push and pop.*

The basic structure of a hardware stack is illustrated in the block diagram of figure 6.11a. In this diagram, the blocks represent registers in which a data word can be stored. Especially note the bidirectional data shifts: each datum shifts to the right on a push and to the left on a pop. Specifically,

If PUSH = 1 and POP = 0,
Datum → [n]
[i] → [i−1], i=2, 3, . . . , n

If PUSH = 0 and POP = 1,
[n] → Datum
[i] → [i+1], i=1, 2, . . . , n−1
[1] = ?

Figure 6.11b shows how a simple hardware stack might be constructed using D flip-flops. This stack has a word length (register size) of 1 bit and a maximum stack length of three words.

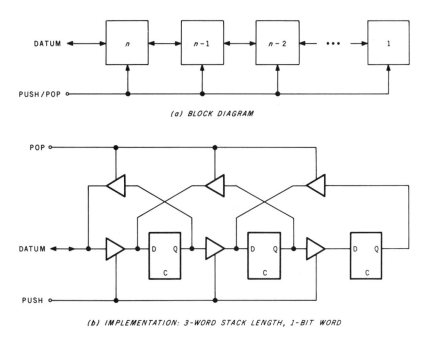

(a) BLOCK DIAGRAM

(b) IMPLEMENTATION: 3-WORD STACK LENGTH, 1-BIT WORD

Figure 6.11: A hardware stack.

For use in general-purpose digital computers, software stacks or *memory stacks* are most common. Typically, in a digital computer a certain portion of memory is assigned for use as a software stack. A *stack pointer* is used to keep track of the address of the top word in the stack. The stack pointer can be simply a location in memory reserved for this purpose. However, where stack operations are used frequently, an extra register is added to the processor to be used expressly as a stack pointer. When this is done, stack in-structions must be added to the instruction set to utilize this new register. A memory stack is illustrated in figure 6.12. In a typical memory stack, data is either pushed to the top of the stack from a processor register (eg: the A register), or data is popped from the top of the stack to a processor register. For example, assume that the address q is initially stored in the stack pointer (ie: $[S]=q$). This means that address q defines the top of the stack. Specifically, q is the address of the location to which the next datum will be pushed, and $[q-1]$ represents the datum at the top of the stack. If a push operation is now executed, the following processor actions occur:

$[A] \rightarrow [[S]]$ (ie: $[A] \rightarrow [q]$: the contents of the accumulator are pushed to the top of the stack)

$[S]+1 \rightarrow [S]$ (ie: $q+1 \rightarrow [S]$: the stack pointer is incremented by 1 to reflect the increased size of the stack)

If a pop operation is executed when $[S]=q$, the following processor actions occur:

$[S]-1 \rightarrow [S]$ (ie: $q-1 \rightarrow [S]$: the stack pointer is decremented so that it reflects the address of the datum at the top of the stack—the datum about to be popped)

$[[S]] \rightarrow [A]$ (ie: $[q-1] \rightarrow [A]$: the top of the stack is popped to the accumulator)

Note that the push and pop operations are defined so that the stack pointer points to the location to which the *next* datum will be pushed. This requires that the stack pointer be incremented *after* a push and decremented *before* a pop. It is also possible to define the stack pointer so that it points to the datum at the top of the stack. In this case, it would be necessary to increment the stack pointer *before* a push and decrement it *after* a pop.

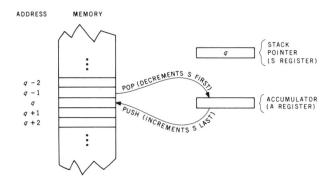

Figure 6.12: *A software (memory) stack.*

By adding a stack-pointer register S to the processor register array, and by adding two instructions utilizing the stack (see table 6.4) to the instruction set, the execution of subroutines can be made quite simple.

Instruction (Op Code)	Machine Cycle	Processor Action	Comments
JMS(m)	1	JMS→[I]	Fetch the operator.
	2	m→[D]	Fetch the operand.
	3	[P]→[[S]]	The contents of the program counter are pushed on the stack.
	4	[S]+1→[S]	The stack pointer is incremented.
	5	m→[P]	The program counter is set equal to the operand, which is the address of the first instruction of the subroutine.
RTS	1	RTS→[I]	Fetch the operator.
	2	[S]−1→[S]	The stack pointer is decremented.
	3	[[S]]→[P]	The stack is popped to the program counter.

Table 6.4: *Subroutine instructions.*

The jump-to-subroutine instruction (JMS(m)) causes the normal sequence of a program to be interrupted. Specifically, execution is transferred to the instruction at address m, which is the first instruction of a subroutine. The jump-to-subroutine instruction differs from the simple jump instruction in that the contents of the program counter P are pushed onto the stack *before* control is transferred to the subroutine. When execution of the subroutine is completed, the stack can be popped to restore the program counter.

The return-from-subroutine instruction (RTS) is used as the last instruction of a subroutine. Execution of the RTS instruction pops the stack to the program counter. This restores the program counter to the value it had before execution of the subroutine, allowing the main program sequence to be resumed. Figure 6.13 illustrates the sequence of instructions followed in executing a subroutine.

The contents of processor registers can be altered while executing a subroutine. Therefore, if the data in these registers are necessary to resume the operation of the main program, measures must be taken to safely store important register data immediately before executing a jump-to-subroutine

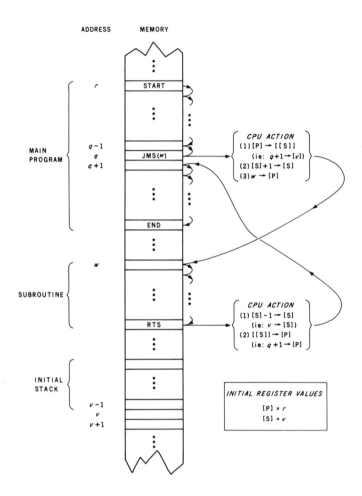

Figure 6.13: *Executing a subroutine.*

instruction. These data can then be used to restore the registers immediately after executing the corresponding return-from-subroutine instruction. It is also common to use the stack for storing important register data. To enable the stack to be used for this purpose, other stack instructions are introduced, allowing the contents of important processor registers to be pushed onto and popped from the stack (see table 6.5). It is especially useful to be able to push from and pop to both the accumulator and the index register. Figure 6.14 illustrates how the push and pop instructions can be used in conjunction with the JMS and RTS instructions to execute a subroutine. In this case, the contents of the accumulator and the index register are stored before executing the subroutine, and the contents of these registers are restored after executing the subroutine.

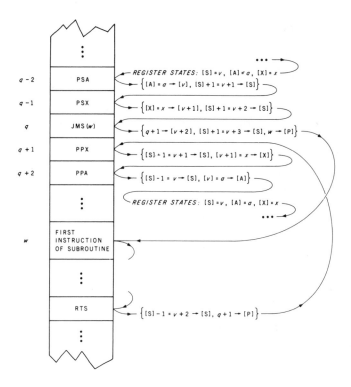

Figure 6.14: *Preserving the contents of important processor registers during execution of a subroutine: push and pop instructions.*

Instruction (Op Code)	Machine Cycle	Processor Action	Comments
PSA	1 2 3	PSA→[I] [A]→[[S]] } [S]+1→[S] }	Fetch the operator. The accumulator is pushed onto the stack.
PPA	1 2 3	PPA→[I] [S]−1→[S] } [[S]]→[A] }	Fetch the operator. The stack is popped to the accumulator.
PSX	1 2 3	PSX→[I] [X]→[[S]] } [S]+1→[S] }	Fetch the operator. The index register is pushed onto the stack.
PPX	1 2 3	PPX→[I] [S]−1→[S] } [[S]]→[X] }	Fetch the operator. The stack is popped to the index register.

Table 6.5: *Stack instructions.*

6.2.9 Interrupts

Most general-purpose processors provide for some type of *interrupt* capability. An interrupt, generally initiated by a signal from a peripheral device, allows the normal program sequence of the processor to be broken while the peripheral device is serviced by a subroutine. After the subroutine which services the peripheral device is executed, the normal program sequence is resumed. Most processors have one interrupt input which is active at all times; such an interrupt is called a *nonmaskable interrupt*. However, many processors also have a weaker type of interrupt input which can be controlled by programming the processor so that *interrupt requests* occurring during certain periods are ignored.

As an illustration of an interrupt capability, refer to the simple digital computer system shown in figure 6.15. In this system, the processor serves two functions: the primary function is to run the main program; the secondary function is to service a peripheral device by executing a subroutine written especially for this purpose. The peripheral device is not used often and, as a result, requires service only occasionally. For this reason, rather than using two processors, it is deemed feasible to share one processor between the main computing function, defined by the main program, and the peripheral-device servicing function, defined by the subroutine.

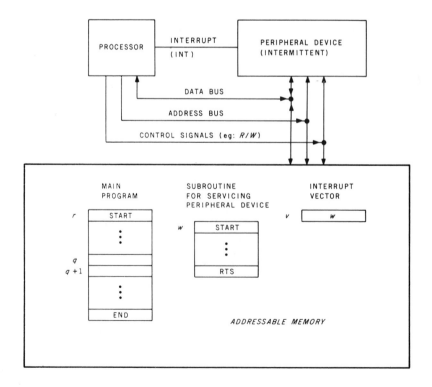

Figure 6.15: *A computer interface using an interrupt capability.*

A processor with an interrupt capability has a special interrupt input (eg: the INT input shown in figure 6.15). A peripheral device requiring service from the processor would signal the processor via the INT line, indicating it is ready to be serviced. At this point, the processor would respond by jumping to the appropriate subroutine. The address of the first word of the service subroutine is called the *interrupt vector* and is always stored in the same location. In the system of figure 6.15, memory location v is reserved for the interrupt vector.

The following sequence of actions is typical of most interrupts. Assume that INT = HIGH is normal and that a negative edge (a HIGH-to-LOW transition of the INT line) signals the interrupt request.

1. While executing instruction q of the main program, the peripheral device signals the processor for service by initiating a HIGH-to-LOW transition on the INT line.
2. The execution of instruction q is completed.
3. $[P] \rightarrow [[S]]$ (ie: $q+1 \rightarrow [[S]]$; the program counter is pushed onto the stack).
4. $[v] \rightarrow [P]$ The interrupt vector w, which is stored at memory location v, is loaded into the program counter.
5. The peripheral-device service subroutine, starting at w, is executed.
6. The last instruction in the service subroutine is a return-from-subroutine instruction (RTS). Upon executing the RTS instruction, program execution returns to the instruction at $q + 1$: $[[S]] \rightarrow [P]$ (or, $q+1 \rightarrow [P]$), and normal program execution is resumed.

6.2.10 Reset and Bootstrap Programs

Immediately after power is turned ON, a special interrupt is generally used to initiate computer operation. In addition to the general-purpose interrupt input which is used to service peripheral devices, most computers have a *reset input*. The reset input, represented by RST, is simply another interrupt having its own distinct interrupt vector. In a typical digital computer, both the reset interrupt vector and the *bootstrap* subroutine, to which the reset interrupt vector points, are stored in read-only memory. As a result, both are immediately available right after power is turned ON. Generally, the primary function of the bootstrap subroutine is to control data transfers from the input devices (keyboards, tape players, etc) to the processor. Under control of the bootstrap subroutine, the input devices can be used to load programs and associated data into external memory and to set the program counter, initiating the execution of a program. The bootstrap subroutine often controls data transfers from the important processor registers to output devices such as LED displays, video monitors, and printers.

A typical digital computer start-up sequence would be as follows. The reset switch (ie: a switch connected between the reset input (RST) and ground) is closed, causing an active transition on the reset input (a HIGH-to-LOW transition of RST). During the first machine cycle following the RST transition, the reset interrupt vector, which points to the bootstrap subroutine in read-only memory, is loaded into the program counter. In the second machine cycle following the RST transition, the processor begins execution of the bootstrap subroutine. Under the control of the bootstrap subroutine, an input device is used to load a program (and any associated data) into main memory. When the program and data are loaded into memory, the program counter is set to the first instruction of this program, and control of the processor is then transferred to this program.

When the input device is a keyboard, the transfer of control to a newly loaded program is generally initiated by depressing a special key of the input keyboard reserved for this function and referred to as a GO key. The keyboard is interfaced to the computer so that it can address any location in memory and cause the contents of that memory location to be displayed on an output device. Under control of the bootstrap subroutine, the processor detects a depression of the GO key and executes a jump instruction, causing the program counter to be set to the address of the memory location presently being displayed. To execute a program which has been loaded into memory (say, starting at location q), display the contents of location q and depress the GO key, under the control of the bootstrap subroutine. The reset-interrupt input and the bootstrap subroutine to which the reset-interrupt vector points are obviously important parts of a computer system.

6.2.11 Status Register (Flags)

The design of both digital computer software and hardware can be greatly simplified if certain data pertaining to the status of the processor are readily available. A collection of such data is generally stored in a special processor register called a *status register*. Here, these data are easily accessed by using special instructions added to the instruction set for this purpose. Each bit of the status register is called a *flag*; each flag either represents the status of one of the processor registers or identifies a mode of operation. The following are typical of the flags stored in a status register:

Carry (C): The carry bit of the status register generally serves as an extra bit for the accumulator in certain arithmetic and logic operations (eg: add, shift left, etc). For example, in a machine having an n-bit accumulator, the result of an add can be an $(n+1)$-bit number. The carry flag C can be used to keep track of the $(n+1)$th bit. Introducing a branch instruction that tests for the state of the carry flag (the BRC (m) instruction of table 6.6) simplifies the writing of sophisticated arithmetic programs which must use the primitive n-bit add instruction as the basic arithmetic instruction.

Zero (Z): The 0 bit of the status register indicates whether or not a processor register is set to 0. For instance, if after executing an instruction, the contents of the accumulator are 0, then $Z = 1$; otherwise $Z = 0$. A useful instruction based on the 0 flag is the BRZ(m) instruction (table 6.6).

Sign (S):   The sign bit of the status register indicates whether or not the binary number stored in a processor register is positive. For instance, if after executing an instruction, the contents of the accumulator is greater than 0 (positive), then $S = 1$; otherwise $S = 0$. Recall the BRP(m) instruction defined in table 6.1 in which the branch depends upon the state of the accumulator. A more general branch instruction BRS is defined, in which the branch depends upon the state of the sign flag (table 6.6).

Overflow (F):   In an arithmetic operation, the most significant bit (the nth bit of an n-bit word) is used to indicate the sign of a number. If the nth bit is 1, the number is negative. The overflow bit of the status register indicates whether or not the result of an ALU operation overflows into the sign bit. If after executing an instruction affecting the accumulator, the nth bit of A is 1, then $F = 1$; otherwise $F = 0$. A useful instruction based on the overflow flag is the BRF(m) instruction (table 6.6).

Instruction (Op Code)	Machine Cycle	Processor Action	Comments
BRC(m)	1 2	BRC$\rightarrow$[I] If C=1 then $m\rightarrow$[P]	Fetch the operator. Branch if the carry flag is HIGH.
BRZ(m)	1 2	BRZ$\rightarrow$[I] If Z=1 then $m\rightarrow$[P]	Fetch the operator. Branch if the zero flag is HIGH.
BRS(m)	1 2	BRS$\rightarrow$[I] If S=1 then $m\rightarrow$[P]	Fetch the operator. Branch if the sign flag is HIGH.
BRF(m)	1 2	BRF$\rightarrow$[I] If F=1 then $m\rightarrow$[P]	Fetch the operator. Branch if the overflow flag is HIGH.

Table 6.6: *Status-register instructions.*

6.2.12   Processor Bus Structures

The block diagram of a processor is shown in figure 6.16. This processor is more complex than the simple one depicted in figure 6.4 in several respects. Notably, the register array is larger in that it contains an index register X, a stack pointer S, and a status register F. Especially important, however, in terms of interfacing this processor with memory and I/O devices, is the addition of a second data bus. With two data buses separated

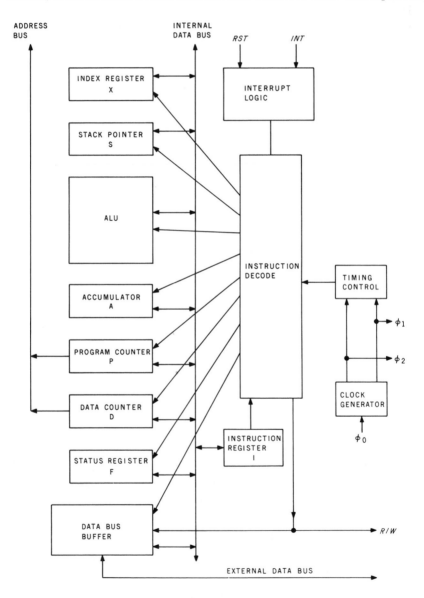

Figure 6.16: *Processor architecture.*

by a *data-bus buffer*, a distinction can be made between internal data transfers (transfers of data between processor registers made on the *internal data bus*) and external data transfers (transfers of data between the processor, external memory, and the I/O devices made on the *external data bus*). By using two distinct data buses, the interfacing of the processor to memory and to I/O devices is simplified considerably. Data must be put on the external data bus only during read and write machine cycles and not during cycles in which internal processor operations are taking place.

The data-bus buffer logic controlling the transfer of data between the internal and external data bus is shown in figure 6.17. With such a buffer, the internal and external data buses are isolated from each other at all times, except during the last half of the execute cycle of either a read or a write instruction. Both the internal and external data buses are bidirectional in that there are transceivers connected to each bus, and the direction in which data is transmitted on the data bus depends upon the state of the transceivers. All the processor registers connected to the internal data bus are transceivers. The data-bus buffer acts as a transceiver for both the internal and the external data bus. In a computer design, memory and I/O devices are interfaced to the processor via the external data bus. Memory and the I/O devices, considered as a single entity, can be viewed as transceivers on the external data bus.

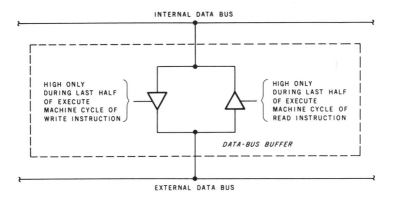

Figure 6.17: *A data-bus buffer.*

In comparison to the data-bus structures, the address-bus structure is relatively simple. The address bus is a unidirectional bus in that data is always transmitted from the processor to memory and to the I/O devices. The only transmitters connected to the address bus are the program counter and the data counter, both within the processor. However, within the processor there are no receivers connected to the address bus. The only receivers connected to the processor are the memory and the I/O devices, both external to the processor. No external transmitters should be connected to the address bus.

6.3   Microprocessors

A typical microprocessor consists of an entire CPU (central processing unit) contained in a single IC (integrated circuit). This remarkable packing of an entire CPU into a single, small, low-power, electronic component, and *not* the particular architecture, is the essence of a microprocessor. At any given time, market considerations and the state-of-the-art in LSI manufacturing determine which microprocessor architectures are commercially available. Thus, given the rate of technological growth in microelectronics, it seems unlikely that the architecture of a typical present-day microprocessor would still be typical in even one or two years. To illustrate, the first commercial microprocessors were 4-bit machines designed for use by logic designers. These microprocessors were generally used to replace complex electronic logic systems in industrial applications, such as control of manufacturing processes, instrumentation, and complex appliances. Although some of these early microprocessors found their way into some bona fide computing applications, industrial applications represented the primary market, and microprocessor designs reflected this market.

The next generation of commercial microprocessors was 8-bit machines; again, the designs reflected the primary market for microprocessors, which was still in industrial applications. However, by this time the impact of the microprocessor was such that many designers were not only trying to replace existing logic designs with microprocessors, but they were also recognizing new, more sophisticated applications for the microprocessors. Demand grew for larger, more complex microprocessors. Also, by this time microelectronic technology had advanced to the point where such a demand could be met. Although the 8-bit microprocessors were not specifically designed for general-purpose computer applications, it became obvious that simple, general-purpose computers, which satisfied the limited needs of many users, could be designed using these 8-bit microprocessors. The 8-bit microprocessor was responsible for the creation of the hobby computer market, which rapidly expanded to include personal computers and small business computers. At the present time, with the incentive of an established market for microprocessors in general-purpose computer application, manufacturers are expending considerable effort developing microprocessors well suited for general-purpose computers. The architectures of the new 16-bit microprocessors reflect not only the improved technology in microelectronics, but also the influence of computer scientists concerned with general-purpose computer applications. This is in sharp contrast to the early microprocessor designs which were influenced largely by the needs of the logic designer.

There is presently little evidence to indicate that the rapid rate at which microprocessor designs are evolving will diminish. Even at this time, it is becoming increasingly difficult to functionally distinguish between a *microcomputer* (a computer using a microprocessor for its processor) and a minicomputer. Given this rapid evolution of microprocessors, it seems prudent to avoid trying to characterize a microprocessor as anything other than a processor contained in a single integrated circuit. To illustrate how a microprocessor is used in a microcomputer design, it is useful to introduce a hypothetical microprocessor.

A microprocessor, typical of those most commonly used at the time of this writing, would have most of the following features:

- von Neumann architecture
- 8-bit data words
- Instructions of 3 words, 2 words, and 1 word—The first word of an instruction is always the operator; the second or the second and third words make up the operand. In the absolute addressing mode, where the operand is the address of the data to be processed, the two-word operand allows for a 16-bit address. Such a microprocessor can address 65,536 words (ie: $2^{16} = 65536$ words; this is frequently referred to as 64 K words). In the immediate addressing mode, where the operand is the data to be processed, only a one-word operand is required to store the 8-bit data word.
- 8-bit data bus—An entire 8-bit word can be transmitted on the data bus (ie: *parallel* data transmission).
- 16-bit address bus—An entire 16-bit address can be transmitted on the address bus.
- A register array of seven registers:

    (a) The accumulator (the A register): 8 bits
    (b) The program counter (the P register): 16 bits
    (c) The instruction register (the I register): 8 bits
    (d) The data counter (the D register): 16 bits
    (e) The stack pointer (the S register): 16 bits
    (f) The index register (the X register): 8 bits
    (g) The status (flag) register (the F register; includes the carry (C) flag, the zero (Z) flag, the sign (S) flag, and the overflow (F) flag): 8 bits

- A two-phase clock—Typically, the processor clock generator uses the timing reference signal ϕ_0 to generate two clock signals, ϕ_1 and ϕ_2. The two clock signals are out of phase with each other, ie: ϕ_1 and ϕ_2 are never HIGH at the same time (see figure 6.18). By having two clock signals instead of one, it is possible to resolve a single machine cycle into a greater number of distinct subdivisions. This allows for the possibility of more activity during a single machine cycle (eg: because the HIGHs of ϕ_2 and ϕ_1 do not overlap, the data bus could be used by the processor for the normal reading and writing of data when ϕ_2 is HIGH, and it could be used to allow a peripheral device to directly access external memory when ϕ_1 is HIGH).
- An arithmetic and logic unit (ALU) that can execute an add (8-bit with carry), an AND and an OR (both 8-bit operations on a bit-by-bit basis), and a shift (left and right)

- Interrupt and reset capability
- Forty-pin DIP (see figure 6.19)
- A thirty-five-instruction instruction set (see table 6.7)

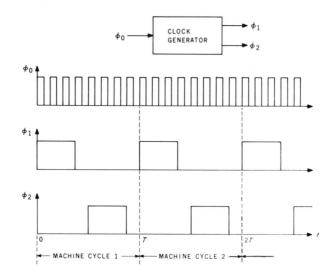

Figure 6.18: *A two-phase clock.*

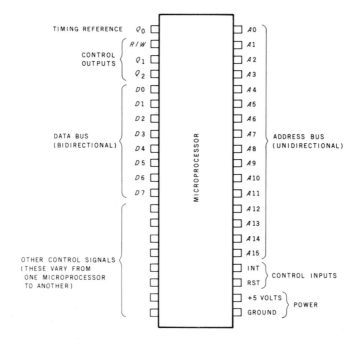

Figure 6.19: *A microprocessor IC.*

	Instruction	Addressing Mode	Number of Words	Processor Action	Flags Affected C Z S F
Accumulator — Store	SRA(m)	Absolute	3	[A]→[m]	. . . .
	SRN(m)	Indirect	3	[A]→[[m]]	. . . .
	SAX(m)	Indexed	2	[A]→[m+[X]]	. . . .
Load	LDA(m)	Absolute	3	[m]→[A]	. x x .
	LDI(m)	Immediate	2	m→[A]	. x x .
	LDN(m)	Indirect	3	[[m]]→[A]	. x x .
	LAX(m)	Indexed	2	[m+[X]]→[A]	. x x .
Status Register	BRC(m)	Absolute	3	If C=1 then m→[P]	. . . .
	BRZ(m)	Absolute	3	If Z=1 then m→[P]	. . . .
	BRS(m)	Absolute	3	If S=1 then m→[P]	. . . .
	BRF(m)	Absolute	3	If F=1 then m→[P]	. . . .
ALU — Add	ADA(m)	Absolute	3	[m]+[A]→[A]	x x x x
	ADI(m)	Immediate	2	m+[A]→[A]	x x x x
	ADN(m)	Indirect	3	[[m]]+[A]→[A]	x x x x
	AAX(m)	Indexed	2	[m+[X]]+[A]→[A]	x x x x
AND	ANA(m)	Absolute	3	[m]AND[A]→[A]	. x x .
	ANI(m)	Immediate	2	m AND[A]→[A]	. x x .
	ANN(m)	Indirect	3	[[m]]AND[A]→[A]	. x x .
	ANX(m)	Indexed	2	[m+[X]]AND[A]→[A]	. x x .
OR	ORA(m)	Absolute	3	[m]OR[A]→[A]	. x x .
	ORI(m)	Immediate	2	m OR[A]→[A]	. x x .
	ORN(m)	Indirect	3	[[m]]OR[A]→[A]	. x x .
	ORX(m)	Indexed	2	[m+[X]]OR[A]→[A]	. x x .
Shift	SHL	Accumulator	1	A register C←7 6 5 4 3 2 1←0	x x x .
	SHR	Accumulator	1	A register 0→7 6 5 4 3 2 1→C	x x 0 .
Stack	JMS(m)		3	[P]→[[S]],[S]+1→[S],m→[P]	. . . .
	RTS		1	[S]−1→[S],[[S]]→[P]	. . . .
	PSA		1	[A]→[[S]],[S]+1→[S]	. . . .
	PPA		1	[S]−1→[S],[[S]]→[A]	. x x .
	PSX		1	[X]→[[S]],[S]+1→[S]	. . . .
	PPX		1	[S]−1→[S],[[S]]→[X]	. x x .
Index Reg.	DEX	Index Register	1	[X]−1→[X]	. x x .
	LDX(m)	Immediate X	2	m→[X]	. x x .
	JMP(m)	Absolute	3	m→[P]	. . . .
	DEC(m)	Absolute	3	[m] −1→[m]	. x x .

Table 6.7: *An instruction set for a hypothetical microprocessor.*

6.4   A Simple Microcomputer

A microcomputer, like any other digital computer, consists of a processing unit, memory, and I/O devices. However, in a microcomputer the processing unit is a microprocessor which is generally a single IC. How the processing unit, memory, and I/O devices are interfaced depends largely upon the bus structures defined by the architecture of the microprocessor being used. Because, at any given time, certain types of microprocessors tend to capture a large fraction of the market (eg: at the time of this writing, the microprocessors which are most popular are 8-bit processors with 16-bit address buses, similar to the hypothetical microprocessor described in the last section), many efficient and effective design practices tend to evolve, which are appropriate for use only with the popular microprocessors. Even more significant is the fact that a large number of commercial MSI and LSI devices are developed that are especially designed to facilitate the design, construction, and software development of specific microprocessors. Thus, when designing a microcomputer, it is important not only to carefully study the characteristics of the particular microprocessor being used, but also to study the family of ICs that have been developed expressly for use with that microprocessor. The approach to microcomputer design will be based on the 8-bit processing unit described in the last section.

An important architectural implication for a microprocessor having 8-bit words and a 16-bit address bus is that a three-word instruction is required for absolute addressing: the operand, which represents a 16-bit address, must be divided into two 8-bit words. Such a microprocessor can address 64 K (or 2^{16} = 64 $\times$ 1024 = 65536) distinct locations. Use of this address space is decided by the designer. A portion of the space is generally used for read-only memory (in which bootstrap subroutines and other frequently used programs, subroutines, and data are stored), user memory (which is used for the temporary storage of programs and data), and I/O devices.

An operand representing an address is divided into two 8-bit words: the *low byte* consists of the lower 8 bits of the address, and the *high byte* consists of the higher 8 bits of the address (see figure 6.20a). Because of this division, the address space tends to be partitioned into subspaces reflecting a two-word address. For example, it is common to partition the addressable space into 256 *pages*, each page containing 256 words. The high byte of the address (A15, A14, . . . , A8) can be used to select a page, and the low byte of the address (A7, A6, . . . , A0) can be used to select a word on the page (see figure 6.20b).

It is often convenient to add memory to a system in 4 K blocks (blocks of 2^{12} = 4 $\times$ 1024 = 4096 words). In such situations, the highest 4 bits of the high byte (A15, A14, A13, and A12) are used to partition the addressable space into sixteen 4 K blocks. Often each 4 K block is further partitioned into four 1 K blocks (selected by A11, A10), and each 1 K block is partitioned into four pages (selected by A9, A8), as indicated in figure 6.20c.

Many possibilities exist for partitioning the addressable space, but in an 8-bit machine the concept of a 256-word page is natural and convenient.

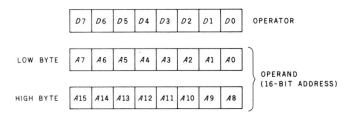

(a) A 3-WORD INSTRUCTION WITH ABSOLUTE ADDRESSING

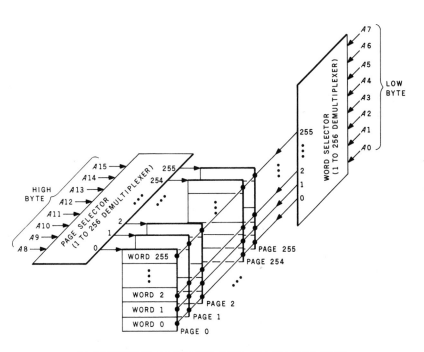

(b) PARTITIONING ADDRESSABLE SPACE INTO 256-WORD PAGES

Figure 6.20: *Partitioning addressable space (8-bit word, 16-bit address).*

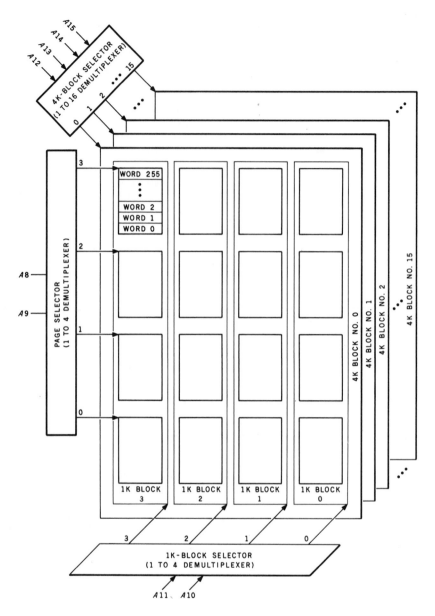

(c) PARTITIONING ADDRESSABLE SPACE INTO 4K-BYTE BLOCKS

Figure 6.20 cont.

In microcomputer design, each unit of the system must be assigned the necessary address space so that programs can control the transfer of data between units. A *memory map* reflects such assignments. For example, consider the case that read-only memory comprises 2 K bytes of memory and is located on pages 128 through 135; user memory comprises 8 K of memory and is located on pages 0 through 23; there is only one input device (eg: a keyboard) which is read at a single address, say the zero-th word of page 64; there is only one output device (eg: a seven-segment LED display) with a single address, say the first word of page 64. In addition, two words of addressable space must be reserved for the interrupt vector. In servicing an interrupt, the microprocessor addresses these two locations for the address of the first word of the interrupt subroutine. If the interrupt subroutine is stored in read-only memory (ROM), then it makes sense to use ROM for the interrupt vectors. On the other hand, if the interrupt subroutine is to be loaded into user memory, and if the location of the first word of the subroutine varies depending upon the application, then it is necessary to provide user memory for the interrupt vectors. In this example, assume that the last two locations in addressable space are reserved for the interrupt vector. Similarly, two words of addressable space are reserved for the reset vector (eg: the next-to-last pair of words in addressable space). Figure 6.21 shows a memory map corresponding to these assignments of addressable space. The design of the addressing logic hardware and the design of the software that will eventually be written for a computer depend upon the memory map.

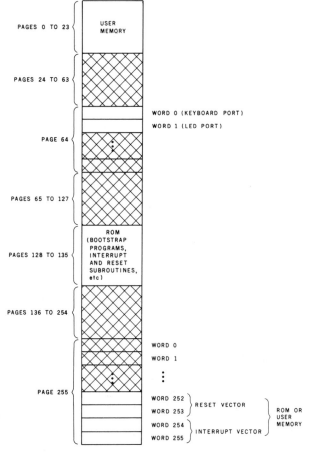

Figure 6.21: *A memory map.*

Figure 6.22 shows a simple microcomputer system. The control-logic block contains the logic for developing the enable signals, which are used to select the various memory blocks and I/O devices. The design of the control-logic block depends upon the memory partitions imposed by the memory hardware and the particular I/O devices that are used.

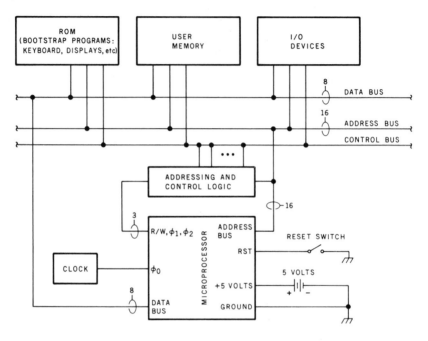

Figure 6.22: *A simple microcomputer system.*

PROBLEMS

P6.1. Use the oscilloscope to observe the important microcomputer waveforms (address bus, data bus, ϕ_2, and R/W) when the store and load instructions are executed. This can be done by running a simple program in which the store and load instructions are in an endless loop (figure P6.1a). The instructions in such a loop are executed periodically, and can be observed on an oscilloscope. For example, running the program of figure P6.1b on the KIM-1 microcomputer allows all the accessible microcomputer waveforms to be observed while the store and load instructions are executed. The three instructions in this program are repeated every eleven machine cycles. By displaying eleven cycles of the clock signal ϕ_2 on one channel of the dual-trace oscilloscope, the waveform of any other signal can be observed on the other channel during one pass through the loop.

Sketch the waveforms of ϕ_2, R/W, A0, A1, . . . , A15, D0, D1, . . . , D15 on the same time scale for eleven machine cycles; identify the fetch and execute machine cycles for each instruction. Note how changing the contents of 0300 from F0 to 0F affects the data bus; note how changing the contents of 0204 and 0205 from F0 to 0F and from 00 to 03, respectively, affects the address bus.

Remember, the data bus is a tristate bidirectional bus. Therefore, care must be taken in interpreting the waveforms observed. In particular, during intervals when the processor is trying to read the data bus and when there are no peripherals trying to transmit data to the processor on the data bus, the data bus is in the High-Z state. At these times, no significance can be attached to the voltage levels on the data bus.

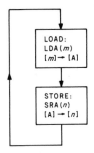

(a) Load-store loop

Address	Instruction		Number of Machine Cycles	Comments
	Op Code	Machine Code (Hex)		
0200	LDA	AD	4	Read: [0300] →[A]
0201		00		(ie: F0 → [A])
0202		03		
0203	STA	8D	4	Write: [A] → [00F0]
0204		F0		(ie: F0 → [00F0])
0205		00		
0206	JMP	4C	3	Jump to 0200
0207		00		
0208		02		
0300		F0		[0300] = F0

(b) KIM-1 program for load-store loop

Figure P6.1.

Appendix

Appendix A1
Solution of Linear Differential Equations

A1.1 First-Order Linear Differential Equations

The simplest differential equation is the linear time-invariant first-order homogeneous differential equation, which can be written in the general form

$$\frac{dx(t)}{dt} + ax(t) = 0 \qquad \begin{array}{l} \text{for } t \geq t_0 \\ a = \text{constant} \end{array} \qquad \text{(A1.1)}$$

It is well known that the solutions of linear time-invariant differential equations are exponentials. Therefore, assume the solution

$$x(t) = Ke^{s(t-t_0)}$$

Substitution of the assumed solution into the original differential equation gives

$$sKe^{s(t-t_0)} + aKe^{s(t-t_0)} = 0$$

Therefore, the assumed solution is a solution for the case that $s = -a$; the value of K is arbitrary. If the solution is constrained by specifying its initial value, then the value of K is fixed, eg: if $x(t_0) = x_0$, then at $t = t_0$

$$\frac{dx(t_0)}{dt} + ax(t_0) = 0$$

Since $\dfrac{dx(t_0)}{dt} = aKe^{-a(t-t_0)}$, and $x(t_0) = x_0$, then

$$-aKe^{-a(t-t_0)} + ax_0 = 0$$

Therefore, $K = x_0$, and the solution is

$$x(t) = x_0 e^{-a(t-t_0)}$$

The linear time-invariant first-order nonhomogeneous differential equation, in which the nonhomogeneous term is a constant k, can be written in the general form

$$\frac{dx(t)}{dt} + ax(t) + k = 0 \qquad \begin{array}{l} \text{for } t \geq t_0 \\ x(t_0) = x_0 \end{array}$$

This equation can also be written as

$$\frac{d(x(t) + k/a)}{dt} + a[x(t) + \frac{k}{a}] = 0 \qquad \begin{array}{l} \text{for } t \geq t_0 \\ x(t_0) = x_0 \end{array}$$

Thus, by using a simple variable substitution, the nonhomogeneous equation can be put into the homogeneous form [equation (A1.1)]:

$$X(t) = x(t) + \frac{k}{a}$$

and therefore,

$$X_0 = X(t_0) = x(t_0) + \frac{k}{a} = x_0 + \frac{k}{a}$$

resulting in the homogeneous equation

$$\frac{dX(t)}{dt} + aX(t) = 0 \qquad \begin{array}{l} \text{for } t \geq t_0 \\ X(t_0) = x_0 + k/a \end{array}$$

Thus, the solution is

$$X(t) = X_0 e^{-a(t-t_0)} \qquad \begin{array}{l} \text{for } t \geq t_0 \\ X_0 = x_0 + k/a \end{array}$$

and since $X(t) = x(t) + \frac{k}{a}$

$$x(t) = x_0 e^{-a(t-t_0)} + (e^{-a(t-t_0)} - 1)\frac{k}{a} \qquad \text{for } t \geq t_0$$

The effect of the nonhomogeneous term k on the solution is the introduction of the additional term, $(e^{-a(t-t_0)} - 1)k/a$. The *transient* part of the solution, $x_0 e^{-a(t-t_0)}$, is still the same.

A1.2 Second-Order Linear Differential Equations

A linear time-invariant second-order homogeneous differential equation can be written in the general form

$$\frac{d^2x(t)}{dt^2} + 2\alpha\frac{dx(t)}{dt} + \beta x(t) = 0 \qquad \text{for } t \geq t_0 \qquad (A1.2)$$

As before, it is assumed that the solution is an exponential, ie:

$$x(t) = Ke^{s(t-t_0)}$$

Substitution into the original differential equation gives

$$s^2Ke^{s(t-t_0)} + 2\alpha sKe^{s(t-t_0)} + \beta Ke^{s(t-t_0)} = 0$$

Dividing through by $Ke^{s(t-t_0)}$ results in the system *characteristic equation*:

$$s^2 + 2\alpha s + \beta = 0$$

Solving for s gives

$$s = -\alpha \pm \sqrt{\alpha^2 - \beta}$$

or, equivalently,

$$s = s_1, s_2$$

$$\text{where } s_1 = -\alpha + \sqrt{\alpha^2 - \beta}$$

$$s_2 = -\alpha - \sqrt{\alpha^2 - \beta}$$

Importantly, there are two values of s satisfying the characteristic equation; hence, there are generally two distinct exponential solutions, ie:

$$x(t) = K_1e^{s_1(t-t_0)}$$

and

$$x(t) = K_2e^{s_2(t-t_0)}$$

where K_1 and K_2 are arbitrary constants.

An important property of all linear differential equations is the property of *superposition*: If $x_1(t)$ and $x_2(t)$ are both solutions to a linear differential equation, then $x(t) = K_1x_1(t) + K_2x_2(t)$ is also a solution of that linear differential equation. Consequently, the most general solution to the linear second-order homogeneous differential equation (A1.2) is

$$x(t) = K_1s^{s_1t} + K_2e^{s_2t} \qquad (A1.3)$$

Again, the values of K_1 and K_2 are arbitrary. However, if the solution is constrained by specifying the initial values of $x(t)$ and $dx(t)/dt$, then the values of K_1 and K_2 are fixed, eg: if $x(t_0) = x_0$, and $dx(t_0)/dt = \dot{x}_0$, then

$$x_0 = K_1 + K_2$$

$$\dot{x}_0 = s_1 K_1 + s_2 K_2$$

Solving for K_1 and K_2 gives

$$K_1 = \frac{\dot{x}_0 - s_2 x_0}{s_1 - s_2}$$

$$K_2 = \frac{s_1 x_0 - \dot{x}_0}{s_1 - s_2} \qquad (A1.4)$$

For the case that $\alpha^2 \geq \beta$, the quantity $\sqrt{\alpha^2 - \beta}$ is real; thus, s_1, s_2, K_1, and K_2 are also real. However, when $\alpha^2 < \beta$, the quantity $\sqrt{\alpha^2 - \beta}$ is imaginary. In this case, it is convenient to define

$$w = \sqrt{\alpha^2 - \beta}$$

Therefore, in terms of w,

$$s_1 = -\alpha + jw \qquad\qquad s_2 = -\alpha - jw$$

$$K_1 = \frac{x_0}{2} - j\frac{\dot{x}_0 + \alpha x_0}{2w} \qquad\qquad K_2 = \frac{x_0}{2} + j\frac{\dot{x}_0 + \alpha x_0}{2w}$$

where $j = \sqrt{-1}$.* Substituting these expressions for s_1, s_2, K_1, and K_2 into the general solution (A1.3) and using standard trigonometric identities [eg: $\cos \theta = \frac{1}{2}(e^{j\theta} + e^{-j\theta})$, $\sin \theta = \frac{1}{2}j(e^{j\theta} - e^{-j\theta})$, $\tan \theta = \sin \theta / \cos \theta$] gives the damped harmonic form of the solution:

$$x(t) = \sqrt{x_0^2 + [(\dot{x}_0 + \alpha x_0)/w]^2} \; e^{-\alpha t} \qquad \sin\left(wt - \arctan\frac{x_0 w}{\dot{x}_0 + \alpha x_0}\right)$$

The linear time-invariant second-order nonhomogeneous differential equation, in which the nonhomogeneous term is a constant k, can be written in the general form

$$\frac{d^2 x(t)}{dt^2} + 2\alpha\frac{dx(t)}{dt} + \beta x(t) + k = 0 \qquad \begin{array}{l} \text{for } t \geq t_0 \\ x(t_0) = x_0 \\ \dfrac{dx(t_0)}{dt} = \dot{x}_0 \end{array}$$

---

*Note that j, rather than the customary i, is used to denote the imaginary numbers. This is not uncommon in electronics where the variable i is reserved for electric current.

This equation can also be written as

$$\frac{d^2(x(t) + k/\beta)}{dt^2} + 2\alpha\frac{d(x(t) + k/\beta)}{dt} + \beta[x(t) + \frac{k}{\beta}] = 0 \quad \begin{array}{l} \text{for } t \geq t_0 \\ x(t_0) = x_0 \\ \dfrac{dx(t_0)}{dt} = \dot{x}_0 \end{array}$$

Again, the nonhomogeneous equation can be put into the homogeneous form [equation (A1.2)] by using simple variable substitution:

$$X(t) = x(t) + \frac{k}{\beta}$$

Therefore,

$$X_0 = X(t_0) = x_0 + \frac{k}{\beta} \quad \text{and} \quad \dot{X}_0 = \dot{x}_0$$

The homogeneous equation results:

$$\frac{d^2X(t)}{dt^2} + 2\alpha X(t) + \beta X(t) = 0 \quad \begin{array}{l} \text{for } t \geq t_0 \\ X_0 = x_0 + \dfrac{k}{\beta} \\ \dot{X}_0 = \dot{x}_0 \end{array}$$

The solution is

$$X(t) = \hat{K}_1 e^{s_1 t} + \hat{K}_2 e^{s_2 t}$$

$$\text{where } s_1 = -\alpha + \sqrt{\alpha^2 - \beta}$$

$$s_2 = -\alpha - \sqrt{\alpha^2 - \beta}$$

$$\text{and } \hat{K}_1 = \frac{\dot{x}_0 - s_2 x_0}{s_1 - s_2} - \frac{s_2 k}{\beta(s_1 - s_2)}$$

$$= K_1 - \frac{s_2 k}{\beta(s_1 - s_2)}$$

$$\hat{K}_2 = \frac{s_1 x_0 - \dot{x}_0}{s_1 - s_2} + \frac{s_1 k}{\beta(s_1 - s_2)}$$

$$= K_2 + \frac{s_1 k}{\beta(s_1 - s_2)}$$

where K_1 and K_2 are the same as the K_1 and K_2 found for the homogeneous case [see equation (A1.4)]. Thus, the solution to the original differential equation can be written as

$$x(t) = K_1 e^{s_1 t} + K_2 e^{s_2 t} + \frac{k}{\beta}(-\frac{s_2}{s_1 - s_2}e^{s_1 t} + \frac{s_1}{s_1 - s_2}e^{s_2 t} - 1)$$

Again, it is seen that the effect of the nonhomogeneous term k in the solution is to introduce an additional term.

For the case that $\alpha^2 < \beta$, the damped harmonic form of the solution results:

$$x(t) = \sqrt{x_0^2 + [(\dot{x}_0 + \alpha x_0)/w]^2} e^{-\alpha t} \sin\left(wt - \arctan\frac{x_0 w}{\dot{x}_0 + \alpha x_0}\right)$$

$$+ \frac{k}{\beta}[e^{-\alpha t} \frac{\sqrt{w^2 + \alpha^2}}{w} \sin\left(wt - \arctan\frac{w}{\alpha}\right) - 1]$$

where, again, $w = \sqrt{\alpha^2 - \beta}$.

Appendix A2

Numerical Solution
of a Simple Integral Equation

Consider finding the solution of the simple integral equation

$$v(t) = \int_0^t F(v(\tau),u(\tau))d\tau \qquad \text{for } 0 \le t < \infty$$

where v is the unknown output variable, u is the input variable known for all t such that $0 \le t < \infty$, and F is a specified function of two variables [eg: $F(v(t),u(t)) = \text{Pos}[(|u(t)| - v(t))/R_S - v(t)/R_L]$. A simple numerical method for obtaining an approximation of the solution to this integral equation is obtained using a zero-order approximation of the integral, ie:

$$\int_t^{t+\delta} F(v(\tau),u(\tau))d\tau = \delta\, F(v(t),u(t)) \qquad \begin{array}{l} \text{for } 0 \le t < \infty \\ \delta \ge 0 \end{array}$$

Clearly, this approximation is reasonable only for small values of δ.
The original integral equation can be rewritten as

$$v(t + \delta) = v(t) = v(t) + \int_t^{t+\delta} F(v(\tau),u(\tau))d\tau \qquad \begin{array}{l} \text{for } 0 \le t < \infty \\ \delta \ge 0 \end{array}$$

Using the zero-order approximation results in the recursive equation

$$v(t + \delta) = v(t) + \delta\, F(v(t),u(t)) \qquad \begin{array}{l} \text{for } 0 \le t < \infty \\ \delta \ge 0 \end{array}$$

Thus, given the initial value $v(0)$ and the input $u(t)$ for $t = 0, \delta, 2\delta,...$, the values $v(\delta), v(2\delta),...$ can be generated.

Appendix B

Laboratory Components, Instruments, and Supplies

The following is a list of the laboratory equipment sufficient to carry out the suggested laboratory exercises.

1. A 5 V power supply (1 A is sufficient)
2. A volt-ohmmeter (a high-input impedance is recommended, but not necessary)
3. A solderless breadboard (a large one is convenient, but one with only a 10 to 14 DIP capacity suffices)
4. A pulse generator or a function generator (a maximum frequency of 100 kHz suffices)
5. A dual-trace oscilloscope (a bandwidth of at least 15 MHz)
6. A microcomputer—A cable should be constructed connecting the data bus, the address bus, and the control bus to a 40-pin wire-wrap DIP socket. This socket can then be inserted into a solderless breadboard, so that the important microcomputer signals can be easily accessed.
7. An 8-bit DIP switch
8. A small screwdriver
9. A combination wire cutter/wire stripper
10. Small longnose pliers
11. AWG No. 22 solid wire (an assortment of colors, including red and black; AWG No. 20, 24, or 26 may also be used)
12. A 25 kΩ potentiometer
13. Two seven-segment LED displays (MAN-52 or MAN-72 are suitable)
14. Six npn transistors (2N3393 are suggested)
15. Ten diodes (IN4148 are suggested)
16. Six LEDs
17. An assortment of TTL ICs (including 7400(2), 7402(2), 7406, 7420, 7447, 7473, 7475(4), 7483, 7485(2), 7493, 74125, 74153, and 74155)

18. An assortment of CMOS ICs (including 4007 and 4011)
19. A 555 timer IC
20. An assortment of common 5% resistors (including 47, 100, 150, 330, 360, 390, 560, 680, 820, 1 K, 1.5 K, 2 K, 2.2 K, 4 K, 5.1 K, 6 K, 8 K, 10 K, 47 K, 51 K, 100 K, and 1.5 MΩ)
21. An assortment of disk capacitors (including 0.01, 0.047, and 0.1 μF)
22. An assortment of electrolytic capacitors (including 1.0 and 2.0 μF)

INDEX

A

Accumulators 344
Adders
  full 212, 243
  half 208
  parallel 243, 244
  serial 244, 281
Address space 372
Addressing 224, 342, 372
  absolute 342
  immediate 342
  indirect 350, 352
Alternating current (AC) 20
American wire gauge (AWG)
    numbers 14
Ammeters 33
Ampere's law 39, 44
Amperes 13
Architectures 340
  simple processor 343
  von Neumann 341
Arithmetic and logic unit (ALU)
    244, 341

B

Batteries 12, 30, 104
Binary systems 87, 156
Binary-coded decimal (BCD) 221
Bits 91, 213
Boolean algebra 156
Bounce, switch 264
Breadboards, solderless 31
Buffers 308
  data-bus 367
  logic driver 308
Building blocks, universal 134, 135
Buses 282, 307
  control 343
  data, internal and external 367
  processor 366
  structures 305, 340
    open-collector 316
    RTL-based 308

tristate
  TTL 317
  CMOS 325
Bytes, high and low 372

C

Capacitors 39, 40
  capacitance 40
  ceramic 74
  charging 54
  electrolytic 74
  filter 105
  identifying 73
  parallel 42
  series 42
Carry 364
Cascading 133, 135
Cathode-ray tubes (CRT) 63
Central logic unit (CLU) 253
Central processing unit (CPU) 340
Charges 3
Circuits, electric 21
  resistor-capacitor (RC) 54
  resistor-inductor (RL) 57
  resistor-transistor NOR 133
Clear 276
Clocks 207
  binary 236
  crystal-controlled 262
  structures 257
  two-phase 370
CMOS logic 188, 208
Coils, air- and iron-core 49
Combinational logic 203
Comparators
  analog 259
  digital 216
Complements 156

Computers
  architecture 339
  digital 339
  stored program 341
  (see Microcomputers, Minicomputers)
Conductors 14
Control signals 342
Constant current source 191
Control units (CU) 340
Coulomb's law 4, 44
Counters
  binary 236
  data 343
  decoding 287
  program 343
  ring 284
  shift 284
  toggle 285
  weighted 287
Current 12
Cycles
  fetch 344
  machine 344

D
D'Arsonval meter movements 33
Data 342
  multiplexed 230
  selectors 224
  transmission, parallel 306
Decoupling inputs 167
De Morgan's theorems 160, 209
Demultiplexers 224
Dielectric constant 4
Dielectric 40
Differential equations
  first-order linear 55
  second-order linear 59
Diffusion currents 93
Digital logic circuit 155, 166
Digital systems 87
Digital-to-analog conversion 291
Diodes 94
  anodes 94
  cathodes 94
  diode circuits 95
  forward- and reverse-biased 94
  ideal 100
  models 99
    forward-resistance 100
    pure-offset 100
  rectifier 105

resistor-diode 96
  reverse breakdown 94
  reverse saturation current 95
  Zener 95, 111
Direct current (DC) 20
Displays
  cathode-ray tube 63
  LED 147, 220, 290, 362
  seven-segment 220
Dividers, voltage 30
Drivers 120, 128
  bi-bus 330
  open-collector bus 316
Dual-in-line packages 185
Duality 160
Dynamic network elements 39
Dynamic systems 236, 237

E
Electricity 1
Electromotive forces (emf) 12
Electrons 4
Enables 225, 278
Energy 7
  stored 39, 43, 52

F
Fan-out 136, 155, 170, 172, 183, 196
Faraday's law 44, 48
Farads 40
Ferromagnetism 45, 50
Fetches 344
Fields
  electric 6, 39
  magnetic 39, 44
Flags 364
Flip-flops 266, 557
  asynchronous 266
  delay (D) 269
  edge-triggered 240, 270, 273
  JK 275
  master-slave 270, 272
  set-reset (RS) 249, 266
  synchronous 266
  toggle (T) 274
Flowcharts 349
Flux linkages 49
Formulas, well-formed 157, 235, 245
Frequency 20
Function generator 61

G
Gates 161
Generators 12
Germanium 91
GO key 364

Graphical methods 98
Ground loops 69
Ground potential 67
Grounds 67

H
Hardware 204
Heat sinks 121
Henry 44
Hexadecimal 302

I
Impedance 320
  output 30
Inductance 44
Induction, perfect 159
Inductors 39, 44
  parallel 51
  series 51
Input/Output (I/O) devices 340,
  363
Input/Output matching 135
Instructions 341, 344
  sets 346
  three-word 372
Insulators 14
Integral equations 107
Integrated circuits (IC) 33, 166, 203,
  235
  large-scale (LSI) 167, 204
  medium-scale (MSI) 167, 203
  small-scale (SSI) 203
Interfacing 304
  CMOS logic and TTL 197
Interrupts
  nonmaskable 362
  requests 362
  vectors 363
    reset 363
Inverters 87, 128
  design 128
  RTL 308
Isolation 135

J
Joules 7

K
Keyboards 363, 364
Kirchhoff's current law (KCL) 22
Kirchhoff's voltage law (KVL) 22

L
Latching 282
Light-emitting diode (LED) displays
  147, 220, 289, 363

Load lines 98, 118, 130
Loads, capacitive 181
  (see Fan-out)
Logic
  block diagrams 161
  combinational 206, 207, 237, 242
    design 208
  complementary metal-oxide
    semiconductor (CMOS) 188,
    193, 208
  current-sinking 173, 179
  design 203, 235
  diode-transistor (DTL) 171
  families 155
    integrated circuit (IC) 167
  functions 160, 162
    universal 253
  resistor-transistor (RTL) 167
  sequential 207, 235, 237, 242,
    245, 248, 339
  tristate
    CMOS 325, 328
    TTL 317
  transistor-transistor (TTL) 176,
    208
    driven by open-collector logic
      314
    features of 7400 series 185
    loading 186
    open-collector 311, 313
    unconnected inputs 185
  two-state 265
Loops, logic 207, 257

M
Machine language 346
Magnetic flux 47
Maxterms 165
Measurements, electric 33
  dynamic 61
Memory 206, 235, 238, 263
  addressable 341
  arrays 300, 328
  cells 206, 238, 327
    strobed 239, 251
  design 329
  dynamic 296
  main 340
  map 374
  mass 341
  programmable 292
  random-access (RAM) 292
  read-only (ROM) 229, 292, 341
  read-write 292, 341
  refreshed 296
  stacks 357

static 296
toggle 240
user 292
Meter elements 33
Meters 33
 ammeter 33
 elements 33
 movements, d'Arsonval 33
 ohm 33, 37
 volt 33, 35
Microcomputers 204, 302, 341, 368
 simple 372
Microprocessors 204, 302, 341, 368,
 369
Minicomputers 368, 372
Minterms 163, 211, 213
MKS system 2
Multiplexers 224

N
NAND 171, 176
Negation 156
Networks 21
 analysis 23
 bridge 26
 diagrams 21
 digital logic 155
 dynamic 54
 elements, dynamic 39
 resistor-inductor-capacitor (RLC)
  58
 responses, damped harmonic and
  exponential 59
 switching 157
Neutrons 4
Newtons 3
Newton's second law of motion 3
Nodes 23
Noise pickup, capacitive and inductive 69
Nonmagnetic materials 45
NOR 133
Number systems, binary 156
Numerical methods 107

O
Ohm's law 13
Ohmmeters 33, 37
Operands 341
Operations, logic
 parallel 243
 sequence of 243
Operators
 instruction 341
 primitive logic 156, 162
Oscillations 60, 257

Oscillators 207
Oscilloscopes 62
 high-frequency attenuation 69
 probes 65, 69
Outputs
 High-Z 320
 Impedance 30, 320
 totem-pole 143, 181, 266, 308,
  311, 317, 318
Overflow 365
Overshoot 60

P
Pages, memory 372
Parasitic network elements 66
Perforated boards 185
Permeability 45, 50
 relative 45
Permittivity 4
Photoelectric cells 12
Physical quantities 2
Piezoelectric effect 262
Plates 40
Pointers, stack 357
Pop 356
Potential 7, 9
Potentiometers 19, 30, 104
Power 15
 gains 120
Power supplies 12
 DC 104, 105
 variations 185
Preset 276
Printers 363
Processors 341
Programs 245, 340, 341, 344
 bootstrap 363
 execution 348
Protons 4
Pulse 62
Pulse generator 62, 258
Pulse train 62
Push 356

R
Race conditions 271
READ 344
Receivers 307
Rectifiers, bridge 105
References, external timing 344
Registers
 arrays 369
 index 349, 353
 instruction 343
 notation 344
 parallel load 278

shift 279
status 364
  (see Flags)
Relays 89
Resets 363
Resistance 13
  equivalent 24
  internal 30, 104
Resistivity 13, 91
Resistors 14
  identification 18
  nonlinear 18
  parallel 25
  pull-down 194
  pull-up 193, 313
  series 24
  temperature effects on 17
  variable 19
  voltage-controlled 191
Reverse Polish Notation (RPN) 246
Right-hand rule 46

S
Semiconductors 14, 91
  complementary metal-oxide
    (CMOS) 188, 191, 208
  doping 91
  intrinsic 91
  junctions, pn 93
  n-type and p-type 92
Sensitivity, switch 88
  analysis 122
  input 89
  transistor circuit 121
Sequences 248
Sequential logic 235, 340
  design 248
  general purpose 245
  programmable 252
Shockley, William 113
Shocks, hazard of 68
Sign bit 365
Signals
  clock 344
  control 342
Silicon 91
Socket strips 31
Software 204
Splitters, phase 181
Stacks, hardware, memory, and
  software 355, 356
State transition equations 241, 248
Static systems 236
Steady states 110
Strobes 224, 239
Subroutines 340, 355

bootstraps 363
Sum of products 163, 165
Switches 87
  bounce 263, 264
  debounced 263
  electronic 91
  input insensitive 121
  switching times 141, 180
  transistor 118
    analysis 125
  turn-on and turn-off times 142
Switching albegra 155, 156, 205, 235
Switching functions 160
Switching speeds 140
Synchronous logic 239

T
T-Delays 238, 269
Tape players 363
Thermocouples 12
Time constant 55, 146
Time-sharing bus 306
Timers 258
Toggles 240, 274
Tolerances, switching 89, 121
Totem-pole output 143, 181, 266
  (see Outputs, TTL)
Transceivers 330
Transformers 52, 109
Transistor-transistor logic (TTL) 176
Transistors 113
  common base, collector, and
    emitter 115
  current amplification 117
  current gains 121
  dependent current sources 115
  design analysis 125
  junction capacitance 140
  junction voltages 126
  maximum current gain (h_{FE}) 122
  metal-oxide semiconductor
    (MOS) 188, 191
  models, Ebers-Moll 115
  n-channel MOS 188, 189
  p-channel MOS 188
  saturation 122
Transmitters, bus 307
Tristate, (TTL) 328
Truth tables 87, 157, 162, 208
  asynchronous 277
  conditional 165
  synchronous 277

U
Units 2
Unstable logic 257

V

Variables
  logic 160
  select 255
  state 242
  switching 156
Video monitors 363
Volt-ohmmeters (VOM) 33
Voltages 7, 9
  bias 94
  dividers 30
  induced 48, 49
  regulators 105, 110
  sinusoidally time varying 20
  sources 12
    ideal 29
    real 29
Voltmeters 33, 35

W

Watts 15
Waves, sine, square, and triangular
  61
Webers 47
Well-formed formulas of switching
  algebra 205
Words 341
Work 7
WRITE 344

Z

Zener effect 94